"NEVER TRUST A WHITE MAN"

I Am Makah, Son of Whaling Nation

ARLYN CONLY

A Journal

COVER ART & SKETCHES by AL ZANTUA
NORTHWEST COAST INDIAN ARTIST

FIRST EDITION

RED APPLE PUBLISHING
Peggy Meyer, editor/publisher
15010 113th St.
Gig Harbor, WA 98329

Printed by Gorham Printing
Rochester, WA 98579

ISBN 1-880222-29-9
Library of Congress Catalog Card Number 97-76424

DISCLAIMER
This is a fictionalized version of actual happenings—as written in my journal—when
teaching at Neah Bay from 1954-1959. Names and descriptions of some people have
been changed in order to protect their privacy or to safeguard a person's character. All
names of teachers, principals, superintendent, and minister are fictitious. Some
students' and other adults' names are also fictitious—except for those who have given
permission to use their real names.

Dedication

To MY MOTHER, Elda Blake Conly, who always said I could . . .

To KEVIN DELZELL, who said, "Why don't you call it 'Never Trust a White Man'?" . . .

To LIDONA AND JAMES P. SHELLEY, who typed my first draft . . .

To MY MAKAH FRIENDS AND STUDENTS, who opened a new world for me through their culture, their traditions, and their spirit world . . .

To THE TEACHER who inspired me to give to my students the traditions that formed me and who said, "You've brought an indistinguishable something up here."

Song for the Makah

GREAT SPIRIT moved across land and sea
    across mountains and valleys
  brought forth the People named Makah
isolated they lived within cedar forests
                near rock cliffs
                beside crashing seas

Great Spirit called the People his own
    spoke to them in voices of wind
    drifts of fog   drops of rain   rush of tides
glory sunsets   herbs for healing   spirit rocks
                for protection
                for guidance

Great Spirit gave them Mighty Whale
    songs to sing to Whale Spirit
    songs to sing to Salmon People
wild flowers on Ocean Prairies
                history   legends
                spirit power

Heart of Great Spirit still echoes the ages
    in throb of drums   in ceremonial dances
    sacred dreams   visions   prophecies
and in the hearts of the People named Makah.

—DARCEA SCHIESL
Tacoma poet and writer

PREFACE

" . . . not meant to be complete life stories—only insights into aspects."

HENRY WADSWORTH LONGFELLOW swept me into the world of the American Indian with *The Song of Hiawatha*. Ever since, emotionally, I have belonged to the Indian world.

Impressions from the poem's romance, pathos, tragedy felt in childhood are with me still.

My dreamy, fanciful, romantic thoughts followed me to Neah Bay, Washington—to the Makah Indian Reservation on the tip of Cape Flattery. There, between 1954 and 1959, I taught in the high school.

I remember that first school assembly. With shakes and shivers—with excitement—I watched Indian students and white students enter the Assembly Hall.

Descendants of Chieftains, Whale hunters, Seal hunters—the Indian students also came from canoe carvers, makers of drums and masks, fishermen, deer and elk hunters.

When these Indian students marched into the white man's school, each one wore his own peculiar—his own absolute—badge of assimilation into the white world.

I too entered the school wearing *my own peculiar—my own absolute*—badge from the white world.

How would I fit in with these young warriors and maidens? Would they accept me? Trust me?

I had come only to teach in a Washington State accredited high school on an Indian Reservation. I didn't come to change the Indians—to learn to speak their language—to learn to weave cedar baskets or mats. I didn't come to collect ancient masks or deerskin drums or whaling harpoons for a museum. I didn't come to study their culture—to ask questions—to write a book or earn a Ph.D. I didn't even bring a camera. I only came to do my job.

Then one day I began to write—to keep a journal—just for me. Just my thoughts, my feelings, my concerns.

I wrote on haphazard pieces of paper, backs of envelopes, pass slips—

anything that had a blank surface. I wrote of days that began and ended in a cultural fog of depression—days of fun and frolic—days of triumph and progress—days shadowed by tragedy and superstition.

Recorded—I tossed each piece into a kitchen cabinet drawer.

When I left Neah Bay, I stared at those pages of journaling—five years of living. What shall I do with them? I nearly sent them to the burning barrels—but changed my mind:

I KEPT THEM!

—*Arlyn Conly*

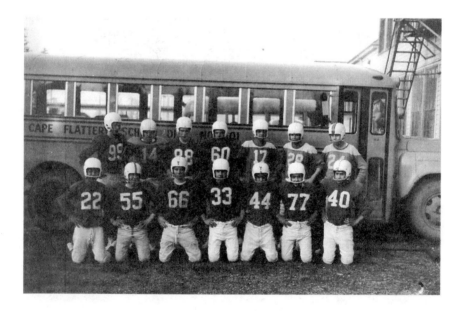

1954-1955

PROLOGUE

Washington State Intertribal Conference
October 1954
Makah Indian Reservation
Village Theater
Neah Bay, Washington

"Never trust a white man! Never talk to a white man! Stand up for your rights!"

Like a gunshot—the voice of the stocky Indian leader exploded to the corners of the theater. The voice hit ME!—there at the Council of Indian Nations.

I sat up in disbelief. Shattered. Wounded. An Indian had blasted white people . . . like me . . . the new white teacher. ME!

Oh, no! Not these harsh words from Hiawatha's people.

I wanted to hide.

The meeting blurred. I was carried back—back to when I was six years old. . . . I remembered listening to my teacher read the rolling lines from Longfellow's *Song of Hiawatha.*

With the flow of the song, I moved into the RED MAN'S WORLD. Enchanted, I wanted the song to go on and on—but it stopped with the shrill of the dismissal bell.

I followed my chattering, first-grade friends outdoors—outdoors where the hazy, smoke-filled air drifted over us—smoke from September's burning leaves.

I couldn't speak of it then—nor understand it then—but now I know what I felt standing in autumn's smoky air. Smoke swirls from the burning leaves had become Indian signals—*Gitche Manito—THE MIGHTY—*called the tribes of men together—called the warriors to his Council.

In my child-mystique—I was there at the Council of Indian Nations—I was kin to Hiawatha's people—my people. I watched smoke twist upward, upward, from the *PEACE PIPES of great CHIEFTAINS.*

That day all life around me pulsed Indian Spirit Power. I felt that power in a hedge of Sweet Syringa—in a scarlet Indian Paintbrush—in a graceful Weeping Willow, an emblem of deep sorrow.

Indian Spirit Power lifted my spirit to the mysteries of the RED MAN'S HEAVEN. Following the pathway of ghosts and shadows—I traveled the Milky Way—watched the fiery tresses of *Ishkoodah, the Comet—*sought my Guardian Spirit—heard chants of Chieftains still echoing the ages.

NOW—TODAY—at a real Council of Indian Nations—I heard a Chieftain chant prejudice: *NEVER TRUST A WHITE MAN!*

RACE PREJUDICE—unrelated to me—only an abstraction that I had heard about—read about—but never felt. Now I felt it. Stunned—it hit me like an ice-cold wind. I shuddered.

Hastily, I glanced around. Were they all looking at me? No. Faces, serious and concerned, gave no clue to their thoughts. But I saw their grievances—their bitterness—etched in deep creases under their eyes—in trenched lines across brown foreheads. I saw their past written in those deep lines and creases—a past I had never lived.

Today—at this Council of Indian Nations—they had come far from the wigwam of Nokomis—over prairies and mountains and rivers . . .

As on a screen, Indian faces and figures passed before me. I was a spectator. The presentation of their whole tragic—tormented—history pointed right at me. There was nothing I could do about it . . .

I didn't feel like taking the usual teacher-meeting notes. It would have been out of place. Sacrilegious. I was an intruder. This was their meeting and I didn't belong here . . .

I had smarted under the surprise attack that had ripped my Hiawatha-world apart . . . but how COULD they trust the white man?

I thought of LESCHI, Nisqually Chief, who met death through the white man's treachery and ruthless greed.

I thought of JOSEPH, Chief of the Nez Perce, and his tragic flight that led to blood on the snow at Bear Paw.

I thought of how the buffalo were slaughtered by white hunters and how the Plains Indians were left to starve on the prairies.

I thought of SEATTLE—great Chief of the Duwamish-Suquamish Allied Indian Tribes—who stretched out his hand—extended his heart—in friendship, in peace, to the white man—*only to find no hand, no heart, could stem the bold invader's reach* . . . the great Chief too knew the sting of treachery and betrayal—broken promises—broken treaties—of the white man . . .

My eyes closed in sorrow and shame—but I could not blot out the many trails of tears.

~

The bus lurched in a deep rut.

The lurch jolted my thoughts back to Tacoma—back to the shrill of the four o'clock alarm. I remembered how qualms struck my stomach. No time to pamper stomach qualms today. At seven o'clock I would begin an all-day bus journey from Seattle to Neah Bay—at the tip of Cape Flattery.

A new teaching assignment awaited me on the Makah Indian Reservation. My thoughts teeter-tottered! How would I fit into this isolated Land? How would I fit into this different culture? History? Legend? Spirit world?

A lone passenger on the rickety bus, I now joggled over the last miles from Clallam Bay to Neah Bay.

The bus lurched again. This time it jerked my thoughts back to the stony wilderness road, once an Indian trail that silently threaded its way to the western sea. Brown feet had walked in secret spirit with all nature beings. Deep-throated voices had chanted praise-songs to the rising daystar.

After many centuries, intruders changed this trail to the western sea.

Road crews with dynamite sticks and blasting powder ruthlessly ripped into the Land. From the force of the high explosives, Earth-Mother erupted into the sky—rocks and boulders crumbled—trees split and cracked—mountain foliage, torn and shredded, lay crushed.

In defiance of this violation, summer's late, last, wild flowers along the narrow roadside bloomed in untamed brightness. Thickets of mountain sumac and vine maples—dipped in Indian red—flamed out among black-green firs, hemlocks and cedars.

The bus driver steered past sheer granite cliffs—dark sentinels guarding the Land. The steady climb broke. He pulled to the side of the road. Stopped.

Why stop on this lonely road? Wild thoughts dashed in my mind: Bandits?

Ambush? Terrorists? Fear in my voice crept out in a dry whisper, "Is something wrong?"

"Yeah. There's a boulder in the middle of the road."

I followed him off the bus—watched him shove the huge boulder over the old trail's edge. It tumbled over and over to the bottom of the ravine. I shivered.

Pushing his cap back over his gray-streaked hair, the driver hesitated a moment. "Along this road I drive with God's hand over me. So far, I've been lucky. Like today. Rolling rocks before me or after me—but I've never been hit by one."

He shrugged out of his dark-blue jacket—slung it over his brawny shoulders. "It turned out warmer than I expected." Starting back to the bus, he continued to talk. "Always some danger to watch for." His gruff voice matched his robust frame.

Before climbing on the bus, he pointed down the road. "Have to be on the lookout for deer. They'll jump out of the brush before you know it." Squinting his grayish-blue eyes, he remarked, "Back in those woods, cougars prowl. But these tawny cats don't come out near the road very often."

My thoughts traveled back into night-black shadows to Olympic wild life: savage cougar—gentle fawn: a blood tryst . . .

Now—on the bus again—the driver gripped the wheel. His blunt fingers—strong and tough—gave me a feeling of security. I lost my terror.

I watched the driver's shoulders and back sway to the bus rhythm. Now left. Now right. He rounded treacherous curves—edged roadside dips. Alert and responsible. I trusted him.

Through the window to my right, I saw smoky-violet mists rise from the rush of waters: STRAIT OF JUAN DE FUCA—once a fabled water passage.

In drowsiness, I envisioned the force of tidal currents' slap and slam against ancient rocks. Halted on the verge of shore, these rocks stood raucous in nakedness—brazen—dark. From their darkness eked a warning . . .

History and legend called out in this changing scene of water, sky and mountains.

. . . and high in this sky—high above the cedar forests—a great bird swooped and swerved in native freedom. Was it the legendary Thunderbird I'd read about or a powerful spirit Eagle?

I tried to follow the mighty bird's upward flight. I searched beyond cloud images—but lost him in the glinting sun-streams of crimson and gold.

Enclothed in this mountain fortress, I sensed being enlightened—being awakened to an irresistible, magnetic pull beyond the jolts and jostles of the bus—an invisible, mystical SOMETHING drawing me into the unknown—from out of the past toward the western sea—to Makah Country.

Suddenly—the end of the road.

Here—the Land of the Makah stretched before me . . .

I stepped from the bus. Alone. No one to meet me.

Now faded, the glinting sun-streams of crimson and gold darkened into purples and shadowed grays.

A seabird's desolate cry echoed my silent desolation.

Only darkened forests, foreboding, loomed around me. Stern, craggy towers crushed me. Treacherous reefs lay hidden in that powerful sea. Black spirits of grotesque rocks watched . . .

I wanted to run. But I walked the path—past evergreens—toward Cape Flattery School District #401. Silence—eerie and awesome—followed me.

At the gate now—I tripped the latch—stepped through—left the silence. Earth—hard under my feet—belonged to Washington State. I was safe.

I opened the door to my apartment—paused—wondered about the year ahead. I had questioned coming to this faraway Land—an Indian fishing village on the northwestern point of continental United States.

Once a friend had cautioned, "You might be crushed by the Great Wheel . . . you had best step back." How could I step back? There was no place to step back to. Besides, all my belongings were here—piled around the room in boxes and suitcases and trunks—all waiting to be unpacked. But I did wonder how I would fit into this strange, detached Land.

 "Hel—loo. Hel—loo," a voice called through the screen door. I turned to face a slight, wiry woman. Old-fashioned, tortoise-shell combs held her gray hair in place. "Oh, please come in," I invited.

"I'm Alta Starks. You're the new Home Ec teacher, aren't you? Mr. Rutledge told me about you last summer." Sharp eyes snapped behind lenses set in flashy frames. "I'm so happy to be first to welcome you."

Before I could catch my breath—another voice—soft—but with strong tones. "Knock. Knock. May I come in? We've all been waiting to meet the

new Home Ec teacher." I turned from one to the other—tongue tied. "Not easy to find someone to come all the way up here—booming fog horns—drowning rains—isolation—scares most people. I'm Jule Craggs, second grade teacher. Mrs. Starks teaches in the high school. You'll have lots to talk about."

Jule Craggs—like the rocks I'd seen on the shore of Juan de Fuca—rugged and sturdy. Her blondish-red hair, with gray sprinkles, pulled straight back, was pinned in a firm braided knot. No make-up. But color from the sun tinged her cheeks. Outdoorsy, I thought. Tramping beaches—poking into driftwood heaps—looking for glass balls and strange, spiky sea urchins—filled her free hours I learned later.

"It's nice meeting you," she smiled, glancing over the stacks of baggage. "You're busy. I'll come over tomorrow." Blunt and straightforward.

At the door Jule Craggs pivoted. "You know the bed is hidden behind those wide doors." She pointed to the far end of the living room. "You'll get used to pulling the bed down at night and shoving it up against the wall in the morning. Come over later for tea . . . if you care to . . . "

"You'll get used to a lot of things," Alta laughed. "Until I came here, I never cooked with gas or operated an oil heater."

Remembering back to that first year, I recalled shaking as I slowly guided a match flame to sources of fire: GAS. OIL. I had clenched my trembling eyelids and waited—expecting a violent explosion to follow. I had wanted to run and hide until it was over.

Alta broke into my reminiscence: "Too bad you weren't here last week to help celebrate Makah Day," she reflected. "The Indians put on quite a show. Dancing. Games. Boat racing. Feasting. The main dish was Salmon—very delicious." Pushing her hair back from her forehead, she went on: "The festival commemorates the day in late August 1924 when the Makah were granted American citizenship."

Getting edgy on the sharp angle of the trunk, I casually remarked, "Oh, I wish I'd known." Mentally, I checked boxes and trunks—thinking how wonderful to have all my stuff sent up here and delivered by water freight.

"As Miss Craggs told you, I teach in the high school. I have all the math classes. Surprisingly, some of the Indian students do very well." She fluttered out a handkerchief—patted her face. "Warm in here. But oh my," she added, "others I can't do very much with. Pretty hopeless, I'm afraid!"

"You'll do all right with Home Ec. It's not an academic subject, and they all love to eat."

Chattering clickety-clack, Alta emphasized, "I'm Senior Class adviser. You're new. I suspect they'll give you the Freshman Class."

I squelched a yawn—hoped Alta hadn't noticed. "Right now my schedule is a bit vague."

"Yes, and they do switch things around even at the last minute. One never knows. Anything can happen here . . . "

In suspense—I waited—but Alta changed the subject.

Her laughter flowed easily. I felt her humor came from a source—at present, unknown to me. Later, I realized that I would need a sense of humor too in order to survive.

"When I received my first teaching certificate," Alta said, "I was only sixteen years old. In the pioneer days of Colorado, a high school diploma qualified for a state teacher's exam. I took it—passed—and the first thing I knew my career began in a one-room, country, school house. I've handled all four years of high school in one room."

Alta took her glasses off—peered through the lenses—again a handkerchief from her sweater rubbed out the smudges. "My! Oh my! I'll never forget my early days in Colorado, Wyoming and Washington. I came here several months ago to complete the spring semester. Some kind of trouble caused the teacher to quit."

As she stood to leave, Alta laughed again: "But I'll stay right here just as long as they'll keep me."

"Oh my!" I thought. What a long, fascinating life lay behind this pioneer teacher of the Old West.

I wondered if she ever kept a journal . . .

 A firm click snapped the door shut. I was alone. Restless—unstrung—not willing to face the boxes and trunks, I escaped to Jule's. She greeted me with "I'm checking my mail. For the last week, I've . . ."

"What a gorgeous kimono!" I interrupted. Dazzled by the elegant black satin, the gold embroidered dragons, the accents in orange and purple, I exclaimed, "It's exquisite!"

"It's an extravagance from Seattle's Chinatown. Have to splurge once in a while," she said, dropping her mail into an Indian basket. "In Chinatown—in a quaint herb shop—I bought a box of spiced tea. Let's have some." Squinting her deep gray eyes, she added, "I hoped you'd come."

Hot spiced tea soothed like an opiate. So did Jule's cheerful calm. I nearly dropped my cup though when her calm burst into contempt. "There's that woman!" Jule scorned. "SHE, I call her. I'd hoped they were rid of her."

Through the picture window I saw a tall, heavy-boned woman in classy gray slacks topped with a red blazer. With meticulous precision she latched the campus gate behind her.

"Who is SHE?" I found myself whispering.

"Who is SHE?" With an impatient shrug, Jule looked at me. "Nobody really knows. Recluse from the hills, I guess. There's an isolated community back in the woods. Some say it's kind of a health resort . . . a group of people came out here from the East Coast to regain their health. SHE came with them, I understand. They grow their own vegetables—don't eat meat—drink herb teas—that sort of thing. SHE lived with them part of the time—often driving to Neah Bay.

"Eventually, SHE met Rudy Buckthorn—a Makah fisherman. They were married two years ago. SHE's now Rega Buckthorn—just a troublemaker and bad influence." Jule squirmed in her chair—lifted her feet to a footstool. "So now SHE tries to run the Tribal Council, school district and village. Typical white woman found on Indian Reservations. I've taught on three and know her type," Jule sneered. "Sometimes it was the Indian agent's wife—can't fit in any other society, so they try the Indians—always want to reform them."

I listened to all this and wondered: Where did I fit in?

Setting her tea cup on the coffee table, Jule rasped in disgust, "SHE dyes her hair coal black, wears hideous, garish eye make-up, uses too much rouge. Reminds me of a circus clown."

The gold embroidered dragons on Jule's kimono shimmered and rippled when she moved. I stared at them. They stared back. A shiver tingled through me—an invisible mystical SOMETHING . . .

Jule interrupted my thoughts. "Let's have more tea. I'll heat some scones."

"Scones!" I almost shouted. "Haven't eaten scones for ages—sounds mighty good to me."

When Jule disappeared into the kitchen, I relaxed against the gold brocade chair cushions. Composed living, I thought, glancing around the room. Jule's reflection of composure linked her life to beach and forest and secret sea.

Smooth-edged seashells in a Makah cedar basket linked the rolling, blue-white surf to an oil painting—on iris-blue draperies, sword ferns mingled with wild flowers. Tracing color lines running through the patterns, I found purple violets, white daisies, golden buttercups. Blends of taupe, buff, russet linked the colors in the hand-woven rug to the rocky shore.

Then—I spotted the driftwood! Propped in a corner, tangled branches reached out in beauty and simplicity. Silvered by sun and wind, rain and waves. Smells of the sea oozed from the seaweed dried on the branches.

To relish the salty essence from the deep, I closed my eyes . . . but a glint popped them wide open. Rising from the cozy chair, I followed the glint to a cedar basket piled with blue-green glass balls—one with a purple hue glistened among the others.

Glass balls: blue ones—green ones—purple ones—they fascinated me.

Tokens from the Orient—with strange, mystic origins—with cryptic, curious markings—with myriad shapes and sizes . . .

Were they ripped from Japanese fishing nets by wind and current—or plucked by spirit fingers to be pushed to Indian shores as totems for Makah lodges?

To me—they were vagabonds, wanderers, mysterious messengers that bounced and tossed in Kuroshio—the great Black Stream from Japan . . .

"Do you like raspberry jam?" Jule's question shattered my reverie. "I made it myself!"

Returning from fantasy, I dealt with an answer slowly. "Raspberry jam? Oh yes. I like raspberry jam."

But the shock of Jule's voice, and the exciting whiff of hot scones, ravished the scents from the sea—banished the mysterious messengers circling the Pacific Rim.

Lured to the kitchen doorway by the exotic smells, I praised, "What a tribute to the sea! Your collection of glass balls is a beachcomber's glory. To me they are messengers belonging to a secret sea of mystery and legend. Did you find them on the beaches at Neah Bay?"

"I found most of them here. Others were gifts. Did you notice the purple one?" Lifting the pan of scones from the oven, Jule continued, "I've always yearned to find a great big one. Maybe some day . . .

"The scones are ready. Let's eat them while they're hot." Picking up the black-lacquered tray, Jule set a plate of hot buttered scones enticingly near me.

She hesitated and then added, "You might as well hear the rest of the story. While in the resort, Rega Buckthorn formed a friendship with a younger woman—Lola. The gossips say that Lola had a degree from a New York college. Whatever it was, it qualified her to do substitute teaching."

Jule interrupted her story to spread jam on a scone. "Well, believe it or not, misfortune fell on the school. Last year—even before the school year had started—the Home Ec teacher suddenly became ill. She resigned, leaving the position unfilled. It threw the school board into a state of panic. SHE saw her opportunity and instigated the hiring of Lola. In desperation, the school board complied. It was a need that had to be met immediately, and SHE wasn't qualified, but Lola was her chance to get into the school.

"Lola blithely stepped in and took over. So did SHE—bossing the job, running the department. Like a bulldozer, nothing could stop her."

Squashed by a bulldozer—not wanting to think—I concentrated on scones.

"Yummy," I muttered—licking crumbs from my lips and raspberry jam off my fingers. "I've never tasted such crusty, luscious scones except at the Puyallup Fair."

"Guess what? I made them from the same recipe."

Then, silence. Warm, secretive, nostalgic.

Jule split the silence and thrust Lola back: "While Lola was teacher, there was always some disturbance going on—some conflict in her classes. The high school staff and Principal believed Lola encouraged a fight between an Indian girl Molly and a white girl Carrie. They said Carrie taunted Molly as coming from an Indian slave family. How ridiculous! We don't recognize that sort of thing. But the girls got into a bloody fight. Knives flashed. Both girls were cut up. I never knew the whole story."

Jule paused a moment. We sipped our spiced tea and nibbled scones. "This year Lola applied for the same job—but she wasn't hired. Her rejection infuriated Rega Buckthorn."

Jule poured more tea. "They claimed Lola needed Washington State certification. But there were deeper reasons—like a way to keep Rega Buckthorn out of the school."

Jule reached for another scone. "SHE's been over to welcome Jacqueline Winters, third grade teacher. You'll like Jacqueline."

A wry wrinkle creased Jule's nose. "They both will be around to pick you over. At least SHE will. Be prepared. You have an enemy in Rega Buckthorn just by being here," Jule warned.

Jule laid her horn-rimmed glasses on the end table. "I become so weary worrying about conditions here: the drunkenness, the immoral behavior, the child pregnancies, the slovenliness and the neglect."

Preoccupied, Jule traced the outline of a dragon on her kimono. Etched lines across her forehead deepened. A shadow of sadness moved over her face. Jule was deeply troubled. "Sometimes I wonder if I want to come back next year."

And I wondered . . . would I be back next year?

I stared at the tea leaves helter-skelter at the bottom of my cup. Must I summon an old Makah Medicine Man to predict my fate? Uneasiness was building in me. Fear gripped my throat.

. . . Lola was not rehired . . . I had her job . . . "You have an enemy . . ." echoes as a premonition.

Shrill, terrified neighs awakened me. Terrified too—I jumped out of bed—rushed to the window. In the misty golden dawn: HORSES! Before my unbelieving eyes, horses wheeled, snorted, screamed. Heavy hoofs pounded the ground and ripped the grass.

Men's bellowing commands shattered the golden dawn: "Whoa! Whoa! Back! Back!" shouted a tall, dark-haired man in a brown and beige plaid jacket. "Rick! Rick! Head off the leader—the Blood Bay!"

In black jeans and a bright red sweatshirt, Rick ran in long strides to face the Blood Bay. "Whoa! Whoa!" he yelled. "Hey! Hey! Back off! Back! Back!"

He'll be trampled, I gasped. But by wild circling arms, Rick turned the Blood Bay around. Speechless, I watched the magnificent, auburn-toned stallion plunge into the milling horses. With frightened squeals, the huge horses bunched. Then, as if by some unspoken command from the Blood Bay, they charged across the school yard and out the west-end gate.

Did I glimpse a mane of pale gold? A palomino? A spirit horse? A ghost horse?

My breathing eased. Flying manes and tossing tails disappeared. I hoped equestrianism wasn't part of the curriculum.

But I would meet with horses often!

And so it was that I entered my new world—in a golden dawn . . .

Voices—at ten o'clock in the morning.

I knew who was coming.

"Be prepared," Jule had warned. "SHE will be around." Struggling to cover the couch with a large, furry, white throw, I turned— and there SHE stood—possessing the doorway: Rega Buckthorn.

My eyes glanced her height—her dyed black braids coiled snake-like around her head. Heavy gold-loop earrings dangled defiantly from pierced ears. Darting cold black eyes impaled me. I couldn't move. SHE has come to possess me! I thought—wildly.

Strides—long and determined—stepped Rega Buckthorn to the room center. SHE jerked her head sideways and shot a haughty smile toward me. Arching her arms in wide flings, SHE pushed me out of her way. "Oh, how clever! I like your interior design. You're an artist. How original! Covering this ugly old furniture with elegant white throws gives a designer effect." Tipping her head, SHE sneered, "The District should be forced to replace these worn-out pieces and install refrigerators in teachers' cottages."

Stuck in shadow, Jacqueline Winters watched the scenario. Then Jacqueline stepped out to introduce herself as third-grade teacher. Amused, she said, "Getting anything done around here takes time. Last year I waited three months for plumbing repairs."

Jule was right. I liked Jacqueline. Soft sunny hair fluffed into a fringe framed her fair delicate features. Her warm charm bloomed in contrast to the cold boldness of Rega.

SHE informed me that three days ago Jacqueline had driven from Morton. "A logging town in the Cascade foothills—as I'm sure you know," she quipped. "Loyal to her home town, she waited to celebrate the annual *Loggers Jubilee*—coonskin caps, log-rolling contests, fireworks—the whole sh'bang!"

Glints from Rega's black eyes bore through every trunk and box in the room. "But Jacqueline was back in Neah Bay in time for *Makah Day*. Too bad you missed the Salmon feast and boat races—a real cultural education." Her eyebrows arched in sarcasm.

Striding toward the door, SHE turned, towering over my five feet. I felt threatened. Repelled—yet fascinated—I heard her say, "As adviser to the Girl's Club, your one big job is putting on the *Mother's Tea and Style Show* in May." Innocuous words—but menacing tones. "The *Mother's Tea* is traditional and *THE* social event of the school year." Lifting her arms above her head, SHE snapped her fingers and swung her hips in cabaret style. "It's time to step up the glamor and really shine. The Village, the District, and the River residents all look forward to it year after year."

In a flamboyant gesture—Rega—forever planted in my mind as SHE—faced me. Her eyes pierced me. They seemed to be everywhere at once. Witching eyes.

Her voice grew gruffer. "Girls make their own garments to model in the Style Show. Better start nagging now. Some girls—the lazy ones—will straggle behind—just sit around and do nothing—until the very last minute." SHE poked a finger—tipped with blood-red enamel—at my heart: "And you'll end up doing the whole garment yourself! I know what Lola went through."

I sensed uneasiness in Jacqueline. "With all these boxes and trunks to unpack, you're busy. We'll come back another time." Jacqueline moved to open the door. Jacqueline's hint—ignored—SHE babbled on.

By this time, Rega's dagger-toned voice stabbed me. "You can't start planning too far ahead." The blood-red fingertip still pointed at my heart. "Begin right now to make your list for invitations. I worked so hard with Lola." SHE rolled her eyes. *"You dare not overlook anyone!"* SHE warned with a chiseled smile. Her chiseled smile turned into a smirk. "Lola nearly missed it."

Rega's eyes—now like thorn points—spiked right through me. Behind these threat-spikes perked a pitying smile: "It's your ONE chance to stand in the limelight to make an impression. Your contract renewal will live or die by the success or failure of the *Mother's Tea*." A sharp-edged smile cut across her lips. SHE wanted to scare me—not help me.

WAS I scared? After all: WHO WAS SHE?

Contract renewal? That could wait. This year's contract hadn't even begun. But I felt squelched.

SHE amused Jacqueline. SHE hexed me. Thereafter—*THE TEA*—an obsessive shadow—haunted my days.

As they walked into the late morning mist, I caught an impish twinkle in Jacqueline's hazel eyes: Message received. Decoded later.

~

LATER brought Jacqueline and Jule to my door. "We couldn't wait to tell you what Rega Buckthorn said about you."

"WOW!" I applauded with a wry laugh. "Tell me, I can't wait."

From Jacqueline's lips erupted: "THAT WITCH . . . WHERE'D THEY GET HER? . . . SHE'LL NEVER LAST UP HERE!"

Darts quivered in my stomach like tiny arrowheads . . . ME! The new Home Ec Teacher! SHE CALLED ME A WITCH!

Jacqueline followed her outburst with a giggle. "I think it's funny."

Jule comforted, "It's obvious. SHE bitterly resents you . . . you were hired instead of her friend Lola. SHE'll make it as tough for you as SHE dares—I warned you . . ."

I stood—stunned—forgot my manners. I finally spoke up, "I'm sorry—please sit down—I'll make some coffee."

"I brought some cinnamon rolls." Jule continued with "SHE's hopping mad because SHE couldn't control the School Board—and another thing—you're petite and dainty—such a contrast to that tall heavy-boned Lola—she's the one who didn't last up here—forget it."

Jule held a rock in her hand. "I found this rock on the beach—it's rather interesting." She placed it in my hand—a small rock with a dip in the center—a salt-crusted barnacle grew on the cusp. "Indians believe spirit-powers dwell in all nature objects. Keep it. This rock may hold spirit-powers to guide and protect you."

A mysterious power welled within me. For this moment—I would forget it—I sharply reminded myself. This was no time to brood over Rega Buckthorn's words edged in ominous black.

The picture-view from the back window—above the kitchen sink—glistened like luminous silk. In early dew, the sun drifted its patina sheen over nearby hills and faraway cliffs. In this brilliance, I fantasized a golden eagle—his great wings tilted in powerful upswing. I wanted to "upswing" too—but I was grounded—stern demanding stacks of baggage stared at me.

Two stiff cups of black coffee started me off: I wound the alarm clock—hung skirts and dresses—filled drawers with sweaters and blouses—tacked up the calendar.

Mid-afternoon hunger urged me to munch on Jule's leftover scones. As if the act produced her, Jule's voice called through the screen door. "Come, let's walk to the village. You can finish unpacking later."

"I'd love to finish unpacking later." Happy to leave my task, I followed her up the narrow trail. We faced into sharp, salty air from the sea. Vital! Spicy! Tantalizing!

From the beach—strong, briny whiffs of seaweed, clams, and mussels stung our noses. From the village chimneys—wood smoke spiraled—mingled with sea smells.

A force of energy filled me—a new intense quality of strength flowered within me. I WOULD MAKE IT HERE!

Jule talked. I listened.

"No one would dare come up here without a full range of immunity shots—especially tetanus—hope you've had yours." Anxiously, she peered at me from under slanting brows.

"Oh, no! Not me!" I protested. "I've never ever had any immunity shots—except smallpox. Shots scare me."

"Well, you ARE brave," she muttered.

I laughed—covering fear. Was I really so brave? Jule had had them all:

tetanus, flu, typhus, bubonic plague, jungle rot—she never took chances.

Lined by tall weeds, the short pebbled incline led to Front Street.

Jule pointed to a small white wooden building to the right. "That's the Post Office. It's not only a place for mail—but a tourist information center and source of village gossip. Same as Washburn's Store—at the other end of the village. There's always some rumor flying about: 'Do you know . . .' 'Have you heard . . .'"

Nearby, a weathered, rickety, public telephone booth had replaced Indian signal codes. In its vandalized open-air enclosure, I heard a laughing brown-skinned girl chant, "You'll never believe it—but I met him in Forks."

We walked on. "Like an Arabian scimitar—the beach curves in a crescent—readily visible in postcard aerial views."

But I wasn't listening. Exhilarated by the picturesque beach curve—dazzled by sun sparkles—I inhaled live, fresh, salty sea air, and thought again: I will make it here.

Jule crashed my thoughts. "You'll notice all village houses face the water. An Indian tradition—handed down for generations—forests must be kept at the backs of the people—kept behind the houses. I guess they believe dark and evil spirits lurk in the forests."

Circling close to shore, seagulls shrieked and squawked. Wings outspread, gulls swooped down to feed at water's edge.

"Seagulls are with us year round," Jule assured me. With a brisk turn she pointed toward the Strait—to a bulkhead-like structure. "That's the breakwater. It's a rubble mound—built of broken stones and loose rocks—heaped in a pile."

Amazed, I asked, "How can loose stones and rocks piled in a mound stay put?"

"They do and the breakwater really works," Jule said. "It's built to hold back the pounding waves from violent winter storms." Jule continued to fascinate me by the breakwater story. "The project was constructed by a corps of government engineers and finished in February 1944. It's 8,000 feet long and runs from this western shore to Waadah Island out in the Strait."

Jule turned—pointed to the eastern shore. "That's where the Waadah Point Coast Guard Station stands—on the shore of the Strait."

Wrenched from the mound of loose rocks—and the Coast Guard Station—my attention riveted on HORSES! HORSES! HORSES! Right down the middle of Front Street. They swished their tails—they twitched their ears—they cloppety-clopped on heavy hairy hooves—right through auto traffic, people traffic, bicycles, and little kids.

This wild band from the Ocean Prairies stomped down the village street with devil-may-care snorts and stomps—*as if they owned the joint.* Among the blacks, browns, the dappled grays, the Blood Bay stood out: the leader—the horse I had seen in the golden dawn. Then, blending with the lawless band—the shimmer of a palomino? A spirit horse? As glimpsed in that early dawn? Or just sun in my eyes?

Horses disappeared. Dogs appeared. Black dogs, brown dogs, spotted dogs, running dogs, barking dogs, scratching dogs, sleeping dogs—dogs in the street, in doorways, on door steps, under porches, under cars. "Better to run over a child in this village than a dog," Jule scoffed.

Soon face to face with a big old frame building, Jule began another story: "In 1931, the first paved road from Port Angeles to Neah Bay was completed. Before then, all supplies and food stuffs—like meat, milk, bread—plus the mail—were brought up by boat. Now most commodities are found in Washburn's General Store.

"The store began as a little country trading post in 1902. It's been enlarged since then. Everything's here—from spinning tops to old whaling harpoons. One of the Makah elders, Perry Ides, trained as a harpooner.

"Just look at those children," Jule interrupted. "They're going to get hurt if they're not careful."

Over old splintery board steps, happy Indian children crawled and climbed, twisted their agile bodies around gray-timbered porch railings. Quick and lively in play, these little black-eyed, round-faced boys and girls mirrored the living traditions of their Land.

Jule bombarded my thought-wanderings: "Let's take this backroad." A dirt path angled between five or six small frame unpainted houses. "Most Indian homes are like these—built side-by-side or askew. They're ramshackle. Nobody ever repairs anything. They just let them fall apart. If doors sag, somebody props them up.

"Wonder where this key belongs." Jule stooped—picked up a brass key—pondered—then dropped it into the pocket of her yellow windbreaker. "I'll turn it in to the school office. The owner might come asking about it."

Walking past two or three more houses, Jule abruptly stopped. "Just look! Broken steps and cracked railings. It's a wonder some drunk doesn't fall and break his neck."

In dismay and disgust, Jule threw up her hands. "Now just look at this mess! Orange crates, sardine cans, and beer bottles scattered with the other trash—covers the whole yard. I don't know why they can't keep their junk picked up."

A vacant lot exposed a network of discards. "What a sight!" Jule stormed. "They smash up their cars—then leave them any old 'which way' and buy another."

Cars in demolition: caved-in hoods—knocked-out windows—cracked windshields—trunk lids ripped off—tires flat. Mixed with scrambled cars: discarded stoves, refrigerators, washing machines—all added to the hodge-podge.

"What a junkyard! What a novelty view for tourists!" Jule paused—slipped her hands in her pockets—looked toward the Bay. "I get so upset struggling to help improve living conditions. I do the best I can with my second graders, but I wonder if I'm getting anywhere."

From the vacant lot, a side road at the west end of town led to the gray-shingled Presbyterian Church. "Oh look, an old-fashioned bell tower! Are there bats in the belfry?" I laughed. "Romance and history exude from old bell towers—they keep secrets too."

"I'm sure they do," Jule said. "This old belfry has heard many things unspoken. Presbyterian missionaries were the first to come to Neah Bay. Let's sit here on the steps a while." She looked toward the water. "It's getting breezy. The tide must have changed."

In these romantic surroundings, I waited for Jule to tell more. "Before this church was built in 1935, services were held in the Mission. The old harpooner, Perry Ides, was the first Makah to become a Christian. He was pastor of the Mission until failing eyesight forced him to retire."

This old harpooner stirred my imagination.

"Breezes are getting nippy. We'd better move on," Jule suggested. At a rectangular one-story unpainted frame building, Jule stopped. "This is the Makah Community Hall. It's not built like the cedar-plank longhouses, but it's a center for all Indian activities. They love parties and start the drums beating for just about anything: weddings, birthdays, baby showers, distinguished guests or ceremonial dancers from other tribes. Some very spectacular and unusual masks and costumes show up at these gatherings."

Back on Front Street, we meandered through late afternoon traffic. Looking—I was being looked at too. Village women wearing bright-pat-terned head scarves—shawls or sweaters strung across their shoulders—stood around gossiping. Some carried baskets of blackberries. Others ran after small children, but all quick-like glanced at me. Curious, black-eyed children turned to stare. Village fishermen—carrying Salmon right out of the sea—looked askance.

Who was the stranger with Jule Craggs? Did anyone guess I was the new Home Ec teacher? What were their first thought-impressions? I wondered. Small in stature—hair pulled back in a pony tail—engulfed in a bright-blue windbreaker—I was guessing too!

 Believed by the Indian tribes to be a Spirit Gift from the Great Spirit, the Medicine Bag became my own Spirit Gift.

> . . . believed to hold totems with spirit power: love charms, healing herbs, sacred bear claws
> . . . believed to possess powerful spirit objects needed by skilled warriors, great hunters, mystic healers
> . . . believed to hold signs divined from *voices heard—powers felt—visions seen*
> . . . believed to be a Spirit Gift from the Great Spirit

When the American Indian Medicine Bag first became part of my cultural belongings—I believed it legend to all tribes. Then one day I asked a Makah friend about its origin, "We never used the Medicine Bag—not the way the Plains Indians did—we do use herbs for power and healing and protection."

From legends and stories—I gathered bits and glimpses into differing tribal concepts of the Spirit Quest or Vision Quests—native to all tribes . . . but the Medicine Bag was different.

• An Indian youth from a Plains Tribe returned from HIS Vision Quest. Objects that appeared in HIS vision: love charms, healing herbs, sacred bear claws, stones with magical powers are found in HIS Medicine Bag . . .

• An Indian youth from a Rocky Mountain Tribe—weakened by days and nights without food or water—forced into fierce struggles with demon spirits—overcame enemies—returned from HIS Spirit Quest. By signs received from HIS Spirit Guide, the youth made up HIS own Medicine Bag . . .

• An Indian youth from a Dakota tribe—deprived of energy by fasting for many days—returned from HIS Spirit Quest with visions: a great bear reared before him—a raven perched on a cedar branch—a creek rippled through a canyon. To understand HIS vision, the youth seeks a Medicine Man—who deciphered the meaning of the visions. They are then put in HIS Medicine Bag . . .

In fantasy, I made up my own deerskin Medicine Bag. Instead of love charms, healing herbs, sacred bear claws, stones with magical powers, I stored my Indian Spirit symbols in it: my olive-shell necklaces, shredded cedar bark, an eagle feather, a black prayer rock. I protected happenings and friendships. I pulled classroom assignments from it—included the stories of the Salmon People and the Whale Spirit—the legend of Destruction Island and Tatoosh Island—the sequence of Star and the Blood Bay stallion. All turned into culture codes to line my Medicine Bag.

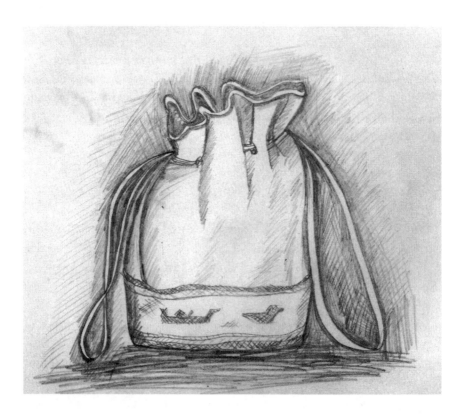

TODAY: Plunged into this culture far different from MY OWN, I was oblivious to the struggles and frustrations of the Makah.

YESTERDAY: Plunged into a culture far different from THEIR OWN, the Makah still shifted in confusion, distrust, and bitter resentment.

A Chieftain had shouted: "NEVER TRUST A WHITE MAN!"

As a white teacher, I was living within conflict—within prejudice.

Did it all begin with the Government schools? I would ask Jule . . . I did.

Then one day Jule began to ventilate her beliefs, opinions, impressions: "When the Treaty of 1855 was signed, the Government agreed to educate Indian children."

Jule viciously attacked the brutality of the Government schools. "All they could think about was to civilize these savage Indian children RIGHT NOW. QUICK! QUICK! QUICK! And the quickest way was to sever all ties with their families—strike out the old customs—rip their language out of their mouths—cut off their beautiful long black hair. Both boys and girls suffered this humiliation and indignity. Tears of protest and anger only brought punishment."

As we sat on the steps, Jule squinted into the late afternoon sun, added more: "I might say here that the Indian prized his long black hair. It defined his Indianism—exemplified 'the Indian way.' Determined to eradicate 'the Indian way,' the white man forced the Indian men to cut off their long, black hair. This degraded and humbled the tribesmen—deprived them of their freedom—their Indianism."

Intrigued by Jule's bit of history, I listened to more: "I get so upset just thinking about how these poor, frightened, lonely, homesick children were treated—snatched from their families—and dragged into unnatural living quarters—compelled to wear uniforms at odds with their native dress—forced to eat foods disagreeable to their taste—coerced into losing their identity—to sabotage their Indianism NOW!"

With profound reconciliation of differences, I harbored Jule's impressions.

Within me grew a longing to reach out—to touch—to fully grasp the essence of living between two worlds—to understand—to value—the heritage of the Makah students who tend to rebel—with silence or aggression.

Some time later Jule added: "From what I've learned, the Government established an Industrial Boarding School—here at Neah Bay. This was in the late 1800s. In spite of its being very harsh and strict, it was one of the

first schools in the United States to add Manual Arts and Home Economics. I guess the Government deserves some credit. But I've heard that many
Makah parents attacked the Government schools with violence and hostility.

"It's important to understand the early background. It makes one want
to work in harmony with the culture—the cedar trees—the ocean—the village—and the school children."

~

Bitter memories of the old Government Boarding School days still fer-
ment from generation to generation.

Once Ernie said, with unforgiving hatred: "I know how they treated my
mother."

Those were the dark years. Tragic memories hover over those who remember.

~

After a while—at Makah parties—at Salmon feasts at the Community
Hall—at Forum (PTA) meetings—at school functions—a spirit connection
grew among some of the Indian people and me.

Entangled in this web of changes, I thought of the Indians as
living not within two worlds but living within three worlds:
. . . the Traditional Makah who seeks to retain language, legends, ancient traditions—to continue their crafts—their way of life.

. . . the Progressive Makah who seeks to abandon native teachings—let
the old ways perish—turn to the new way—the white man's way.

. . . and the White Culture whose Government imposed new codes
that changed the lifestyle of the Makah.

Yet, Ada, a Makah elder, said, "I glad when white man come—we not
worry anymore about other tribes making war on us."

But Ada also voiced sadness, "Our old people not understand the new
way. Many drink whiskey to forget."

Within this intertwining of worlds, past lives emerge minute and insignificant in contrast to the present magnitude of life around us all.

How vast! How great! How powerful! How sad!

I felt all these things at once—omnipresence—and I was a living part of
it all—part of a changing culture—part of a changing world.

"I HATE YOU!" hissed Dolly.

With a backward jerk of her head, she spit. Her target: Corky. Horrified—I froze. My first day. My first class. And there I stood—speechless—benumbed.

I stared at this feisty girl with honey-colored curls. Defiance glared from her blue eyes. Spite twisted her sun-tanned cheeks. She stamped her foot—knotted her fist—shook it under Corky's freckled nose. "Don't you dare touch me!"

Rage and anger distorted Corky's face. His temper matched the red blaze of his hair. "The gym-bag was mine in the first place," Corky shouted, snatching the bag from Dolly. "Besides, I only loaned it to you—you stole it!" He scrutinized the leather strap—continued to yell: "Remember, stupid! It was before school was out."

Even with the clang of the bell, their quarrel went on. Exasperated and frustrated, Dolly wheeled, kicked the gym-bag in Corky's hands, shoved him against the desk and stomped out.

Stunned and shaken, I wanted to wheel and stomp out too . . .

~

Later, at the end of that first day of confusion and disorder, I realized these kids were just back to school—right off beaches, off fishing boats, off camping and hiking trails—still high and wild from MAKAH DAY! They had had no time to adjust to the classroom, so they shoved and pushed and yelled into their first class—Freshman English—MINE!

Will tomorrow be better?

 Those first days: shock and confusion stalked me. Was Dolly's unexpected outburst, "I hate you!" to set the pace for classroom behavior?

Struggling in this vortex of the unpredictable, I faced so many demands— so many questioning, suspicious eyes—so many violent, quick flashes of anger.

~

I was shaken and troubled by disheveled, unkempt Indian children. Boys and girls from elementary grades—to junior high—to high school— came to classes ill-groomed, slovenly, with grimy hands, dirty fingernails. With pain and despair, I sorrowed for these children of Makah—forced into an unnatural, alien, white culture.

Boys, more often than girls, marked my attention: rumpled pants, crumpled shirts, stained T-shirts, stiff black hair standing on end.

Did they sleep in their clothes last night? I wondered.

By the time most girls reached the boy-crazy stage—the "in-crowd"—they affected a contrast. With divergent lifestyles—family backgrounds—personality traits—girls, aspiring to date, emerged to attract, to appeal.

~

In this state of perplexity—in this existence of contrasts—I strived for order, for discipline, for respect.

In the midst of resistance and indifference, I found a spark of willingness, eagerness, and even friendliness.

This spark ignited COURAGE! Courage to open my Medicine Bag of class schedules and assignments. Did hidden messages, secret codes, surprises lurk in the deeps of my Medicine Bag?

I soon discovered each assignment carried its own code of communication and system of signals.

Freshman English concealed a hidden message: distress signals flashed hot anger. A presage? (As initiated by Dolly?)

No flashing red lights or sirens escorted American Red Cross Home Nursing class . . . but when I pulled out Food and Clothing assignments—an alarm blasted: "THAT WITCH . . . SHE'LL NEVER LAST UP HERE!" In my mind I answered that curse with a war cry—my battle strategy—forming on yonder skyline to May: The Mother's Tea and Style Show!

A deep corner of my spirit bag held a request—a surprise—an after-school instruction class in Nutrition. No menacing threats here—no warning voices. Kelly—Makah—graduating senior—aimed his talents for a chef's career. Soft-spoken, polite, appreciative—Kelly's resolve to learn inspired me with an end-of-the-day impetus.

From the bottom of the Bag erupted: TYPING! The last period of the day—down in the basement—next to Boy's Shop. No sirens shrilled—no SOS calls—no war drum's alert. This group of juniors and seniors created their own secret codes of behavior.

And that wasn't all! Secret codes, disentangled—announced: No Girl's Athletic Director hired this year. So they posted me as Girl's Education Supervisor. WOW! To keep score in a basketball game or girls' soccer, I could not! Poor me! I might teach a class in clog dancing—but there were no clogs.

From a deeper dig into my Medicine Bag, mysterious voices whispered, casting me as adviser to both Girl's Club and Freshman Class . . . and another SURPRISE—assistant adviser to the school paper, *THE CHIEFTAIN*.

My mind twirled and spun like a top. "THAT WITCH . . . SHE'LL NEVER LAST UP HERE!" twirled and spun in my mind too!

No time to think. No time to question: Would I last UP HERE?

All day I whirled and thrashed from one class to another. I distributed textbooks, assigned lessons, took lunch counts (free lunches for Indian children), signed pass slips, learned names, listened to giggles, to flashes of temper: "I did!" "You didn't. You weren't even there."

And so those first days I moved in partial shock. To absorb this bi-racial school atmosphere demanded time:

Time to think. Time to adjust. Time to accept.

Time to place life in my medicine bag.

~

"How do you like it up here?" eagerly asked the school kids of a new teacher.

UP HERE meant the high, wild, windswept Makah Indian Reservation at Neah Bay, Washington—a spread of forested Land that stretched to the tip of Cape Flattery. This historical Cape—a headland—hangs above the turbulent swells of the North Pacific Ocean . . . THERE the swells crash against the splashy breakers from the Strait of Juan de Fuca.

UP HERE on the Cape—on this high point of Makah Land—spanned an arc of timeless sky and water—ageless cliffs—forested hills—mighty sea boulders.

UP HERE in this rugged wilderness the Makah was one with the Land . . . and me. I was swept into the mystique of the Makah culture:

. . . sounds of their harsh guttural ancient tongue

. . . power-beats from their primitive drums

. . . ceremonial dances with their native masks and costumes

. . . chants from their spirit songs

UP HERE I walked the pebbled beach where once stood the Spanish Fort—tramped the muddy trail to the Cape named Flattery by English sea captain James Cook—lived the legend of Tatoosh Island and Destruction Island told by a Makah storyteller.

UP HERE the Indian Spirit World spoke to me: Guardian spirits—Storm spirits—Whale spirits—Spirits of sea and wind—Spirits of fog and rain. Even wild flowers on the Ocean Prairies spoke spirit life—as did pebbles along the beach path and star fish left on the shore. All belonged in the chain linking the natural world to life . . . to *my* world . . . to *my* life.

UP HERE where the wild flowers flourished . . . I watched blue-bells toss sassy heads in wind and rain. I tendered wild violets nestled in purple bunches. Before my eyes, yellow-headed thistles spotted the rough terrain—brilliant tops of Indian Paintbrush enlivened the Land.

UP HERE spirits of the Rainbow flashed colors that exalted my psyche: a sunrise flamed bright and brilliant—vivid blue, scarlet, and gold—as seen in that first golden dawn. Sunset hues flamed orange, purple, magenta—colors that staggered my senses—as did storms that raged and lashed the sea-tossed waves that leaped awry.

UP HERE in the legend of Tatoosh and Destruction I learned native people—long ago—believed trees, mountains, rivers were inhabited by spirits in human form.

UP HERE the Makah's band of wild horses roved. Like a shadow on the periphery—I glimpsed the mystical palomino—the golden horse in that first dawn.

UP HERE I became one with the splendor, the beauty, the majesty of the Land and its People: an old harpooner—a medicine woman—a basket maker—a descendant of the great Chief Seattle.

All these and the quick jerk of an earthquake became memory totems for my Medicine Bag.

 It's like entering an exotic bazaar in Afghanistan—where hundreds of tiny brass bells tinkle—to beckon tourists into the market place.

Only it's not Afghanistan—it's Neah Bay! Tinkling brass bells turn into tinkling olive-shell necklaces—the exotic bazaars turn into craft shops along the crescent curve of the beach.

From Alta I had learned that in August 1924 the United States Government granted all Native American Indian tribes citizenship.

Jule scorned in ridicule: "Citizenship in their own native country."

To commemorate this Spirit Happening—this vital extension into the white world—Jule recalled that in 1926 the Makah Nation set aside a day in late August—called forevermore: MAKAH DAY—a day when progress and tradition meet.

I know about PROGRESS:
- Automobiles—from Cadillacs to Volkswagens—dot the Land
- Telephone wires carry messages in and out of Neah Bay
- Power from electric lines replaces longhouse fires—torches soaked in Whale oil
- Motels offer lodging to tourists and guests
- A school building with double-entry doors replaces the old government building and school
- A general merchandise store offers an easy way to obtain food supplies
- Village restaurants stir cravings for seafood
- Churches of differing sects call villagers to worship

But I want to know about TRADITION—the old way—before white man:
- Salmon tied on sticks to bake around an open, wood fire
- Olive-shell necklaces tinkle on costumes worn by little children

skipping along the crescent curve
- Teens—vivacious and bubbly—line up for tug-of-war on the waterfront
- Dugout canoes set to race on the bay—paddlers, vigorous and energetic, stand ready
- Bone-game teams compete day and night in the Community Hall
- Zettah—down where the old Spanish Fort once stood—bakes bread in the sand

Under the rippling waves of the Stars and Stripes, the Tribal Council chairman introduced speakers.

"One year Perry Ides was invited to speak," Jule said. "He spoke with fierce pride of past prowess of the Makah as a great whaling nation. He also mentioned Tribal scholarships offered to honor students."

After speeches, native competition in games and sports ran amok. Villagers and guests joined in heightened festivity—a time of enlivened activity—a day of hilarious excitement—of spirit power—of fervor and laughter—a mood of rejoicing created by an air of jubilant energy. Zesty, spicy—the aromatic whiffs of Salmon and Indian bread enticed all to the serving tables.

~

With the setting of the sun, drum beats and chants of the Welcome Song called everyone into the Community Hall—to a Spirit Happening that revived the old ways:

   . . . a time to honor ancestors, elders, young Native Americans of today
   . . . a time to remember the SALMON PEOPLE, who send from the sea their fattest and tastiest fish
   . . . a time when sacred family dances—guarded for generations—spring into life
   . . . a time when dancers in elaborate costumes—ancient headdresses—striking masks—whirl and chant, lurch and twist
   . . . a time when the thunder of native drums stirs the race-blood
   . . . a time when primitive songs echo through the cedar boughs
   . . . a time when the Makah culture becomes their own again
   . . . a time when the Makah blocks out the progress of the white man—to be themselves

"Before the rains start, let's walk down to the dock to watch the fishing boats come in."

So, another wilderness adventure began when Jule and I stepped onto the wood-planked pier. "Always a chilly wind out here. That group of wooden buildings at the end of the pier is FISHERMAN'S MARKET. It's called the CO-OP. An important port for commercial fishermen—Indian and white. Hundreds . . ."

"Look!" I interrupted—pointing to the beach. Before a wood fire a lone Indian boy sat on a log tending a huge Salmon. "Oh, the Makah have baked fish this way for hundreds of years," Jule shrugged her shoulders.

Relaxing against the pier rails, Jule followed ancient ritualistic steps to baking Salmon . . . as she remembered: "First the Indians praise the Salmon People for the fish—the Salmon is split, cleaned, and spread out flat—the head and backbone are removed—the old way. Ancient methods are still used to tie the fish on a stick frame. The selection of sticks and tying materials is like a ceremony. I understand each tribe has its own secret methods."

ROASTING SALMON

Jule gazed across the Strait—then back to the lone Indian boy. "Salmon cooked this way has a woodsy, smoky flavor. Incredibly delicious. As long as the sea gives Salmon, there is never hunger or famine."

From the Indian boy—from his blazing wood fire—from the baking fish—I felt the primitive rise around me. A Land of ancient traditions and customs . . . what Indian girl would choose to bake Salmon in a gas oven at 350 degrees when she could bake it around a wood fire!

Cultural collision: Stick frame and beach fire versus baking pan and gas oven!

~

"Here they come!" Jule waved. "Hello! Hello!" she shouted—circling her arms in wide arcs above her head. "We're just in time to welcome you back!" Small fishing boats idled to the dock. Jule rejoiced: "The hatches or fish-holes are loaded with an early fall catch . . . gold from the sea . . . gift from the Salmon People!"

Tingles of excitement slithered through me. Merging with sounds, sights, and smells, I nearly forgot to breathe. Sudden activity erupted! Rousing, boisterous noise burst through the late afternoon. Shrieks of signal whistles clashed with lusty commands from skippers. Shouts and halloo's crossed from boat crews to dock crews. Hefty arms slung heavy ropes—that creaked and groaned when cinched to dock cleats.

Squealing, squawking, flapping seagulls out-screamed the clank and clang of pulley chains . . . and over it all, sloshing slaps as sea-green water thrashed against boat sides and dock pilings.

Glued to the interworkings of fishermen, boats, dock, and sea, I jumped at Jule's remark, "During peak runs, hundreds of fishing boats, Indian and white, are out in the waters around Tatoosh Island, off Cape Flattery, and in the Strait."

Looking toward Tatoosh and the Cape, I also sighted Vancouver Island across the Strait. Still wilderness. Turning to Jule, "I've never stood on a wilderness fishing dock before. Fish were just fish—bought in a fish market."

And now, as I watched, fishermen and boat crews—with cruel-looking gaffing hooks—lifted the ocean's gold from boats to unloading platforms.

"After the fish are unloaded, where do they go from here?" I asked.

Jule broke her gaze from the lively activity. "After unloading, fish are placed on weighing scales and then sorted and graded. After the basic steps in handling, fish are iced down and shipped to Seattle, Port Angeles and other markets. Eventually, processors kipper, can, and dry or smoke the fish and send them out to markets worldwide."

The force of the evening wind increased. Jule shivered. "I help my second graders locate Neah Bay on the map—help them understand the importance of fishing as one of Washington State's greatest natural resources. These Makah children live in the center of Northwest history."

Sundown now.

We turned our backs on sights, sounds, smells of FISHERMAN'S MARKET and the Strait of Juan de Fuca. "I wonder if my second graders will remember the story of Juan de Fuca and the Strait some historians believe he discovered. I love to tell historical stories. They're just like legends. And right over there on the beach—she pointed to the west end of the village—Spanish explorers erected a Fort—the first white people to settle on Land that is now Washington State."

Like an unexpected intrusion from the past—the builders of the Spanish Fort seemed to bolt into life. I could believe I saw red and yellow banners—the standards of Spain—wave over Neah Bay. I could believe I heard hammers pounding to acclaim possession—heard footsteps of conquerors strutting over the pebbled beach.

Did Jule? . . . My fantasy vanished when she spoke up, "In 1778, Captain James Cook—England's famous explorer—out here looking for the Northwest Passage—sailed up the coast—saw a craggy headland, a Cape—jutting into the sea. Close by stood a steep flat-topped island—Tatoosh, we now know. Encouraged, Captain Cook hoped for a safe harbor, but with further scrutiny he decided not to risk sailing his ships between the Cape and the island. He turned his ships away from the treacherous rocky shore—named the jutting headland Cape Flattery. In his journal he wrote that the Cape had flattered him into thinking it a safe harbor."

I could not interpret Jule's thoughts . . . had she too felt the mystique of the historical scene—felt the vibrations from the past? Had she been far away in mind—then returned to intrigue—to tantalize?

"A trail leads to the very tip of the Cape. It's a muddy scramble of about half a mile—a tramp through forests of sword ferns and thick foliage. Tangles of roots and old wooden planks cover the trail. Once there, the timelessness of space spreads before you. "

Now, in silence, I followed Jule down the narrow path—lined with tall weeds—to a world apart.

 "We don't need no white school," scolded bold and bossy Genevieve. "Grandparents and elders show girls how." Prejudiced? You'd better believe it!
Families—still stubborn and resistant—grimly clutched old Indian ways.

That first morning, shy giggly girls entered the Home Ec kitchen. They gaped in awe. "This room is bigger than our house."

Had I read into their thoughts? Some tiny houses seen on my walk through the village WOULD fit into this large classroom.

Through the over-sized windows, September's sun streamed in—flashed on Home Ec kitchen equipment. Strange and unusual—these implements of white culture aroused curiosity and suspicion—and giggles! And stares!

I answered their stares with a question: "You've all seen the huge gas stove in the Community Hall?" Coy smiles answered my question. "The gas stoves you see here are just like the one in the Community Hall, only smaller," I explained, opening an oven door. "You can bake Salmon in the oven instead of on sticks around the fire." Genevieve turned up her Makah nose—sniffed—looked away. Just giggles from the others.

When a match to the pilot flame forced a scary pop, they all jumped back! It scared me too.

The girls followed me across the room to the refrigerator. "In here we keep milk, eggs, butter, and sometimes leftovers." Huddled together, they watched my every move. "This is the freezer compartment. Frozen meat and fish keep in here for a very long time."

What did they care? I wondered. Were they really interested? In their lifetimes they had survived without gas stoves and refrigerators.

In defense, Erma spoke up, "We don't need a refrigerator. We smoke fish the old way. We dry it for winter. We dry clams for soup. We use roots and dried onions."

"We have a cook-stove," commented serious-faced Elizabeth. "My mother cooks Salmon in a skillet." Thick, black braids wound around her head—distinguished Elizabeth from her classmates.

Four sinks—like huge ominous caverns—demanded exploration—but with caution. "This faucet turns on hot water. This one turns on cold water. Would you like to try the faucets?" Giggles and shaking heads answered my question. Genevieve—in a mood to ridicule—said nothing.

Further inspection included lifting garbage-can lids—moving prongs on towel racks—opening and closing cupboard doors—fingering white enamel-top work tables and wooden desk chairs.

"After you are served lunch from the school kitchen, you bring your trays in here. You eat your lunch in the Home Ec kitchen with all the other high school girls."

"What's in there?" Genevieve scowled, pointing at the pantry door.

Just then Simon walked in to unload food supplies. I unlocked the pantry door. A mysterious dark room loomed for inspection.

Simon snapped on the light switch. "Did you expect the village ghost?" he teased. Did shy giggles hide fears?

Spicy scents from cinnamon sticks, whole cloves, oranges and apples flooded from the pantry.

"Have an apple," invited Simon—biting into a crispy, crunchy, red Delicious. But the girls shook their heads—refused Simon's coaxing.

The bell rang. My prejudiced girls skipped out.

How would I manage the Mother's Tea with these giggly, prejudiced, little Indian girls . . .

"THAT WITCH . . . SHE'LL NEVER LAST UP HERE!"

Editing *The Chieftain* write-ups, a sharp knock at the door jarred me.

"Here's a story to read," Alta scowled, handing me a magazine. "A man, woman, and boy are brought together in a romantic woodland setting. The love theme, though well written, turns out to be a ghost story," she added in disgust. "I thought you might like it though. Will help break the monotony."

MONOTONY! No monotony in my life. I'm too busy.

Bewitched by a haunting love story, Alta had invaded my "underground retreat." Test papers to correct, lesson plans for tomorrow, food orders to call in, School Carnival coming up, Open House, Freshman Initiation Party, Halloween, and the school paper to get out on time. Everything coming BANG! BANG! BANG! How could I find time to read a story? It's been forever since I've read one . . .

One day at the end of sixth period, Dolora asked, "What do you do in the evenings? You just go over there and mysteriously go underground. Why don't you come out and do things with us?"

Do things with us, I thought. The Pool Hall, drinking and dancing half the night?

Lovely, vivacious, dark-eyed Dolora has small children. Married? I don't know. In my classes are several teenage mothers. One of them lost a baby during the infantile-flu epidemic in Tacoma a year or so ago.

Once before, Cerena had mentioned that when high-school pregnancies occurred, girls dropped out to have their babies. Then, in a year or two, they often returned to pick up graduation credits.

Spunky girls—they grappled with class schedules and routines. Some days an ill child kept a mother home. "Where's Dolora today?" I might ask. And someone would answer, "One of her children is sick." But with make-up assignments, girl-mothers moved along with the class.

A fierce ambition to receive a certificate of graduation held the girl-mothers to a steady pace.

~

Again I was reminded of a conversation with Cerena after school.

"Several times since I've been here, fourth- and fifth-grade girls have quit school to have babies," Cerena despaired. "It happens through incest, older men attacking them, and many girls have been molested by school boys. It's a very tragic situation and nothing is done to protect these innocent children."

"What becomes of the baby?" I asked.

"If the mother can't care for it, a grandmother or other relative or friend takes the infant. Some families have secret herbal remedies to induce abortion, I've heard. Most formulas are lost or forgotten by now." Then Cerena added, "There are many wicked people out there in that village."

Cold and clammy this night. Fog horns moaned a doleful monotone of drizzle and doom.

I heard a rush of footsteps. Debra stood in the doorway. "It's spooky out here," she shivered, stepping into the room. "With all the groaning fog horns and everything else that's going on, Breck's about ready to quit."

Debra lay her coat over a chair, settled herself near the stove. "Breck's at school—meeting with Mr. Perkins and other teachers. It's about the behavior of some of the kids. Several of Breck's sixth graders are pretty rough stuff."

Always the last one to hear the latest gossip—the latest scandal in the village—the latest blow-up in the Tribal Council—the latest problems in the classroom. Was it part of my job—my education—to accept, to understand—a CULTURE far different from my own? I believed so.

Like huddling over a witch's brew, I listened. Debra weighed her words before speaking. "It's only hearsay, but Breck's heard one of the new teachers is becoming a nervous wreck, just about to fall to pieces."

"Oh?" I questioned—filling coffee cups—setting out a plate of shortbread.

"It's a problem with the kids—mostly football players." Debra removed her earrings. "These are too pinchy. Anyway it sounds to me like a kind of ganging up to scare him half to death. Bold and pushy—these big football players move in around him—like they're going to scalp him—and he's terrified."

"I know what you're talking about," I laughed. "They do the same to me—but one thing I know—those bold and pushy Red Devil Champions soon found out they could not intimidate or frighten me. When they hunch their shoulders—and move in around me—I just look up—smile sweetly—and shove them out of my way—and they throw back their heads and laugh! laugh! laugh!"

Today after school I joined Jacqueline in Jule's classroom for coffee. Alta was not included. Jule rejects her.

Autumn sun flushed the room with warmth. A cozy place to relax, unwind, chit-chat . . . but I found Jule's lusty background of gossip and scandal unsettling.

While Jule poured out coffee, she poured out gossip: "White women at some river-lodge resort—nothing but immoral drunks—indiscriminately exchanging husbands. Husbands—drunks also—and womanizers. That's what the gossips say. These women," Jule scorned, "come to the village—toss their heads so high falutin'—snubbing everybody. I have no use for any of them." Jule refilled our cups—opened a jar of cookies. "Then there're certain village men and women who have their own indiscreet rendezvous, the whole place reeks with gossip—most of it's probably not true."

Jule's gossip—not my interest. Mine is focused on my teaching assign-ments, the kids, and how I would cope. I hoped she'd change the subject, but she rattled on: "Watch out for Minnie Atwater, a white woman. She's two-faced—a real troublemaker—interferes with teachers—bosses the Princi-pal—tells him how to run the school and athletic department. She objects to textbooks, luncheon menus, football schedules. Then, of course, she sticks her nose into Tribal Council and village affairs."

All this time Jacqueline and I sipped—munched—listened.

Jule walked around the room—checking desks—talking constantly: "Tribal Council members want to kick out all white teachers—hire Indian teachers. At least that's what we hear some want."

White teachers! I was one. Qualms hit my stomach again: "THAT WITCH . . . SHE'LL NEVER LAST UP HERE!"

I forced my thoughts back to Jule's chatter: "Cerena and Brad—elemen-tary teachers—she's so pampered and spoiled rotten," criticized Jule. "Brad is so much older. He treats her like a child." Adjusting the pins in her hair, she added, "I'm only guessing but Brad was probably a country school principal and Cerena one of his students. A very kind and gentle man—he fell in love with the young and beautiful Cerena. It must have been some-thing like that," Jule decided. "Cerena's health barometer teeter-totters from fair to poor—all in her head."

Helpful? All this unsolicited blabber just confuses me more than I al-ready am.

Finally Jacqueline changed the subject: "Arlyn's already heard Rega Buckthorn's opinion of her:

"THAT WITCH . . ." You know the rest." Jacqueline snickered, "I still think it's funny!" Not funny to me—not at all.

But I pumped up my courage—looked at my lipstick smear on Jule's cup, "I've never been called a witch before—but a witch can call upon magical powers—spin a spider's web." But my courage nearly failed: "SHE'LL NEVER LAST UP HERE!"

My turn to change the subject. Reminded of my coffee chat with Debra, I offered a bit of news—a new teacher's episodes with the bold and pushy Neah Bay Red Devil champions: "One of the new teachers is falling apart. Ed's short for a man—walks around tippy-toes to appear taller—most of his school kids are taller than he is." Reaching for a raisin cooky, I went on, "They're kind of ganging up to scare him half to death. Indians! Scalping! They're living it up. When those bold and pushy champions crowd in around him, he's terrified. He's becoming a nervous wreck. Ed's afraid to stand up to them. He's thinking of leaving, Debra told me."

"Oh yes, I've seen him around," Jule commented. "He came in a couple days late. I can believe he'll have a hard time around here. He's small for a man—not big and brawny like the champions. They would compare their broad, powerful shoulders to Ed's skinny narrow ones—his pale, thin face with light blue eyes to their native deep black eyes—their wide Makah face, robust coloring, and black hair to Ed's blond, flat hair. I can understand these football players would try to intimidate a man unlike themselves. You're short too—but pretty and cute—and a woman. That makes a difference."

I laughed. "One thing I know. The bold and pushy Peninsula champions found out soon enough their scare tactics could not intimidate or frighten me. When they hunch their shoulders and crowd in around me, I just smile sweetly and push them out of my way. These Red Devils throw back their heads and laugh, laugh, laugh."

So did Jule and Jacqueline. Laughter lifted the depressing gossip.

Picking up purses and books, Jule gave us one more bit of information: "A prominent Makah elder donated ten acres of his Indian Land for the school property."

Drifters . . . sent to this Study Hall . . . corrupted and violated. Not belonging . . . these vagabonds . . . kindled fire bombs by their attitude: "You're not my teacher. I don't have to!"

"Sidney, sit down." I pushed for obedience from my regular kids.

"I am sittin'." Mischief oozed from his grins and impish black eyes.

"There's no such word as *sittin'*," I retorted.

"There is so. I'm sittin' right here."

"Well then, study," I strongly suggested.

"I am studyin' . . . I'm studyin' you."

"Well, I'm not your History or Biology . . . "

Roars of "Haw! Haw!" split the air waves. Hopes for a peaceful Study Hall shattered into unpeaceful pieces.

The last period of the day I face the typing class—in a room down in the basement—next to Boy's Shop. By day's end, everyone is either tired or mad or sad or lazy.

Members of the high school football team are in this class.

CHAMPIONS! Neah Bay Red Devils: Champ, Jack, Jerry, Tom, Scott, Lester and Mac. All Indian. Voices roar as they attack the keys—chanting, "We are from Neah Bay! Rah, rah! Rah, rah, rah!"

What's going to bewilder me next? These first days were full of surprises . . .

One Tuesday the class collapsed before it began. Tom casually handed out balloons in Mardi-Gras reds, purples, yellows. Color and noise erupted. Balloons tied to typewriters and backs of chairs bounced to and fro. Balloons floated in lazy paths up to the ceiling.

With fists full of peppermint candy, Jerry and Champ strolled into class. A happy boisterous love song from Champ incited a round of titters from the girls. "O come to my tent, my beloved . . ." he yodeled.

Then Tom announced, "Today's my birthday!"

So what! I thought. Do you have to desecrate all I ever learned in PRINCIPLES OF EDUCATION? So now I stand and twiddle my thumbs while you celebrate.

"Bosoms!" shouted Champ, as he stuffed balloons under his T-shirt.

"PG!" announced Scott, as he stuffed one under his belt.

HORRORS! Will this day never end? But soon the merrymakers steeled to class routine—heads bowed over typewriters—fingers struck keys in rhythmic clickety-clack.

Birthday favors—still tied—floated and bounced. Others popped, lay mangled on the floor—like I felt some days—mangled on the floor.

 I still recall the Village road—rutted and narrow—that led to a sign nailed on a tree: CAPE AREA TRAIL. RUGGED, HIGH CLIFFS. EXTREMELY DANGEROUS. ENTER AT OWN RISK.

I took the risk—followed the muddy trail to the Cape. Sword ferns—thick and majestic—brushed my shoulders. Scattered within this wilderness headland—huckleberry, blackberry, and salal bushes grew in abundant ecstasy.

October sun-glimpses squinted at me through mingled branches of cedar, spruce, and hemlock. Stepping over tangles of conifer roots that spread across the trail—I hurried on.

Then—a clearing—the trail ended. I stood on the tip of Cape Flattery.

Before me spanned an arc of timelessness—great, wild, wonderful—sky and water unrolled in an endlessness of space.

Flanked by ageless cliffs, mighty sea boulders, forested hills—the Cape reached out forever into never-never-land.

North Pacific waves roared and hissed and slashed against the cliffs below. Mysterious water-echoes rippled through caves and hollows under the Cape. Near the ocean shore—Kwat'utal's Jaws—the savage rocks of legend or imagination—snapped black and cruel 'neath a snarl of white foam.

Held captive by this Land of history, legend, spirit power—I became one with the Indian world. I heard the wind chant spirit songs—felt the tug of centuries gone—listened to Indian prophets whisper the coming shadows . . . I watched a seabird swoop down the sand-strip toward the Point of the Arches—mighty off-shore sea stacks ruthlessly pounded by North Pacific storms.

Dazzled and thrilled by the elements of timelessness and endlessness, I forgot I belonged to the real world.

All at once an illusive spirit voice told me it was time to go—time to go back to the real world.

I turned—walked the trail to the Village.

 Some days I feel such defeat—such complete—absolute—uselessness. I remember SHE called me a witch and declared I'd never last up here.

I remember a friend advised I had best step back—lest I be crushed by the Great Wheel.

I remember having read somewhere: "It is too soon and too vast to see everything in the first moments of seeing."

I remember WHERE I am: This is Makah country—a wilderness—untamed—wild—rugged.

The little children seem so mysterious. They look at me with their startling bright black eyes. They question: Who are you? Where did you come from? What are you doing here?

"For the first year they just look at you," an older teacher consoled me. "It takes a whole year for them to get used to you."

After all, these native people exist in the depths of transition. White culture imposed wrenching changes. The Makah struggle to survive within these drastic precepts—to survive within conflicting cultures.

Echoes from their past—haunting memories—reliving the old days—before white man came, Natah remembers.

~

In the meantime, how can I work with the Freshman English class? How can I break through the Freshman barrier of "play and giggle"? Were they questioning me—an outsider?

 "Let the talents die! There are enough crafts in the museums." How could a prominent Makah woman say that at a school assembly? Did I sense a tone of arrogance? Of defiance? What a squelching reply to a teacher's question: "Why don't you teach native Makah crafts to keep the talents alive?"

By that shattering statement, did the answer seek to banish ancient talents—or was this scourging to dissuade white people from learning native skills?

~

Later, Jule clarified, "Bitter feelings of defeat still exist. Several years ago I learned an old Makah woman, filled with unrelenting hatred of the white man, scorned, 'They've pushed us back as far as they can on this old rock—now they want to steal our crafts.' Other Tribal members, stung with resentment, fiercely resist white people learning their crafts."

I remember—at the assembly—one of the elders emphasized that some Makah do not want to lose their Indianism—they want to preserve *their old ways—their language—their crafts.*

 Hoping he'd be unnoticed, Scott slid into his seat—his head slashed and bruised. Grumbling and growling as usual, he made no intelligible comments.

Jack, with lesser grief, sheltered two bandaged fingers. Woozy from a hangover, he rested his head on the desk.

Champ slid into his seat—cradled his head in his arms—"I backed my car down an embankment . . ."

The girls giggled in silly response.

Kirk Hall, the Lummi Indian, was sober. But I questioned his sobriety when he asked, "Would you have went with me to the dance Saturday night?"

"And get my head all banged up?" I shuddered.

Kirk's handsome Makah friend Duke grinned, "We'd protect you."

"Thank you, Duke, but I think I'll hibernate on Saturday nights."

Not members of the class, Kirk and Duke had drifted by to check on the casualties.

LUNCH HOUR: Noise! Rowdiness! Shoving! Jostling! PANDEMONIUM!

An open doorway—through the Home Ec Room—a short-cut to the lunch line—a fast-lane for Freshmen boys to reach the lunch line FIRST!

But today—a foggy, misty morning—fog horns blared disaster on the rocks near Tatoosh—and the girls waited for lunch too . . .

"It's about time for those Freshmen boys again," forewarned Dolly—staring at the wall clock. "They always get out of Shop early."

"Those smarty-pants boys make me tired," blazed out spit-fire Cheree. "They rush through here every day like they owned the place."

"It's just so they can be first to lunch," scoffed Annabelle in flippant mockery.

"I have an idea!" burst out Cheree—her dimples *popping.* "Come, Daphne, help me!" They dragged a desk chair to the door. Tipping it, they hooked the sturdy back under the doorknob.

With a final, determined check-test on her IDEA, Cheree gloated, "This will fix them!" Her words hissed through tight lips.

BUT—when the door stuck—those kids crashed right through!

Bodies thudded to the floor. Groans! Grunts!

Faces grimaced. Shock! Surprise!

Breaths belched out. WHOOSH! WH-I-I-ISH!

Then began an enterprise of commotion: frantic hilarity! Twisted bones and flesh wiggled to disentangle a snarl of arms and legs and heads.

"OW! Take your elbow out of my eye."

"HEY! That's my neck you're pinching."

"I can't find my arm!"

"It's under my back, stupid!"

"OH! OW! I think my head's cracked!"

ENTERPRISE is scholastically categorized as *venture calling for courage and energy.* Freshmen boys! An over abundance of courage and energy—THERE!

Replace the door? We did. Bought it with our own money—out of the Freshmen Class treasury.

Of course—it was all MY fault! I was Class Adviser!

 Above the booming bawl of foghorns, Indian drums thudded in mystic beat.

"Drums!" I thrilled. Calling to us—coming to meet us.

"The drumbeats are like messengers of welcome carried down from an ancient Makah tradition," Jule explained. "The Makah singers welcome guests with a traditional chant in answer to the drums."

Were the drumbeats the fog mists whirling me to some secret tryst—to the power—to the mystery of this Land and its People—that reached far beyond my first ceremonial—to that *invisible, mystical SOMETHING* that pulled me to this Land?

. . . Land sanctified by the Great Spirit. Land, that I took for granted, the Makah worshipped as their Earth-Mother—Land was LIFE—SPIRIT—STRENGTH—POWER—Energy-power that flows through all beings.

As we walked, Jule broke the mood. "You'll see Helen tonight. She's one of the Makah dancers and singers—an Indian princess—proud of her long line of Whaler-Chief ancestors. Helen's great-great-grandfather, a Makah Chieftain, was among the signers of the 1855 Treaty of Neah Bay." In stifled tones, Jule muttered, "I call Indian Treaties *invaders, desecrators,* of Indian rights."

My thoughts skipped back one hundred years to that historical moment—to the bold invaders' reach—to the signing of the Treaty of Neah Bay. I now walked over this Makah Land . . . felt the fog leave its moistness on my face and hands. Were ancestral spirits—signers of the Treaty—watching? listening? Tremors shivered through me.

I WATCHED. I LISTENED.

Enchained in this now-time Land by primitive drums and ancient chants—I moved apart from the ruthless invaders . . . I moved as one with great-great-granddaughter Princess Helen, maid of Makah.

Jule crashed my reverie. "We're here," she announced. "Watch out! Don't stub your toe on that broken step."

Drums pounded in the background. Mysterious. Exciting. Spirit-stirring.

Was I bewitched? Was I mesmerized by this Indian and white gathering? Facetiously, I shifted my vision, searching for an old Makah Medicine Man. Instead, Jule touched my arm. "That's Perry Ides over there—next to Reverend Dale-Smith. Perry, as you know, was the first Makah to become a Christian."

I remembered the old harpooner—briefed by Jule on our walk through the village. He stood a staunch reminder of the old ways—but also a progressive leader into the new ways.

Happily, greedily, I loved every moment. I smiled at people I knew—at people I didn't know—waved to kids from my classes.

"Oh, looks like Minnie Atwater's Boy Scout Troop is serving tonight. She's just another troublemaker," Jule sputtered.

A little Indian boy in a Boy Scout uniform set a plate of baked Salmon, mashed potatoes, creamed corn, carrot and cabbage salad before me. Looking into his sparkly brown eyes, I thanked him, praising, "You look handsome in your uniform." He beamed with pride.

"Butter is on the table," Jule commented. "Bread slices are served in those small oblong Makah cedar baskets . . . and never anywhere will you taste Salmon as delicious as this! Fresh out of the ocean, fish has a piquant, zesty flavor. Then, when tied on sticks and baked around an open fire, the flavor is enhanced by the tang of wood smoke—hard to describe."

Jule was right. The woodsy smoky flavor WAS hard to describe.

Desserts ran amuck! Pies: pumpkin, apple, gooseberry, and peach. Cakes: German and red devil chocolate, lemon chiffon, confetti, angel food—piled high with gooey white frostings. With her last bite of gooseberry pie, Jule said, "Village ladies, Indian and white, bake the cakes and pies to donate to these community gatherings." She glanced around, "I thought I might see Helen, but she must be in the kitchen or dressing in one of the back rooms."

Boys from the Scout Troop removed plates and dinnerware, bread baskets, and leftover pies and cakes. "It's time to leave the tables now," Jule noticed. "It's customary to clear tables, fold and place them against the back walls. Then the floor is brushed clean for the dancers."

In jig-time, expert sweepers had brushed the floor from clutter and crumbs. "Let's find front-row seats," Jule suggested. "You won't want to miss anything." No, not tonight. Not at my first ceremonial.

At this first Indian and white festival—I devoured the beat of drums, the noisy chatter and laughter, the brown and white faces. Soon a powerful silence swept over all. Children stopped pushing and shoving. Laughter and talk quieted. Swept into the silence too, I forgot Jule. Then she whispered, "Here come the dancers. They'll sing and dance the traditional Welcome Song."

The action of the dancers set in motion the black Whales and red and black Thunderbirds painted across the backs of the ceremonial robes . . . significant symbols of this whaling tribe.

After the Welcome Song, another dance group moved into place. "That's Helen." Jule spoke in low tones, pointing toward a graceful dancer. As if floating, Helen blended as one with the dance movements. Fringes trimmed her costume of a light brown fabric. Orange, blue, yellow, green beads and olive shells decorated the bodice and skirt. Olive shell necklaces tinkled to Helen's dance-steps. Her black hair with gray strands hung in braids down her back. A bright-beaded headband added glamor to her costume. Then, like a flash, Helen and other dancers vanished.

Another flash and out came a high-stepping solo dancer. "The Medicine Man Dance," whispered Jule. A black and white cedar-bark mask with wild red eyes and strands of flying long black hair covered the dancer's face. Rattles clattered in his hands—his stamps and lunges, twirls and twists, evoked feelings of terror and danger—of tension and fantasy. Right out of a legend, I thought. Then, with a sudden forward rush and a series of whirls, he too vanished.

Drum thuds slowed. The slackened pace called performing teenagers. Signaled by a THUMP THUMP from the drums, the dancers rocked in gentle motion. As they rocked, they sang.

"This is the Paddle Dance," explained Jule. The dancers dipped the air as a paddle dips the water. Jule quietly hummed words that fit the dance:

> O paddle dip . . . dip
> strong and deep
> O paddle dip. . . dip
> into the sea
> Guide my canoe
> wherever I go
> O paddle dip . . . dip
> strong and deep . . .

Tonight . . . beyond the invaders' reach . . . I lived as one with drum-beats, rhythmic chants . . . and the maid of Makah.

I had walked into a new culture—I had felt mystery, spirit power—with every drumbeat—every rhythm of the chant—every turn and twist of the Medicine Man Dance—originating from some primordial energy thousands of years ago.

In sleep—I twirled, twisted, stomped, and lunged.

In dreams—I floated with the bending grace of Helen, maid of Makah.

 "Fleas—fleas—fleas!" ranted Jule on our way to the village the-ater. "Blood-sucking pests—they hop, leap, skip—they eat me up and are driving me insane—I'm constantly at war with them—I spray, spray, spray—but they find me anyway—so I scratch and scratch—end-lessly."

"I've heard of cat and dog fleas—but not people-fleas," I said.

"You'd better believe there are people-fleas. Cerena and Jacqueline point blank refuse to go to that flea-infested theater. Mrs. Starks' Christian Science seems to protect her.

"Those miserable biting critters—they even leap off the grade school children—even out of their hair. Some of my second graders scratch and dig until their arms bleed. Poor kids," Jule sympathized—rubbing her arms.

"If you ever find one at home—grab it fast—plunge it into a glass of wa-ter. Wet—they can't jump. They won't die though—unless their hard shell is cracked. Use your fingernail to press the flea against the glass—when you hear a crack, one more flea is dead." I shuddered. "This way is best—if you don't have spray."

"Yuk! To kill a flea . . . may I never find one."

~

"I can't understand why you never find any fleas," wailed Debra. "They are all over Breck and me. We have Tuffy but he doesn't seem to make any difference."

"Oh, but I have! One night I felt something crawling on my arm. I reached for the light, threw back the covers, and there it was."

"What did you do with it?" she asked.

"I grabbed it and threw it on the floor."

"Oh, no, Arlyn, you didn't!"

But I did!

I touch the Ocean . . . the Ocean that speaks in countless moods—in myriads of tempers deep and dark—cold, vast, mysterious—it may rumble in gray danger and power—it may flirt in sassy wicked mirth—it may sigh in deceitful calm, only to burst into rage—erupting waters that plunge into violence—into storm breakers—that pitch against Tatoosh Island—that smash against beaches and rock towers near Destruction Island.

On this bright October day, I followed sun and blue skies to where I touched the Ocean—where I felt the energy—the mystique of water, space, shadow—where wave and wind echo of shipwrecks, tempests, Whale songs—dip of canoe paddles—and flutter of canvas sails—where—today—the Ocean rolls—heaving and boundless—its voice gentle—softly spilling over wave tips.

Out here I revel in the freedom of sky and sea—in the spacious reign of sand. Low, low the tide this day—reaching to the edge of the world—waves ripple to soft foam.

Turning from the Ocean of space and shadow, I walk over wild rough-rutted earth. From shore to far cliffs—this earth is called Ocean Prairies by the school kids. Sandy, rocky—the Prairie is covered with wind-stunted oaks, misshapen dwarfed junipers and grizzled pines.

Among these shrubs, the Indians' horses range.

"Our horses are sorta wild," a school boy grinned. "Us boys ride them across the Ocean Prairies." With a faraway look in his eyes, he said, "The leader is a Blood Bay stallion. There's a star on his forehead. None of us can catch him."

THE HORSE THAT FLAMED IN THAT FIRST GOLDEN DAWN?

Ignoring me, the huge horses roved—cropped tough-bladed grasses and stubborn prairie weeds. I scan both oceanside and prairies. To my left, autumn's sun glosses the bronze-gold back of the magnificent Blood Bay: a warrior stallion! Resplendent he stands against the copper sky among yellow-headed thistles.

In the sunlight, the white mark on his forehead shines like a Star Spirit. Transfixed, I watch. The warrior horse jerks his head impatiently—nostrils quivering. Does he sense danger? I tense—hold my breath. Lowering his head, he grazes again. I release my breath slowly.

Then among the dark-colored horses, I spot the shimmer of a golden mane. A palomino? I blink my eyes. Is it a trick of the sun? A few seconds ago there was no palomino.

THE SPIRIT HORSE THAT GLIMMERED IN THAT FIRST GOLDEN DAWN?

Mesmerized by the powerful presence of sea and sand, do I envisage the golden horse—a spirit stallion that guides the lawless band? By chance, one sent by an old Makah Medicine Man?

Somehow I can accept this thought on Makah Land. Here, NO THING is impossible . . . not even a golden spirit horse . . . visible one moment . . . gone the next.

I hear a muffled whinny. My attention shifts to a pearl-gray mare and her newborn foal. Uneasy, wary, she paws the rocky ground.

Miraculous happenings appear too fast: the Blood Bay—the spirit horse—the pearl-gray mare with her colt.

Captivated by these wonders of the Ocean Prairies, a thought flashes: I grasp their images of power, vitality, freedom, and put them in my Medicine Bag to become my Indian spirit symbols.

Then I wander down to the shore to gather beach treasures: sand dollars, crooked bits of driftwood, black swirls of dried kelp, and barnacle-crusted rocks and shells.

The wind changes. The tide turns. Scooping up my beach findings into a paper bag, I hesitate. At my feet—imprisoned in sand—nearly lost in pebbles and broken shells—a coral-colored point reaches toward the tide. I brush away the sand and broken shells—then lift a tiny tiny starfish. Turning it in my hands, I marvel at this five-pointed totem from the sea: a fragile shell—empty of life.

Sun-warmed—yet chills shiver through me. My spirit reaches out to this little sea creature with a star-shaped shell. Once a bit of life, it was free to skim the crystalline waters—free to follow light lines from a glinting rock to an under-sea chalice. It tumbled, twisted, turned in phosphorescent wave troughs. Glowing. Shimmering.

Then one day—near Makah shores—there—trapped by an angry sea—it was spit upon the beach. Struggling—the tiny starfish cries to its life tide, "Come back for me." But the tide never comes.

Tenderly, I hold the tiny starfish—sun-dried, hard, and stiff. To me, this tiny five-pointed totem carries a spirit-line to the force, beauty, freedom of the sea, the wind, the sand—the mare and her colt—the mystical golden horse—and the Blood Bay with his own star.

All sea creatures—like the starfish—have guardian spirit power. It guides and protects the finder.

I found this starfish . . . STAR! That's what I'll call him . . . STAR! Perhaps he'll be my Guardian Spirit—my Guiding Star.

Awed by this allusion, I move with the mighty rhythm of the incoming tide. Winds slap waves. Iridescent bubbles of foam tumble over sand. Burst. Vanish.

Aware of Star's spirit, I can't drop him in the paper bag. I carry him in my hand.

A shrill cry strikes the stillness. Startled, I turn, clutching Star.

Something has frightened the mother horse. From behind a jagged black boulder, I watch in horror. A raven-black horse—his hammering hoofs tearing stubbled stems—rears. A defiant roan—ears flattened—bares yellow teeth and snaps viciously. Squealing, the huge horses bunch, crowding too near the wobbly-legged newborn. In panic, the mare throws back her head, paws the air and screams again.

The Blood Bay stallion squeals in answer to her outcry. Pitching his powerful head, the copper-toned warrior rears, whirls. His ripping hoofs hack clumps of leftover summer flowers. He plunges into the milling horses. He shoves and nips the riotous animals away. They turn, scattering. Their strong, hard-muscled hind legs kick the prairie sod into leaping clods.

Tense, alert, the leader watches his restless band. He turns toward the mare. With brief, soft snorts against her neck, he consoles her. Secure again, the mother horse nuzzles her foal.

My eyes glimpse a shimmer. Is it the palomino? Yes. He moves—a golden light—to the side of the colt. Then he is gone.

I look for the spirit horse to appear again . . . but instead, five Indian boys crawl from behind a prairie hillock. Had their nearness triggered the fears of the mother horse? Heedless of danger—with ropes in hand—the boys close in. Fascinated, I watch. A spirit-rapport guides each boy to a marked horse of his own. He slips his rope over the horse's head—grabs the mane—flings a leg over the horse's broad back and races off.

Bareback, wild, free, swift—they skim the Ocean Prairies. For a time they belong to their Indian past—pencils and books forgotten.

Then, as returning through a secret sea corridor, they draw rein and canter back across Ocean Prairies. Horses left to graze, the boys walk back to the village—to school yards—to pencils and books.

I too come back from the Ocean Prairies. Sitting on the floor, I spread my beach trinkets before me. STAR must have his own lodge. I lifted him—with his stiff spiny points reaching for the tide—lost in sand and broken shells. Now I know where he belongs.

Spearing the deeps of my deerskin Medicine Bag, I find Rock: drab, sad looking. A hollowed dip caves Rock's center. I feel a Spirit blazes within the hollow. On Rock's cusp a lone salt-crusted barnacle clings. From this sharp-ridged crest, a stream of silver mica leads to Rock's secret power.

I place Star in Rock on the coffee table as my totem of Indian-Spirit Power.

Whenever I look at Star—my tiny totem—I shall always know I have seen the workings of unwritten laws of the Ocean Prairies: a place where Makah Land is embodied in a tiny tiny starfish—in the mystery of a golden horse—in the protective power of a Blood Bay stallion with a star on his forehead.

~

Today after school, Debra and dog Tuffy walked home with me. Over tea and crumpets, we gossiped.

Abruptly the chit-chat chopped off. Debra pounced. Grabbed Tuffy's jaws. Forced them open. Probed.

"He's got your starfish!" Debra shrieked.

"Oh, no!" I gasped, terrified.

Not daring to move, I could imagine the tortured crunch that would gnash Star to bits. I squeezed my eyelids tight, covered my ears and pleaded:

"O Guardian Spirits
Protect Star.
Bring him back to me."

. . . and they did . . .

"I found him!" shouted Debra.

I couldn't bear to watch. From somewhere—between teeth and tongue—she pulled out Star— nearly drowned in dog slobber. But Star was mine again.

How did Tuffy find that speck so small in Rock on the coffee table?

Did Star smell like beef jerky—Indian pemmican—dried Salmon—even like dried starfish?

Poor doggie. I couldn't blame his instinct—nor forgive his rape.

~

In Remembrance: Like the doggie, I too knew the shock of intrusion.

A party at the Community Hall!

Girl's Club? Class party?

Somebody was always having a party.

And I was always stuck making coffee:

In those enormous, foreboding, gray-granite coffee pots.

After a while, I learned to deftly tie the coffee in a cloth and precisely drop it into a pot full of water—and—forget it.

But don't let the pot boil over.

. . . I remember I was looking for someone or something and burst suddenly into one of the back rooms: SURPRISE, SHOCK, RESENT-MENT etched on Indian faces.

Unknowingly, by my intrusion I had invaded a sacred cultural sanctuary: Makah women cooking fish heads!

Startled and offended by my rude rush into the room, they dropped everything—stared—gasped.

But I had never expected them to be THERE.

They relaxed though when they discovered it was only me. We all laughed . . . and I left them . . . with forgiveness . . . to their cultural delicacy.

Like ducking in and out of rain storms—I ducked in and out of the school's lunch-room kitchen—an escape to the Indian cooks: Deena, supervisor, and her jolly assistant, Marta, both warm and friendly—with them I felt secure.

Frazzled by student behavior—I sought their consolation—my Prop Pals. With endearment—I enfolded them in my Medicine Bag.

"I could scream bloody murder, tear out my hair, and jump off the Narrows Bridge," I wailed. "I should have stayed home."

"I pour coffee—hot, good. We don't want you jump off Bridge," said Marta, concerned.

Grateful for the hot stimulant, I poured out my distress: "Before class could get started—Sidney tripped Helmer—they landed in a horrible crunch. I was sure I heard neckbones crack." Deena and Marta threw up their hands—shook like Santa Claus. Like his—their laughter rolled merrily!

No laughter in this for me . . . "Then on top of that . . ." with a disconcerting sigh, I groaned,

"Corky and Dolly split eardrums with their piercing shrieks. No one would listen. No one would study . . . Jesse drew outlines of Thunderbirds and Whales on the blackboard . . . "

"You okay. You okay," chuckled Deena and Marta. So my Prop Pals turned my troubles to the sunny side of despair. From them I learned about Makah humor.

Strong and supportive—their laughter inspirited me—propped me when I skidded. So propped, I survived until the next time.

My bright purple purse! Its mysterious contents labeled: DANGER! KEEP OUT!

"Heh, heh," snickered Lester. "Something from out of science fiction? All those fringes—looks pretty kooky."

They teased, "Do you carry a flask of whiskey?"

"No—it's only perfume."

On Delora's wrist I dabbed a drop. That signaled every freshman to dive for my desk. Wrists thrust so close under my nose all but cut off breathing. But each wrist—touched with a drop of *Tigress*—wore a cleaner spot all day.

"You WAS!" Vehemently shouted Jesse from the back seat. "You WERE!" I corrected. "Never say 'You Was!'" "You WAS!" Jesse persisted.

"You WERE!" I insisted.

"But we've always said it that way," grimly persevered Jesse. "Why do we have to change?" (*Implying: Who do you think you are to come up here and teach us to say YOU WERE when we've always said YOU WAS?*)

"English grammar rules over which I have no control," I blithely remarked.

 A stifling chill washed over me: SHE just walked into the school building—but I brushed away the clammy October fog and followed Jule.

"An anthropologist will speak tonight on the Makah as great Whale hunters," Jule informed me. "This particular anthropologist has worked among the Makah for twenty years. The whole town goes into a tizzy when she comes—she's very popular—highly respected—speaks excellent Makah.

"The Makah language is harsh and guttural—very difficult to speak. Language experts declare Makah cannot be written—but tonight's speaker claims she *has* written it—she's a terrific person in her field. Well, here we are." Habitually, we pushed through the double-entry doors.

"To look at the speaker," Jule said, "you'd never dream she is a famous writer, professor, lecturer, researcher of mankind—organizer of anthropological expeditions—that sort of thing . . ." Looking around the assembly room, Jule added, "She's very mannish—wears gray or khaki-colored clothing—wears sturdy black or brown boot-type shoes. . . . There's Jacqueline—let's sit with her." After greetings, juggling purses, removing wraps, Jule whispered, "The speaker is that tall slender woman talking to Mr. Perkins."

I gazed at this distinguished woman—a renowned anthropologist—one who has worked to recapture the ancient culture of the Makah—to revive lost traditions—to preserve language—one who reads messages from fog, cedar trees, whales. Silvery-gray hair—swirled back into a bun—gave her an aura of individuality—of distinction—of sensitivity.

After routine formalities—after announcements that welcomed back returning teachers—gave recognition to new teachers—the Principal introduced the speaker as one *who will discuss the Makah as a great Whaling Nation.*

"WHALE!" shouted the speaker.

"A giant form sighted in distant waters: Spouted! Lunged! Splashed! Dived!"

Sparked to attention at once, I was captivated—caught up in a spell!

With vigorous accents, the speaker continued: "Since the first Makah dared crash through dangerous, tumultuous waters to harpoon Whale, the Makah was marked a great whaling nation.

"Imagine this gigantic mammal-of-the-sea! An exhibition of mighty strength! A source of invincible power!" A dynamic speaker, the anthropologist, shook her arms in animated gestures. "How was it possible for the Makah harpooner—with only a primitive, handmade harpoon—to overpower this king of the sea!

"Think sizes! Compare sizes! A single man against the strength and power of one mighty Whale! Think of it! Hunters in hand-carved whaling canoes—out on that great ocean—could be smashed to bits by one blow of the Whale's tail." A calm overcame her. She lowered her voice, "Makah whalers knew they could not succeed in the hunt without Spirit Power.

"The safety of the crew was dependent on one single man: THE HARPOONER!" Like Perry Ides, I thought. In her hand she held an object: "See this—a mussel shell—picked up on the beach. With massive strength the harpooner thrust his primitive, mussel-shell-tipped spear into a vital spot near the Whale's head. This was to avoid the dangerous swipe of the wounded mammal—the location of the Whale's vital spots were revealed to the whalers through prayer and Spirit Power."

My energy so riveted to this vivid narration that my body became rigid.

After the power and activity of the hunt—after the harpooner thrust his spear—I relaxed.

The anthropologist's next words jerked me into a secret place: "In a sacred, secluded, forest shrine, whalers observed strict rites prior to the hunt. They obeyed secret rules for fasting—chanted secret prayers—or the Whales would not come. Ceremonial bathing was vital to attract the Whale Spirit. After the bathing ritual, the body was rubbed and brushed with herbs and nettles. Bathing purified the body—cleansed and set the mind in readiness for Spirit Guides or Spirit Powers to assist in the hunt."

I thrilled to the speaker's intense and lively scenario of Guardian Spirit help—the need of Spirit Power to conquer the Whale.

"Powerless without Spirit help, the harpooner—the Whale-hunt leader—prayed alone in a forest cave of his Whaler ancestors—asking his Whale spirit for protection and guidance during the hunt.

"After the harpooner had plunged his spear—fastened to strong ropes of twisted cedar bark—he may have chanted a song to the Whale—asking not to be taken out to sea but brought back to the beach of the village.

"Songs were given to the harpooner by his Whale Spirit . . . spirit songs are kept secret—never sung in public."

The speaker paused . . . I sensed a faraway look in her deep gray eyes. Was she out on the great North Pacific—tossed by erupting waves—feeling the fearful moment before the harpooner struck his mark? Whatever led her away—she focused back to her lecture: "To kill a Whale was not for greed or money. In the old days before white man, a successful hunt was to secure food and oil for the people. It offered social position and rank to the bravest and strongest.

"Before we adjourn, I wish to add that spiritual ceremonies revolved around the capture of the great Whales. To honor the Whale Spirit—inherent Whale songs and dances from the old days—with enormous feasts—lasted for many days. Spectacular costumes and displays of magnificent headdresses appeared at these ceremonies."

She clapped her hands together and said, "Well, my time is up! . . . In conclusion: *One word to the Makah Nation: I urge you to revive the richest parts of your culture—keep your individualism—your distinguished personality. Be yourselves. Stay yourselves.*"

After the meeting, Perry Ides greeted me with a happy, approving laugh—always jovial—friendly.

Once upon a time—in old Indian days—Perry Ides stood a great Whaler: A HARPOONER!

Did he quest his Spirit Guide? Did he fast and bathe to find his Whale Spirit Helper? I must know. Some day. Some day. If I ever find enough nerve . . . I am going to ask him!

~

WHALING NOTES

Later, I learned more:

I learned from Deena—my Prop Pal: ". . . whalers waited for spirit power—spirit direction—to tell when it was time to go out . . . correct timing was a gift from the Great Spirit. After ceremonial bathing the harpooner rubbed and cleansed his body with a tree bark that caused lathering—given to him in secret so the Whales would allow themselves to be caught."

I learned from a Makah school boy: " . . . harpooners developed massive muscle power to throw heavy, killing spear. To build strong muscles in arms and shoulders, harpooner practiced lifting and throwing larger and heavier rocks. Paddling canoes make big muscles."

I learned from Mrs. Dale-Smith: " . . . a successful hunt opened the way to social power, tribal rank, food for the people, and oil. Oil was wealth—a valuable item of trade with other tribes. Later the white man infringed. Whale oil was burned in the lighthouse on Tatoosh."

I learned from Natah: " . . . sometimes after Whale harpooned—he turn and rush whalers out to sea—very dangerous for men in canoe . . . hunters pray and pray to Whale spirit to turn Whale around—bring our men back to village. We wait on beach—we pray and pray to Great Spirit to bring our men back . . . some whalers lost in waves—not come back—we very sad." Tears filled Natah's eyes—she dabbed them away.

 Arrows of rain sliced at the window panes. Winds ripped at the double-entry doors—slapped the flag at the top of the pole. Clouds choked all the sunlight.

"Geez, it's ghoulish in here. Dark as midnight."

"Yeah, and it's only one o'clock."

"Turn on the lights, somebody."

"Same as sitting in one of those old ghost houses waiting for something to happen."

"Something will. It's Halloween, remember?" Ribald smirks. Smart-alecky guffaws.

Following my class into the library, I flipped the light switch. Dark corners lightened. Dull-jacketed books brightened. "Simmer down, now. We'll be called to assembly as soon as the speakers arrive."

I saw three dark figures, distorted by rain patterns against the glass. Makah Tribal Council members. Weaving ghostlike in the wind, they hurdled the school-yard mud puddles and pushed through the double-entry doors.

A bell signaled assembly: Halloween.

The kids edged into seats and listened. The Tribal Council Chairman looked out over the Assembly Hall. Hands in his pockets, he cleared his throat, "Once again it's Halloween. Once again the Council comes to ask your support and cooperation to help combat vandalism, fighting, drunkenness.

"Unlawful, destructive Halloween activities must be stopped. We urge you young people to work together with the Council. Now—tonight—is the time to start."

Never before had I seen a face of such awesome seriousness. His heavy black brows scowled in grim ferocity. I stared at varying shades of guilt on sober faces. I wondered if all I'd heard was true.

In conclusion, Mr. Wagner said, "By helping yourselves, you are helping other people. You make it very difficult for the Council when you don't comply with rules and regulations of the Reservation. Do your part as a member of the community and stand as an example for a clean and sensible Halloween. The Council will set curfew."

Dismissed, the students filed out, not looking at each other.

Later that afternoon, grade school children merrily bobbed for juicy red apples, tangled in taffy pulls, popped corn, and pinned on the donkey's tail. Busy little craftsmen carved sassy grins in plump pumpkins, cut out slinky black cats and evil-looking witches. For sure, there was one with a wart on her nose! Wide-winged black paper bats, eerie goblins, spooky ghosts flanked window panes. Scissors snipped white paper bones. Linked together they made a hollow-eyed skeleton to hang in shivering suspense.

Teachers, turned witches, served delighted children, turned ghosts and goblins. Spicy apple cider, ladled from a frosty glass bowl, became a sticky bitter brew dipped from a black-night cauldron. Orange-frosted cookies and licorice-black cats became nightshade pastries brushed with ashes—acrid sour.

My first Halloween in Neah Bay did not even bring the giggly, tittering, elementary kids to my door. Not the usual pranksters either. Nobody knocked for treats. Nobody soaped windows.

Where were all the kids, I wondered. I was disappointed. Who would eat all the candy bars and gingerbread?

After three more Halloweens, I didn't expect either grade-school goblins or pranksters at the door. Jule always had an answer for everything: "Halloween is a non-Makah tradition—but it has become a night to dread, to fear. Teenagers and younger children use it as an excuse for drunkenness. And, of course, full of whiskey, they live it up. The very word seems to give license to bloody fights, acts to-get-even, and destruction of property. It's a very difficult time. The Council sets curfew—but Tribal police can't be everywhere."

~

Recalling the Tribal Council Chairman's fear-frets of "expected difficulties," I dreaded the morning after Halloween.

First period—all was normal. No bruised or battered bodies—no whiskey smells.

" . . . only a few roadblocks changed the village scene," Mr. DeLong told me.

The Council's urgency for a "clean and sensible Halloween" paid off.

~

Separate from Halloween, the traditional Halloween Masquerade Dance was a school activity—usually scheduled on the last Friday in October.

Ghosts and goblins from Junior and Senior Classes spiced up the Community Hall into a facsimile of an old haunted lodge.

To hide the mundane boring walls, Lester—Kelly—Lissa—and Kitsy hung black crepe paper from the ceiling. Pumpkins splashed orange dots against the stark black walls. Curling in twisted loops, black and orange streamers hung—to waffle over heads of dancing masqueraders. I hoped the loops would stay put.

Under the same star-specked sky, young village identities stalked in masquerade. In the chill spectral darkness, they sneaked through the shroud of night. In disguises from Washburn's Store they arrived as ghosts, zombies, Frankenstein, a flashing green-eyed witch. A scarecrow's eyes ogled through slits in a papersack mask. They stalked in near the huge, black, gas stove that squatted in the corner.

Huddled in sheets and caped in gunny sacks, carnival strangers bumped and shoved in the beginnings of frenzy.

Teacher revelers poured apple cider—offered plates of doughnuts and cookies. But who would drink apple cider when whiskey stirred these masqueraders into madness and craziness?

A long black skirt and red cashmere sweater admitted me as Spirit Guard to Red Devil champions. A true wizard, Coach Rick magically divined a tall, pointed, black hat to plop on my head.

A hat for a Witch?

A cap for a Jester?

Guessing games for the kids?

"GRR-AAA-RR-HH? Grr-aa-hh!" growled a lumbering grizzly. With long spiked claws, he struck at dodging kids.

"You can't reach me," squealed Rose Mary, jumping sideways.

"Nor me," shouted Lester bumping Kitsy.

The grizzly swung out a clumsy bear foot, tripping Dolly and Jesse.

Tumbling in a heap, they rolled on the floor shrieking with laughter.

From the black night, unknown identities continued to silently step across the threshold: a clown, a gypsy, a pirate.

"Who are you? Cheree?"

"Guess again."

"Karla? A witch with a wart on her nose."

"Who's behind the red-devil mask?"

"Scott, of course. No one else is as tall."

"All the football team are wearing red-devil masks."

"Not Champ. He's got a surprise he said."

Greetings. Guesses. Who is behind the gypsy mask? Whose eyes stare from the slits in the papersack?

Rising into an air of hilarious fun created by the imagery of the mysterious—the unknown—they waited—waited for the first notes from the jukebox orchestra.

Choosing partners, they rushed into the dizzied frenzy of the novelty dances of today.

Though I loved to watch the ancient dances of the Makah, tonight I loved to watch the fast-paced dancers of the new generation.

They whirled. They wheeled. They collapsed into each other's arms.

Somewhere I read: " . . . dancing releases inner demands for uncontrolled expression." It was here tonight: uncontrolled expression!

Then it was midnight. Curfew time. The last notes from the jukebox dwindled into the darkness.

After the masquerade, dancers disappeared. Where did they go?

 By November the fog was oppressive.

I had awakened to a morning of fog so thick the edge of the porch ran off into nothingness. My world was crushed by smothering tons of smoke-like vapors. Even the warning horns on Tatoosh blared louder—more menacing—like a sledge hammer booming days and nights of terror.

Snared in black choking fog, morning thoughts became a cloying nightmare. I had decided not to come back next year—not to another year of despondency—of feelings of not succeeding—of failure.

Then—after school—Cerena had invited me to her room for coffee. Her voice softly-toned, rhythmic, carried a message: "There is not so much rowdiness in the halls since you came. It's all because of you and your influence—the girls are better groomed—I give you all the credit. It is something intangible—something you don't do by force—but by day-to-day contact."

Hot, strong, stimulating caffeine had helped lift my depression. And now this boost from Cerena . . . if Cerena could impress me enough.

I remember she spoke quietly, "Wait to decide about coming back. Take more time. You've brought an indistinguishable something here." Deep within me, I heard again: "THAT WITCH . . . SHE'LL NEVER LAST UP HERE!"

Now, Cerena reached beyond my desperation. She inspired me to value my own personality and background—to continue giving to this culture the traditions that formed me. Cerena contained a spiritual, intuitive touch—a gentle loving way.

Her voice continued in soft persuasive tones: "There is something here for you and you want to find it."

I had melted to the caresses of her voice—heard again: "YOU HAVE BROUGHT AN INDISTINGUISHABLE SOMETHING HERE."

I remembered the bus ride: The mystical SOMETHING pulling me to this Land . . . pulling me to this rocky Cape. A spirit message?

 . . . and I'd like to know who pounded on my door—with all his ferocious might—at three o'clock this morning!

Not Thunderbird Spirit. Not Whale Spirit. But a Red Devil!

" . . . just to let you know we're back from the game. We won. We're still the Red Devil Champions!"

" . . . *but you didn't have to knock the door down and scare me half to death.*"

The next day at school I asked, "Which one of you guys?"

Coy remarks—nothing but sweet Red Devil innocence and angelic smiles—Red Devil Frivolity!

"Simon, you wouldn't."

"Champ, you wouldn't."

"But Sidney, you would . . . and I'll bet it <u>was</u> you . . . and after all I've gone through to keep you on the team."

But I never found out! Those Red Devil Champions would never tell!

 Will the frenzied fury of the first November storm drive us to destruction? Will the storm spirits smash in houses, tear down hillsides, split open mountains, rip up roads, and swoop in the gnashing sea?

Where did it all begin? Where is it going? Where will it end?

That was last night.

This morning, teachers gathered in the school office, their thoughts awry in panic and helplessness. With them, I stood "bright-eyed and bushy-tailed." This was exciting! My first coastal storm. I loved the wind, the rain, the waves.

"Have you heard the news? Neah Bay is declared a disaster zone."

"We might be in danger," Alta murmured—her lips tight and stiff.

"How could we?" I asked.

A shiver ran through her. "Well, these hills might slide."

I'd thought of that too. What if the great stone cliffs crashed down? What if they were ripped from their moorings and shoved the hills and us into the icy-blue Strait of Juan de Fuca?

Hey, LISTEN! The newscaster just announced Neah Bay is in isolation.

Hey! That meant no mail, no milk, no bread, no meat, no roads.

Glued to the radio, we listened to reports with despondent anxiety.

Hillsides, rain-heavy and sodden, slid over the logging road.

Creek Road, between here and Jack's place, reported under water.

Rain-stabs knifed a cliffside near Sequim—rocks, sticks, and mud slogged over the road.

Oozing mire ground to a stop across the highway near Clallam Bay.

Soft, muddied earth, in one massive 128-foot slide, skidded onto the road at Sappho.

At Pysht, over-filled streams lifted water levels to a flooding nine feet. Nearby families evacuated.

Later, School News published: "No first grade teacher today." Beach roads on Genny's shoreline—swallowed by breakers—surged in from the Strait.

And still tonight, the might of Makah storm spirits fights on. As in barbaric ritual, they drum their strength against the house. They send wind puffs down the chimney to whiff out specks of black soot. These ebony specks smear over my cheeks and arms and hair. I feel messy and wish the wind would blow away.

Waiting, I think of the ocean: wild, fierce, mysterious.

What's going on out there in the darkness?

Violence!

Booms and crashes!

Feisty spirit winds shriek.

Breakers plunge to whack the shore in smacks and blows.

Gales and spouting seas collide against Islands, Tatoosh and Destruction.

Spindrift leaps, scatters and falls in tiny salty drops.

By morning, will the tempest ebb? Will the violent voices of Makah storm spirits fizzle out? If we listen, will we hear them speak in drizzle and fog?

 Not always discouraged and ready to quit, I remembered Jerry's speaking up: "You're always so happy. What's there to be happy about?"

"It's a happy time. It's Thanksgiving."

"What's there to be thankful for?"

"Yeah! Who cares about Thanksgiving?" grumbled Barney.

Barney—an Indian boy with stiff, unwashed hair—scorned Thanksgiving. In his neck creases, dirt-lines caked. Soiled and greasy—his shirt collar stood agape. Pants and sweater stained and crumpled—as if slept in.

∽

Once a visitor said to me, "Indians are filthy dirty and stink! How can you stand it up here?"

I cringed . . . shriveled inside . . . a cut by the uncaring—the uninformed. In defense, I explained, "Before the intrusion of white culture, there were no unwashed bodies—no dirty clothing."

Looking past her, I remarked, "Since I've been here, I've heard Makah elders say that the first rule of the Great Spirit was body cleanliness—bathing purified the body. Unwashed bodies displeased the Spirits. No boy could find his Spirit Guide in an unclean body."

 Feature article from *The Chieftain*, school paper . . . by Lester:

One day I was walking down the hall just like an ordinary student going to class, when all of a sudden I smelled something and it smelled something like meat and it smelled like, well, anyway, I thought it was the chemistry class. But I followed the terrible odor and went smack dab in the middle of the Home Ec room and heard Miss Conly roaring like a lion so I took off like "Mabeline" yelling, "Miss Conly, you musta left your purple handbag in the oven." But she said, "Calm down, boy." I calmed down and I said, "What is that awful smell?" She said it was a meat roll and I said, "Ohhh!" with a sad look on my face. Then I stooped over to look at it. WOW! Some kinda meat wrapped around mashed potatoes and it looked about six weeks old.

A little later I heard another roar and Miss Conly rumbled in like a Cadillac doing 95 with some kind of strange plant. It had something in the middle shaking as if it were mad or something. It had green legs with large white spots on it, with dark green spots on the white spots. It had six or eight limbs or legs. I asked her where did you get that thing from, Dark Africa or the Light Edges of Africa?

You oughta see it. Shake Rattle and Roll.

Then she told me what it was!

A salad . . . lime jello . . . with dots of marshmallows . . . on a plate of lettuce . . . enhanced by exaggerated imagination!

 Merrily, Cheree hippety-hopped into nutrition class. In one hand she grasped a jar of peanut butter. In the other she waved a box of soda crackers. "A hand-out from the school lunchroom," she giggled.

I didn't giggle. With a sting of sarcasm—I thought: High-style *nutrition—white man's way*: peanut butter and soda crackers, white flour, white sugar, white bread, syrup, candy, canned peas, creamed corn, tomatoes, and Kool-Aid.

Sadly I shook my head. White man's way brought Reservation Indians a mouthful of decayed, broken teeth, dentures in children, small pox, tuberculosis, and drunkenness in all generations.

~

A few days later, in her typical frisky gait, Cheree skipped into class. Her joyous mood enhanced her dimples—brightened her eyes. "Guess what? My grandmother Ada and old Natah will visit our Nutrition Class today!"

. . . and so I learned about high-style-nutrition—the native Makah way:

"Before white man," Ada began, "our Chiefs brought Great Whale from Ocean—whalers sing songs to Great Whale. We have Whale meat, blubber, and oil. We dip our food in Whale oil—oil in carved bowls from red cedar tree."

Ada lifted her arms in praise. "We bless Whale with big feast—we praise Great Spirit for our food—lots of food. Now we eat out of cans." A scowl quickened—then faded. "We give prayers of thanksgiving at every meal . . . every day Thanksgiving day."

Untying her head scarf, Natah spoke up. "We use all parts of Whale— even intestines to hold oil—men carve knives and chisels from bones."

Natah closed her eyes before she spoke again. To think? To remember?

"Before white man, Indian woman dig wild carrot, potato, many roots in ground. We use stick—like this . . ." She picked up the blackboard pointer—fingered the sharp end. "Digging-sticks made from cedar or fir— I show you . . ." In a digging-motion, Natah described how the wild vegetables were pried out of the ground. "We dig roots near Ocean Prairies— fern stalks in woods—we find wild herbs—many ways we use herbs." Natah replaced the pointer. She touched Ada's shoulder. "You tell about berries."

"Lots of berries." Ada smiled in remembrance. "Berries everywhere. We pick huckleberries, salmon berries, blackberries. In woods we find wild currents and gooseberries. Near Ocean Prairies good cranberry bog. We dry berries for winter. We dry rose hips—sweet—good dessert," Ada chuckled.

A quick glance at the clock: Coffee Break. Happy to please their elders, Cheree and Annabelle perked coffee and buttered tea breads.

Elated and excited by their stories, I thanked Ada and Natah. "What a privilege—and what fun— to have you with us today! I love hearing stories of the old ways. I hope you'll come again." They smiled and beamed. Their warm smiles and friendly manner gave me a feeling of approval and acceptance. Overjoyed, I relished—within myself—a presence of spiritual messages.

"THAT WITCH . . . SHE'LL NEVER LAST UP HERE!" But I knew I would last up here.

Slices of hot buttered orange and cranberry breads—strong hot coffee—served by the girls—delighted their tribal elders. "We baked the breads in cooking class," Cheree said.

"So good," Ada smacked her lips. "I make Indian bread—not fancy bread."

"And I've never made Indian bread," I admitted. Ada and Natah threw up their hands—burst into laughter. "We show you."

"Girls tease to make Indian bread. So tomorrow they will teach me. A learning experience for me.

"There's not much class time left. Tell us about the Salmon," I encouraged.

"I tell about Salmon," Ada offered. "Lots of Salmon—our rivers full with Salmon—men fish in Great Ocean too—catch big Salmon. Salmon our good food—we eat it every day. We bake it on sticks around the fire—big outdoor fire. Sometimes we fry it in skillet—we put it in soup. For winter we smoke lots of Salmon and clams—we dry Salmon and clams for soup."

Class dismissal bell rang. "We go now."

The primitive Makah never heard of vitamins, minerals, and essential amino acids—Whale and Salmon provided essential dietary oils—wild vegetables and herbs supplied them with vitamins and minerals. And here I am to help school girls re-learn the value of foods that preserve teeth and protect health.

Today's girls won't find vitamins, minerals or essential amino acids in peanut butter and soda crackers, candy or Kool-Aid—but who cares? Only me?

Eyes on the stars—today's girls dream about their weekend dates—and who is going with whom and where!

Three basic needs of life?

Food—clothing—shelter?

"OH, NO! MEN! MEN! MEN!" shouted Annabelle.

~

"Today it's your turn," I greeted the class. "You teach me—I learn to make Indian bread."

"Can we? Can we?" the girls shouted all at once.

They jumped into excited action—put out mixing bowls—hunted for flour and baking powder—spoons and skillets—jangled instructions.

"All you do is mix flour, baking powder, and water into a dough . . . then bake it in the oven or fry it in a skillet. If it's fried, it's called *Indian fry bread*," explained Annabelle.

"Ada always kneads the dough—but you don't have to," Cheree said, adding flour to a bowl.

"When the bread is done, can we eat it with butter and some of the jam we made?" asked Kitsy. "We don't have butter very often—and never jam."

And so, they added baking powder to flour—stirred in water—mixed all into a sticky dough— rolled it in flour—cut the dough in pieces and fried it in skillets. Kitsy and Rose Mary baked their Indian bread in the oven— interesting comparison—flavor—texture—color.

"I learned to make Indian bread from Ada. She never measured like you taught us to do. She just dumped all together," Cheree giggled, turning her skillet bread.

"In the old days, they baked bread in hot sand," whispered Elizabeth.

"My Aunty Helen tells a legend about the first Indian bread," contributed Marie.

"Bread's done! Let's eat!"

~

INDIAN BREAD OR BUCKSKIN BREAD . . . Legend submitted by Helen Peterson (Makah), Neah Bay, Washington

Years and years ago, in the time of my great-great-great grand-mother, there was a shipwreck on the most westerly point of the United States of America, which is now known as Neah Bay. In the cargo of this ship there was a good deal of flour which the Indian people who found the wreck did not recognize.

One Indian said it could be used to decorate the face when the ceremonial dances were being held. Another thought that the sacks, at least, could be used for clothing.

One old woman, however, took some of the flour to her home, added water to it to make a paste, and put cakes of it in the camp-fire, covering them with hot ashes. When the ashes were finally cool, after two hours or so, she brushed them away, and had a tasty bread.

Since that time many cakes of Buckskin bread have been made in the same way, in many campfires. During the years since the days of my great-great-great grandmother, however, we have added baking powder and salt and sugar to the flour, and we no longer bake in the campfire, but rather in a modern stove and oven. The Buckskin bread, however, is still as much a delicacy to us as it was to them when the first old lady swept the ashes away.

 Hard and fast the rains hit. Cold and black tonight. I wait in this rain forest.

Kids from Journalism Class will come at seven o'clock to run me through the rainfalls. It's Activity Night at school. We'll write and type and rush and speed to meet the deadline for the Thanksgiving issue of *The Chieftain*. It *must* be out tomorrow.

Teachers wait for tomorrow. Wait for road reports.

Last week's Storm Spirits still *rock 'n roll, rattle and shake*—I quote from Lester's favorite cliché.

All week slugging rain bolts walloped hillsides. Washouts and mudslides and rolling rocks scattered from here to Clallam Bay. Will they block our exodus from Cape Flattery for the Thanksgiving weekend?

As I wait, I remember Cerena's remark: "There is *something* here for you, and you want to find it."

Something waiting here for me?

. . . and I am to wait until I find it?—in a rain forest? Gutteral with malice, SHE she rasped through the cold, black night: "THAT WITCH . . . SHE'LL NEVER LAST UP HERE!"

TODAY: Nostalgic smells of Thanksgiving drifted from the school kitchen. Spicy, tantalizing: gingerbread, raisin cookies, pumpkin pies, bubbling cranberry sauce. Holiday time! Festival time!

TOMORROW: Deena and Marta—happy and bubbly too—plan to treat the school kids to a traditional American Thanksgiving Feast. Savory smells of turkeys—roasted to a golden brown—stuffed with sage dressing—will waffle down hallways—into classrooms—into the lunchline. Here kids will pick up trays heaped with foods of Thanksgiving . . . the air crackles with excitement!

THANKSGIVING DAY: Traditional Reservation families will bake Salmon, boil potatoes, open cans of corn or peas, make coleslaw and Indian bread . . . same as any other day.

For some Reservation children, there will be nothing to eat—only snacks of potato chips and beer—until school reopens on Monday.

~

Ada lifted her arms in praise. "Before white man, every day was Thanksgiving. We bless our food at every meal. We give prayers of thanksgiving to our Great Spirit for great Whale and Salmon."

Lowering her arms, she sighed, "Our old people struggle with new way. Not understand white man's way. Some drink whiskey to forget. Young people drink too."

 Vibrant! Intense! Dramatic!

A splash of sundown colors emblazoned the sky. Under this brilliance of scarlet-pinks and blue-purples, Jacqueline drove us back to Neah Bay after Christmas vacation.

Relaxed—I mind-traveled: I reached an inner realm—praised the Great Spirit for glorifying his Indian Land—all along the Strait of Juan de Fuca.

In this inner realm, twilight's celestial shades brushed crested peaks—touched spirit lakes—enraptured ravines—grazed fabled rocks.

In this inner realm, I felt inspired—lifted in spirit. Fleetingly, I dreamed to a day in May: The Mother's Tea and Style Show. I pictured an arbor of wild roses and purple lilacs. The school girls—as maids of spring—blossomed in hostess roles and as models.

In this inner realm, time stood in stillness. Ghosted mists gathered among the Olympic crests. I sensed a hush. A quietness filled my mind-travels. Then I heard chants. Voices called. Echoed. Hillsides returned ancient drum beats from Makah past—but today was Makah present.

As we topped the last road curve, lights from the village dissolved the inner realm—chased away the scarlet-pinks and blue-purples. My Dream-Tea vanished . . .

"Lazy girls!"

SHE had cast a long shadow. "THAT WITCH . . . SHE'LL NEVER LAST UP HERE!"

But I faced tomorrow . . .

Monday! After a weekend of . . . I wonder what . . .

I'll hear about it in the morning.

~

Dawn roared up like thunder over Neah Bay High School.

Lightning struck the staff of *The Chieftain*. Barely dragging, students stumbled into class, half-asleep, one eye open, one eye shut. Primed for Monday-morning-before-class buzz sessions, I leaned against the blackboard–waiting–listening:

"Oh, my poor head!"

"I could die right here on the floor."

"Wish I'd stayed home."

"There was another fight at the dance Saturday night. Scott's in the hospital at Forks."

"I heard he got drunk and some guys from Clallam Bay beat him up."

After I marked Christine absent, she walked in late–reeking! Helmer yelled, "I smell liquor. I smell whiskey."

In the absence of the Principal, Jacqui, at the attendance desk, had admitted Christine in error. I recoiled. I wanted to walk out. No–to run. To hide.

I shifted to my desk to take attendance and wondered who could concentrate on news assignments and editorials. Friday was due-day.

Perhaps tomorrow's dawn would bring no thunder.

～

Before classes–this Monday morning–my Prop Pals–clued me in on another accident–a Junior High boy–seriously injured–driving while drinking–in hospital at P.A.–blood transfusion.

～

At last. The dismissal bell. The day was over. Silence moved through the building. The memory of yesterday's sunset inspiration receded and my spirit plummeted after talking with Ruth.

Coming to clean the room, she spoke of her niece Celia. "She's in your cooking class."

I recalled Celia's long, shiny, black hair, expressive eyes fringed with thick black lashes, her tiny figure. "Her gentle ways and soft voice remind me of you."

For a moment Ruth's eyes brightened, and then saddened. Leaning on her broom handle, she sighed. "Celia and Jesse lost their mother when Celia was four years old. I kept the children for six years." She looked down at the floor. "Then after their father remarried, he took them away from me. It nearly broke my heart. I thought I couldn't bear it. I cried for days and days. I still cry." She paused. "We have no children of our own." Grasping her broom handle more firmly, she continued, "Their father and stepmother are heavy drinkers. I hope Celia and Jesse don't."

Her spirit drooped. Ruth brushed floor dirt into a pile. Then she stopped—looked at me. "Drinking among the young people is terrible nowadays and getting worse and worse."

I gasped. Ruth hurried out to clean the Study Hall.

The Mother's Tea and Style Show. SHE. Everybody drunk.

In imagination I pictured maids of spring weaving and toppling, stumbling into tables and chairs. Who would stay sober long enough to bake cookies, write invitations, light candles?

SHE's taunting voice gutted through whiskey fumes: "Your contract renewal will live or die by the Mother's Tea."

I believed I would die . . .

~

The brilliant March sun warmed the cold window glass. Swift spring winds scattered cloud patches across the dazzling blue sky. A day for adventure! And I was wasting it!

Here I sat correcting test papers. My thoughts wandered from the squiggles on the paper to the Ocean Prairies. What's going on out there? I wished . . .

A knock on the door bumped me from wishing. I opened the door to Jacqueline—geared for adventure. "Get into your boots," she insisted. "Let's drive out to the Ocean Prairies. The day's too sunny to waste inside."

"I can't wait! I'll be ready in a minute."

Zippered and buckled into a storm-proof, hooded jacket, I climbed into Jacqueline's car. Joggling over the furrowed road, Jacqueline swerved to miss ruts and puddles from yesterday's thudding rain. Today—on Ocean Prairie sand—snappy seawinds whisked our words away—but called us to follow prairie trails and wooded paths.

Clustered against rocks and mixed with winter weeds, March wild flowers dared to bloom. Battered by gusts and chopped by cutting rains, they had survived to grow and blossom. Strong roots gripped Earth-Mother and held fast.

~

Some village school girls, like the wild flowers, were battered by harsh and ugly living. Kept awake all night by family drinking quarrels, they left hovels to come to classes—tired, sleepy, hungry. These school girls lived in whiskey-rain. Will they survive to grow and blossom?

THEY WILL. They were the wild flowers: the blue violets, the red-orange Indian Paintbrush, the white daisies, the yellow buttercups. Strong, tenacious roots gripped Earth-Mother and held fast. The girls will survive.

But will I survive the Mother's Tea?

~

Signals from an approaching March storm routed us from the Ocean Prairies. By evening, white patches in an earlier dazzling blue sky turned gun-metal gray. Swift winds turned heavy and rough. Rain pelted window glass, and wild flowers struggled in cold, wind, rain . . . sending ME messages.

~

After our ramble to the ocean, I felt my spirit rising. Wild flowers of primitive culture talked back to me:

ON STRAWBERRY HILL
wild blossoms, petals ivory white,
bow to the wind, call to summer suns

BLUE VIOLETS
knelt among grasses
silver rain sleeted
tiny fearless blossoms

YELLOW BUTTERCUPS
a dash of golden gaiety
touched by spindrift
bend to the sea

WHITE DAISIES
in seaside patches
whip and bob
to storm winds, whistling

WILD ROSES
spin webs of desire
to catch a love flower
in a dream once told

SALMON BERRY BLOSSOMS
merry dancers ruffled by sassy winds
whirl in scented silence
whisper cryptic messages

INDIAN PAINTBRUSH
spirit of firelight
of burning dawns and scarlet sunsets
of the blazing daystar
of primitive love-fire

WOODLANDS
deep deep, the forest green
what wild sensations
what primitive passions
fill the center self, fear the unknown
what beckons? what intrigues?

~

"I'll bring Helen Peterson to see you after church Sunday," Jule promised. "She hardly ever comes over here. Doesn't like to pass the trees."

MAKAH ROYALTY: PRINCESS HELEN. She came from a long line
of Chieftains and Whalers. For hundreds of years, this rugged wilderness
has been her Land.

Today, Helen dared to pass the trees. Trance-like, I watched. . . . Her
mature body moved with gentle grace on its own mysterious spirit power.
In native style, her graying black hair hung in braids. Strong blood-lines
forged in her broad face—high cheek bones revealed her Makah beauty.
Her charm and poise, her gentle elegance, spoke of her high-born lineage.

Below a wide brow, deep brown eyes searched mine. Speechless, I
stood face to face with an Indian Princess. Helen spoke first, "I came with
Miss Craggs." Soft, full lips curved into a smile. "This is for you . . ." An
olive-shell necklace strung with blue beads nestled in my hands. Before I could
find words to thank her, Jule walked up the steps. "Smells like coffee cake!"

Still in awe, I finally managed to speak. "From your recipe, Jule. Come," I motioned. "Sit down. We'll have coffee cake and tea—ginger tea from India and coffee cake from Neah Bay . . ." I jabbered on.

"Next time I come, I'll bring you some Makah tea," Helen promised.

Trifle chatter see-sawed over the tea cups between Jule and me.

Abruptly, word-trivia stopped. "Missionaries! It's missionaries again!" Inflamed by anger, Jule raised her voice. "I've just read that a remote wilderness tribe in Alaska has been forbidden to hold Winter Ceremonials. DEVIL WORSHIP declared a sect of black-robed religious men."

Jule's anger calmed. She looked at Helen. "Indians aren't pagans—Indians don't worship idols."

Helen remained silent. We all remained silent—until Jule burst out again: "One outrage after another has been forced upon the Indian. I've worked and taught among several tribes. I feel every injustice personally."

Jule released a long sigh, but her anger lingered on: ". . . and then the American government sent out agents who were never trained to understand the culture of their charges. Dumb bunnies. They just blundered year after year—not knowing or caring."

Braced in her own deep silence, Helen had listened.

She closed her eyes—relaxed against the overstuffed chair. With a look of subtle disdain—masked by gentle laughter—Helen recalled an Indian agent's letter to the Bureau of Indian Affairs about the Makah: ". . . can't make farmers out of these people," she quoted.

"*These people,*" quickly interjected Jule, "were great whalers, seal hunters and fishermen. Not farmers," she sputtered in disgust. ". . . besides, who could farm in a rain forest—and who needed to?"

"Our Land gave us all we needed or wanted." Setting her tea cup on the window ledge, Helen indulged in memories: "The Makahs are a whaling nation. My father was a whaling chief." I sensed power—pride—in her statement.

". . . when I was a little girl, my mother and my sister, aunts, and cousins would all go to Ozette to meet the whaling boats . . ."

For a moment, Helen drifted off to become a child again at Ozette . . .

"We had such fun!" With dreams in her eyes, Helen recalled, "We children gathered beach wood. We helped the women build fires on the sand. When the men came in, we had hot soup ready and hot bread baked in the ashes." Still dreamy eyed—still remembering: "We still talk about those happy days at Ozette."

Gesturing with outspread arms, "We had tons of seal oil. We dipped our baked potatoes in it. We used carved oil dishes—oil made dried Salmon and clams and berries taste better."

A loud door knock resounded.

"Sounds like it's on my door," Jule said moving out to the porch.

"I'm over here," she called.

A little boy responded, "It's a fish. My mother sent it."

Jule stepped back into the room. "That was Jason, one of my second graders. His mother sent a fish wrapped in a newspaper."

"Jason's great-grandfather was a Whaler," Helen confided. "But now the family is poor. In those days, Whale oil was wealth. It was used in trade with other tribes, but things are different now."

～

My Makah Princess of today excels in crafts, language skills, a storyteller in the old tradition. And in the old tradition, she swirls—a graceful dancer—and chants her spirit songs.

After Helen walked away, her soft laughter—leaden in sadness—lingered—haunting me. But I felt her peace—like tender, silken nightwinds.

Since childhood, Helen had watched the white man push to the rim of the western sea. She had met the assault—over which she had no control.

Resigned. Peaceful. Helen sighted, without visible rancor, the inevitable decline of her people:

"The Shadow of Their Destinies
They Saw Approaching Year by Year
and Murmured Not . . ."

~

Six o'clock in the morning! Up and sipping coffee!

As I sipped, I felt a mounting exhilaration. This morning The Reverend Perry Ides will give the sermon at the Presbyterian Church.

Watching the April dawn filter shadows on the meadow, I groped beyond my knowing for stages that formed Perry's life. I couldn't ask him, but I remember a school assembly last fall. A Makah elder spoke of his early childhood: "When I was a boy, we learned our lessons outdoors. We began our bathing at five years." I remember how smiles deepened the wrinkles in his cheeks and under his twinkly black eyes. "We called it *our ducking.* Early every morning we took our ducking in the ice-cold river. Shivering and naked, we ran home where our mothers had hot soup ready for us."

Another time the old Makah spoke at Forum (PTA): ". . . when I was a boy, we had our classrooms out under the trees and on the beaches. Our grandfather or an uncle was our teacher. They taught us how to survive on our Land—how to find our food—how to fish and hunt—how to paddle a canoe. They taught us all we needed to know."

In this way did Perry begin his lessons to survive in the rough and harsh Land of his ancestors?

I can believe that early in his boyhood Perry was empowered by the Great Spirit. He learned spirit power permeated all life—from spirit rocks to mighty Whale spirits—and that he would find his own Spirit Guide on his vision quest.

I can believe that somewhere in his youth Perry knew he was destined to follow storm-tossed seas to harpoon Whale.

His "knowing" called for spiritual and physical readiness. Years of arduous, vigorous training determined success in the hunt.

As harpooner, Perry would hold the most dangerous position in a Whale-hunt canoe. Only the strongest and bravest dared to seek this stage. Too heavy to throw, the harpoon must be lifted by a mighty, powerful man and plunged into the Whale's vital spot. The success of the hunt and the lives of the hunters in the canoe depended on the first vital plunge of the harpoon. Directed by his Spirit Guide, Perry always succeeded.

~

Then one day Presbyterian missionaries invaded Makah culture. Perry Ides, harpooner of the Whale, stood awakened by the Spirit of Christ. A new way of life opened for him: the Christ Life.

This time his classroom: the sanctity of the white man's church. His teachers: dedicated missionaries. His lessons: to learn to speak English—to prepare for the ministry.

In his new life style, The Reverend Perry Ides became teacher, loved and respected. He taught his people to live the Christ way: to accept a new Spirit Guide, Jesus of Nazareth . . .

Finishing coffee, I returned from fantasy—back to reality. I dressed hurriedly, met Alta, slid into a pew at the Presbyterian Church.

This morning the old harpooner stood as elder of the Makah Nation—mighty energy in the village—Tribal Council adviser—school board member—staunch supporter of the Church.

How I admired and enjoyed this Makah harpooner of the Whale—still among the strongest and bravest—first of his Tribe to become a Christian! I beheld him with deep affection. He was always warm and friendly. And I loved his booming laughter. And laughing, he once said, ". . . I guess we'll have to adopt you. What would you think of that?"

This morning—at the pulpit—he focused strong, powerful—a proud Makah—poised, dignified. In sincerity and devotion, his simple direct message, spoken in deep resonant tones, hit the vital spots—like the plunge of his harpoon: "Each one of us here has his own purpose in life, and we are to accept HIM (Christ) as our Master and Savior. If we are not happy—if we are disappointed—we are not living the Christ Life. Through Him—within ourselves—do we find our happiness."

~

Over and over—again and again—I needed to be reminded of Perry's message about happiness. Through the many days when I felt so distraught—so discouraged—when I wanted to run away—hide my head in a rain bucket or in a sand dune or under a driftwood log—the days when I felt so lost—as in a forest (like my classroom)—with the great trees (like my students) pushing in on me as far as they could come. It was darkness and oblivion. I couldn't see my way out.

As in *Ulalume*, "In the ghoul-haunted woodland of Weir—then in the misty dankness," Edgar Allen Poe mentions a crystalline light:

". . . we safely may trust to its gleaming and be sure it will lead us aright . . ."

So with Poe, I trust to a gleaming, to a crystalline light that will lead me aright . . .

 The Mother's Tea and Style Show—creeping relentlessly closer, closer, bringing me to my fate.

Haunted by the serrated edge of SHE's voice: "THAT WITCH! . . . SHE'LL NEVER LAST UP HERE."

But . . . I WAS here, though terrified. "I" had a degree in Home Economics. SHE did not. Neither did Lola.

- · I could plan a tea party from beginning to end.
- · I could arrange flowers on a tea table, serve cookies and tea, light candles.
- · I could instruct a sewing project and write invitations.
- · I understood color psychology and the importance of eye appeal.

Side-stepping ugliness and hunger—after a Saturday on Ocean Prairies—I concentrated on the Tea. But I could not cut off the black edge on

Home Ec spirit.

SHE in shadow, waited. Waited for me to fall flat on my face. Determined not to fall, I began priming. My battle cry called for the original, creative, artistic—and the girls would help me . . .

～

The Girl's Club president absent, I opened the meeting:

Happy chattering—accented by squeals and giggles—brought members of the Girl's Club to a Tea-planning Pow Wow in the Home Ec room.

I gathered my weapons and war gear. Huddled around council fires, I plotted my battle strategy.

"Let's begin with a name," I suggested. "May is the month of spring time and flowers. Think of the wild flowers out on the Ocean Prairies and in the forests." The eager faces before me glistened with rising interest. "Who will volunteer the first name for the Tea theme?"

Too shy and withdrawn, Sara and Sue Anne smiled and shook their heads. Too stubborn and balky, Genevieve, Erma, and Lorna just glared. "We don't need no name. We never did before," grumbled Genevieve in disapproval.

"Oh, shut up, Gen. You're just an old grouch," lashed out Kitsy. "This is going to be fun!"

Becky shrugged, eyes cast up to the ceiling. "I have one! WILD FLOW-ERS!"

I remembered the wild flowers nestled in their oceanside settings—and the wild flower verses.

Name selections were chalked on the blackboard: May Flowers, Flowers of Spring, Ocean Prairie Flowers, and Wild Flowers. But when it was time to vote, Wild Flowers and Flowers of Spring tied.

"Now, Miss Conly, you'll have to vote," Kitsy laughed, pointing at me.

Barely breathing. Tension rising. The girls waited. I broke the tie. "WILD FLOWERS!" Shouting and clapping, they jumped up and down, ecstatic over a name. I too was ecstatic. Before me—in vivid vitality—moved talent, art, drama, imagination.

I WOULD SURVIVE THE MOTHER'S TEA . . . AND THE GIRLS WOULD HELP ME!

～

At the Pow Wow table: "For general chairman of the Tea, you'll need to nominate candidates and vote."

"Put Lissa in charge. She's a senior and president of the Girl's Club," dictated Genevieve.

Cheree glared in rebuke. "Lissa isn't even here. She'll be late. Let Miss Conly run the meeting." A tap from the gavel silenced the chatter.

"At our last meeting we voted on a name," I reminded the girls. "In planning, use your imagination. Bring the wild flowers off the Ocean Prairies and put them in decorations, in Tea favors, in centerpieces for the tables, and in corsages for your mothers."

"I know what we can do . . ."

"Let's paint wild flowers on the invitations."

"What colors shall we use?"

"How many invitations will we need?"

"Oh, this is so exciting!"

I loved their enthusiasm . . . SPIRIT RISING . . . ABOVE THE BLACK EDGE.

All eyes, laughing and happy, peered at me.

"For general chairman of the Tea, you'll need to nominate candidates and vote," I suggested, just as Lissa entered the room. "Oh, here you are, Madam President. You're just in time. We were ready to nominate names for Tea chairman," handing her the gavel.

Genevieve stood up. "I nominate Lissa. Everybody vote for Lissa. Okay?"

"Yea! Yea! Rah, rah, rah for Lissa!" Shouts of approval shot to the ceiling—WHOOPEE! THAT SETTLED IT! Not exactly according to Robert's Rules of Order, but "like grandfather, like granddaughter." Once someone remarked: "When there's a dispute at the Tribal Council meetings, Perry Ides shouts and stomps and pounds the table and *that settles it!*"

Lissa's dark beauty concealed patterns of passion and delight, mystery and a will-'o-the-wisp charm—an elfin personality. But Lissa stood first with her classmates. Capable and progressive, she ranked a leader—a true daughter of Makah.

A sharp strike of the gavel brought the meeting to order. Poised and confidant, Lissa inspired harmony. "First, we'll make our guest list. We can begin by checking last year's list. Some families have moved away, but new ones have moved in. We must include newcomers."

SHE! IMPALING EYES, GRITTY VOICE: "YOU DARE NOT

OVERLOOK ANYONE."

... "Rose Mary and I will write the invitations and mail them out," volunteered Cheree. "We'll paint a wild flower on each one."

"What an original idea! It will enhance the wild flower theme and give an individual touch to each invitation." I rejoiced. Eager minds and hearts were answering my battle cry. But I wasn't ready to lay down my war gear. Not yet.

Lissa began to assign specific jobs: "Bonnee, will you and Jacqui work together on the table decorations and centerpieces?" This will eliminate confusion and last-minute scrambles. I was elated.

"We'll want corsages for our mothers and special guests," broke in Kitsy. "There should be plenty of flowers in bloom by that time."

"If there's enough money in the Girl's Club treasury, we can order corsages from a florist in P.A.," suggested Lissa. "We've always wanted to, but there's never been enough money."

Genevieve objected with a petulant, "Nah, nah. It's too much money. You can make your own."

Exasperated, Lissa ignored Genevieve. "Check the treasury, Daphne, and then we can decide."

Lissa continued her assignments. "We'll need two or three of you to help set up tables and to help Art bring in folding chairs."

SHE! THREATENING. VOICE COLD. GRUFF: "START PLANNING FAR AHEAD OF TIME OR YOU'LL END UP DOING IT YOURSELF."

... "I'll help," quietly offered Elizabeth. Black-haired maiden—her serious brown eyes set in strong Makah features—Elizabeth never pushed or bossed. Willing and eager—to please—to help.

"It wouldn't hurt the boys to carry in chairs," giggled Cheree. "They're always hanging around anyway."

Lissa thanked her tribal classmates, adding, "You'll want others to help you. The boys may be in basketball practice just when we need them. We'll have to decide who to ask to pour coffee and to serve punch. We'll need someone to be in charge of the guest book. There'll be last-minute decisions, but this will get us started. Is there a motion to adjourn?"

"Let's get adjourned," demanded Genevieve. "I gotta go practice basketball."

"Before you leave," I reminded them, "remember to buy fabric for your skirts. Don't wait until the last minute. Try to find skirt material with bright spring flowers."

"Don't count on me," grumbled Genevieve. "I got no time."

I broke the bickering with, "It's nearly bell time. We'll meet again Friday. Be thinking of ideas for the program."

⁓

Lissa spoke first: "I have an idea! When I was in sixth grade, our class put on a play in pantomime. We could do scenes in pantomime and work out dance movements with the wild flower theme. We can practice in the gym."

"THAT'S RIGHT!" Kitsy shouted with ardent enthusiasm. "I was in that class too. Pantomime is fun! We'll be the *wild flowers!*"

"Let's do it!" Rose Mary said in excited agreement.

"WONDERFUL!" Overjoyed, I nearly forgot my role as teacher.

⁓

Restless, I tossed. Turned. In dream movements, shadow images seeped through mist. In sleep, I paddled a spirit canoe across a vastness of black water. Were Makah storm spirits pushing me into neverness—a void— a time of nothingness? Was it SHE? Was it Lola? Was I to be shoved overboard—left alone in the spaces of sea?

Then, etched against the darkness, a message: MAY 6, 1955, THE MOTHER'S TEA AND STYLE SHOW. My first. I was terrified.

In rough, uneven accents, I could hear my voice croak: "As adviser to the Girl's Club of Neah Bay High School, I welcome you . . ."

At the end of the shadow images: SHE! Arrogant. Dominant. Critical. Waiting.

A sudden bolt of thunder exploded the shadow images. A million lightning facets shattered the black waters. My heart pounded. My breath strangled in my throat.

That ruthless wrench from sleep crumpled my spirit. I had collided with real earth-powers. I felt trapped in conflict. But the storm spirits in an electric storm would move on and out. SHE WOULD NOT! Neither would Lola! . . .

Many times I had declared: I WILL SURVIVE. But three o'clock in the morning brought doubts that chiseled in.

· What if I trip and fall flat on my face?
· What if my voice cracks?

- What if I start to shake?
- What if my knees knock together?
- What if I start stuttering?
- What kind of an impression will I project to the mothers, grand-mothers, and guests?

Most of them I had never seen before. Like being under an old Makah Medicine Man's all-seeing power-eyes—one blunder—one foozzle—one twist too soon—one slip too late—one candle too short—and ZAP!

Enough of these creepy thoughts. I crawled out of bed. Downed two strong cups of black coffee to drown out the demon spirits. I drew a deep breath, looked up for inspiration to instill courage, strength, confidence, endurance . . .

~

In a spiritless mood, I reasoned: Today is Monday, May 2. The Tea is Friday. I sipped coffee, looked out the back window. The rising daystar crept over the ridge of hills, spread a warm red glow over Neah Bay High School. Caught up in the marvel of the sunrise, my spirit lifted. My thoughts clicked through the dawn's warm red glow. Five days of frantic frenzies stretched ahead. That meant millions of last-minute details crammed into the last five days.

Frenzied details flipped and flopped in my thoughts: first things first—last things last. Did I really know which came first or which came last? Finalities? Fatalities?

I pushed! I pulled! I tugged! I coaxed! I demanded!

THE GIRLS! THE GIRLS! THE WILD FLOWERS—WONDERFUL, WONDERFUL, WILD FLOWERS! THEY WILL PULL ME THROUGH.

AND THE BOYS! BOYS! BOYS! In imagination, they seemed to be everywhere. Sidney led the pack. I saw boys crawling on the shelves! In the cupboards! Under the sinks! In the sinks! Hanging from the ceilings! Hypnotized, they followed a fragrant trail of sugar and spice to the Home Ec kitchen. They pestered and teased and planted themselves in my path, begging for goodies, wanting to help.

"Can I do something?"

"Hey, let me carry that."

"Are there any more broken cookies?"

"Scoot, scoot, scoot!" I glared at them. "Scoot! Scoot!"

"Can we watch the program? We promise not to make any noise."

"Oh yes, yes. But for now, shoo! Shoo! Shoo!" And I thought of my grandmother flapping her apron at chickens. What would she think of me now, I wondered. I remembered her asking, "Arlyn, aren't you afraid to be up there with all those Indians?"

⌒

In the Sewing Room . . . Two days before the Tea

Suddenly we were jutting full speed into finalities—or fatalities! I didn't dare think.

SHE in shadow—waited . . .

In the sewing room, we measured and cut—stitched and fitted—wound bobbins—turned hems.

All but Genevieve. "Oh, Genevieve, sweet Genevieve."

"I got no time to sew. Don't you know we gotta beat those Camp womans at the game tonight? I got no time. You do it."

And give you an "A" I thought . . .

Seams stitched—waist bands in place—hems up. But at the zipper they panicked and shouted "HELP! HELP!" Wild flowers indeed!

In sweet refrain, I heard Genevieve: "YOU DO IT!"

And so, I did it! I stitched in seventeen zippers. BUT WE MADE IT.

⌒

In the Home Ec Kitchen:

Contrary stubborn little Indian girls forgot their old resentments.

All tasks throbbed as to drum beats. With jaunty cheerfulness, the girls stirred flour, baking powder, and water into a dough for Indian bread (Genevieve's demand). They kneaded the dough like they had watched their mothers do.

"Little Indian girls didn't ask questions. We listened and watched— then did. That's how we learned."

Like a warrior maiden, Genevieve stood by to boss the jobs.

Sue Anne and Sara opened cans of pineapple juice and squeezed oranges for punch. Freshmen girls cut bread into diamonds and hearts for open-faced sandwiches. Jacqui's slight-of-hand technique rolled flaky pastry for native gooseberry tarts. Bonnee, Rose Mary, and Annabelle baked fancy cookies—crisp lacy ones, butterscotch crispies, confetti surprises, frosted lemon bars, chocolate bon-bons. Jane, Daphne, and Elizabeth plotted and planned over schedules.

~

"What'll we do about flowers and greens for the centerpieces?" wailed Jane. "We don't have forever. It never stops raining. And where can we find purple lilacs and wild roses? The rains ruin all the blossoms."

Cheree's words tumbled over each other. "Ruth and Ada have purple lilacs in their backyards. Let's ask them."

"There's a hedge of wild roses near the old jail and down by the creek," offered Daphne. "If we hurry, we can pick them between sprinkles."

So, Jane, Daphne, and Cheree dashed out between raindrops to gather flowers.

~

Two hours later, placing cookies in storage jars, I felt eyes piercing through my back. I turned . . . and "what to my wondering eyes should appear" . . . not a spirit canoe and eight tiny warriors, but Simon and Sidney. Shining round faces aglow—mischievous black eyes a-twinkle—sozzled by drizzles, their black bangs plastered foreheads—drops of rain clinging to strong brown arms loaded with spring foliage.

Speechless, I stared. BOYS! BOYS! What now, I thought. Like scorpions, they stung my days—exploded my dreams. So unexpected—an offering. Before me, this message: "We like you." I felt myself withering under the smoke from their peace pipes.

"Can you use these? Huh? Can you?" Shyly, hesitant, Sidney voiced a plea.

"Can you use these? Huh?" questioned Simon.

"These" . . . from the soggy, sopping forest: kinnikinick, Oregon grape, new green horsetail shoots, salal leaves, new spring ferns—startling green—sleek and glossy from the rains.

"What magnificent spring greens. Looks like the forest just walked in. Thank you. Thank you for bringing them to us. How did you ever know they were just what we needed? The girls will love them."

"Can we help? Huh?" Simon questioned. His urgent eagerness to please leached the scorpion's sting—and so I forgave their Makah "gifts of humor." I remembered how Deena and Marta had propped me with their Makah gifts of humor.

"You are truly Red Devil champions, and I thank you again for these woodland greens." Warmly overcome by their show of affection, "Take the greens to the gym. The girls will be thrilled. Greens are needed for centerpieces and in decorating the arbor." Lifting his hand in salute, Simon took off in a run. Sidney, beaming like a Cheshire cat, followed.

Soon I followed. Entering the gym, I paused in amazement. Quick, skilled fingers, tipped with bright nail enamel, cut stems clipped off undersized or over-sized leaves, discarded blossoms, discolored and faded by rains. The artists had wired, tied, and fashioned each centerpiece into a unique design.

"You asked for original, artistic, stylized creations! You have them, Miss Conly!" Jacqui called out.

"You have indeed created charming centerpiece arrangements," I praised.

Arms akimbo, Jacqui stood back to admire their works of art. "Beautiful! Just beautiful!" she boasted. To express her exuberant mood, Jacqui whirled in pirouette. Cheree joined Jacqui, and both girls swung off into lively dance steps.

. . . my mind in a dizzying whirl—I unscrambled last things from first things . . . first things from last things

. . . and now to transform the latticed white-wooden arch into a flower arbor

. . . nondescript, dejected—the arch leaned at a haphazard angle against a storeroom wall—rescued, but . . .

"We need more flowers," cried Bonnee. "We used most of the purple lilacs and wild roses on the centerpieces—but we have some leftover greens that the boys brought."

"Why can't we 'borrow' crepe-paper flowers, leaves and vines from the decorations we use for the Valentine-Sweetheart Dance?"

"A great idea, Jacqui!" Rejoicing, the arbor-team skipped off . . .

Later at the gym: twisted and twined, wired and thumb-tacked, crepe-paper roses, yellow daisies, blue iris, carnations nestled among forest greens and vines had indeed transformed the nondescript arch.

"You girls have created a glorious impression!" I applauded. "All the wild flowers on the Ocean Prairies have blossomed on this beautiful arbor."

"It's an arabesque! A legend of flowers!" I praised again.

To surprise me—several wild flower maidens swung into rhythmic whirls and bends of their dances . . .

". . . your dancing is graceful and effective—it will work in with the wild flower (Ocean Prairie) verses perfectly."

"We added spins and reverse turns from our Makah dances." Lissa knew how I loved their Indian dances.

Entranced by fragrances from purple lilacs, wild roses, and forest greens—by determined girls pulling together to wallop our guests with a Tea to outshine all Tea's for all times—I bathed in a brightness that lifted the dark shadow: "THAT WITCH . . . SHE'LL NEVER LAST UP HERE!"

~

. . . AND AT LAST WE WERE READY! WE MADE IT! . . .

~

THE MOTHER'S TEA AND STYLE SHOW—Friday, May 6, 1955
Stark. Accurate.

The hands of the clock ticked on—on to two o'clock.

Time stood in stillness for me. But not for the WILD FLOWER MAIDENS.

With spirit and vitality of Ocean Prairies—the Wild Flower Maidens admitted mothers, grandmothers, and friends. Happy, poised, self-confident—each on her own spirit path—pinned on flower corsages, the totem of endearment.

. . . and the arbor: interlaced with flowers and leaves and forest greens stood—an arabesque—a legend of flowers—a gateway into the auditorium.

There I waited and watched. Drawn into a mysterious vortex, I became one with the activities inside—one with this ancient Land—one with its people—one with the Wild Flower Maidens.

Exalted, I stood uplifted by a strange moment of belonging. As quickly as it came, the moment faded. The fierce stress of knowing I really wasn't ONE after all crushed like a blow from a war club! I WAS DIFFERENT.

Would they accept me? SHE hadn't. Neither had Lola. "THAT WITCH . . . SHE'LL NEVER LAST UP HERE!" still hung over me like the sword of Damocles.

My thoughts switched from that debasing reflection. I sought again the mystical realm that had lifted me into a vital sense of belonging . . .

The background music stopped. Lissa whispered, "Miss Conly, the guests are waiting . . ."

Shot back to Earth-Mother and The Tea and Style Show, I mobilized my defenses. I turned my battle cry into a Welcome Song. I "stretched out my hand—extended my heart" as Chief Seattle did.

I extended my own kind of peace pipe, hoping to remove the long shadow SHE had cast.

OUT THERE—SOMEWHERE—SHE LISTENED.

I welcomed guests to the annual springtime Mother's Tea planned by the Girl's Club of Neah Bay High School.

Again I whirled in the vortex. FACES—known and unknown—waffled before me. As I heard my voice speak, the whirling stopped. "It's been exciting and fun to work behind the scenes with the girls. They've all contributed talent, creativity, and artistic skills in all phases for this yearly event. Did you like the wild flower painted on your invitations?"

I paused, smiled a *bewitching* smile. "Boys helped too! They dared the storm spirits and brought back forest greens for centerpieces. Thank you, boys. We really appreciated your help." At the far end of the auditorium, a few dark heads bobbed around the door. In a quick series of bobbings, heads disappeared out of sight.

I began again. "In the Style Show, each girl will model a full-circle, flower-patterned skirt fashioned in sewing class. I am delighted with the results." Turning to Lissa, I introduced her as Style Show moderator. "This talented and capable senior girl is Girl's Club president and Tea chairman. She will announce the program and Genevieve will operate the record player. The program-theme includes flower dances—an unusual presentation in pantomime especially for you. I know you will enjoy it!" (I-got-no-time Genevieve wore her old skirt.)

The program, released to Lissa, freed me to unwind. Ever aware of the mystical presence of the Makah culture, I wondered: Would I step back again on what I was beginning to call my *Spirit Path*—searching, searching, for something in the past?

Instead, my senses—captivated by the scene in front of me—focused on Lissa, a now-time maiden with roots deep in Makah soil. Exotic flower prints danced on her skirt of black. Her dark beauty stood out, inflamed by the brilliant color-splashes of orange, purple, gold, magenta, copper. A streak of sapphire blue threaded through the color-splashes. The bright gem tones enhanced the soft texture of Lissa's skin and shiny black hair.

In the soft melody of her voice, Lissa welcomed the guests: "Speaking for all members of the Girl's Club, I am happy that you came. Our program will be presented in pantomime. Our theme is WILD FLOWERS. We decided it would be fun to pretend to be wild flowers from the Ocean Prairies and the forests." Lissa's smile sent messages of joy and harmony to all present.

"As the girls step through the arbor of flowers, you can pretend with us that each one is a special wild flower." A nod from Lissa told Genevieve to start the record player.

"Our background music is *Waltz of the Flowers* by Tchaikovsky. We made up our own dances."

Through word-pictures from the wild-flower verses, Lissa brought the daisies, buttercups, Indian Paintbrush off the Ocean Prairies. In the silent motion of pantomime, spring maidens bowed to the wind, tossed sassy heads, swayed to forest intrigues, whirled in flippant breezes. And with arms uplifted, praised burning dawns and scarlet sunsets.

During the interlude, June sang *The Indian Love Call.*

The romantic mood of the melody, with the pure natural power of June's voice, kept me on the spirit path. I thought of the tiny girl trained to chant the old tribal songs—how June chanted war songs in her fringed deer-skin tunic trimmed with bright shells and colored beads—how the war drums quickened the pulse! I shivered. Indian Spirit Power?

In the now-time, June's spirit gift of song surrendered the old for the new. Today her song spilled word-fragrances and echoed a spring-time conspiring.

~

Entranced, I mingled among the girls and their mothers, grandmothers, and guests. Compliments, like a shower of star-flowers, poured over me:

"I've never seen a more beautiful tea table, and the girls were so lovely and lady-like," praised Mrs. Meredith.

"This is the nicest and loveliest Mother's Tea Neah Bay has ever had," smiled Greer Walter. I knew she had seen them all from the very first.

"My Makah grandmother can't speak English, but she liked the Tea," whispered Sara. "She wants you to keep this. She carved it herself." In my hands Sara pressed a tiny cedar canoe. Speechless with joy, I held the sacred gift. Again . . . back on the spirit path where the old culture touched the new.

Then, I heard Ruth's remark, "Wasn't this nice? And to think Miss Conly even invited me. I was so pleased."

Zettah quietly moved to my side. "The refreshments were so pretty and delicious. Your welcome speech was just right," she smiled in approval. Zettah knew how I had fretted. I laughed. "Could you tell I was shaking all the while?"

~

Sunday morning after the Tea there was a bake sale in the vestibule. After church Jule came over. She handed me a box. "I bought Greer Walter's famous poppy seed cake."

"Sounds delicious. I'll make coffee. I've heard of Mrs. Walter's prize cake." I turned to fill the tea kettle.

Jule spoke right to the point. "You made a lovely impression at the Tea. Both Indian and white mothers expressed to me how fortunate the girls were to have the guidance and instruction of one with such dignity and humility."

Overwhelmed. Tongue-tied. I hadn't expected *that* kind of praise.

"They all made a point to tell me it was the loveliest and nicest Mother's Tea ever held here.

"It was so nice to see the girls do things themselves instead of Rega Buckthorn and Lola flouncing and strutting around. SHE and Lola always pushed themselves ahead to be sure everybody saw them," Jule muttered in disgust. "You looked so pretty and modest in a flowered skirt like the girls."

Immersed in my own Elysium, I changed the subject. "Did you notice the bleeding-hearts design on my skirt? Rita made my skirt for me. She wanted extra credit. As Genevieve would say, 'I got no time!'"

The tiny red hearts in the design—entangled with sprays of stems and leaves—entangled my heart. I couldn't resist. Bringing my skirt from the closet, I pointed to the leaves. "I suppose no one noticed, but leaves outlined in black—attached to red hearts—suggest Red Devil colors. Loyal to my champions, I must be!"

Basking in heavenly bliss—rapturous joy—ecstatic—the overflow of compliments at the Tea—and now Jule's added comments of approval—of acceptance—had lifted the black edge. I forgot about SHE and Lola.

TRIUMPHANT! VICTORIOUS! I HAD SURVIVED!

 Obsessed with an eagerness to help—and not being in touch with long-standing race conflicts—I had blindly overlooked an explosive issue.

When asked: "What can our Tacoma DAR Chapter, through the National Committee on American Indians, do for the Indian students in your high school at Neah Bay?"

In my thoughts, flashed: A CITIZENSHIP TROPHY.

. . . and why not? What an incentive for Indian students! A motive to improve grades—to work for a Tribal scholarship—to stimulate leadership skills in school relationships and village affairs.

My flash-thought materialized:

Proposed—discussed—accepted—by National DAR and Neah Bay High School staff.

But in this bi-racial—Indian and white—community, we overlooked RACE PREJUDICE.

Once again it hit me! "NEVER TRUST A WHITE MAN!" This time not at an Intertribal Conference.

Like a smoldering forest fire, subtle embers of prejudice and resentment waited . . . and I, thoughtless—innocent—ignited flames.

So wrapped up in the DAR trophy being for Indian students—a mark of distinction for them—a status symbol for them—that I failed to consider how the white parents might react. But a crack on the head—by the proverbial two-by-four—awakened me. Outraged by the discrimination, they stomped into the Principal's office: "We resent this! We demand an explanation! We demand equal recognition for white students. We'll set up a Citizenship Trophy for white students!"

THIS THE PRINCIPAL DOES NOT WANT!

Neither did I. Neither did staff members.

A monument to widen the breach?

No. Not here. Not at Neah Bay. Not when all over the world, efforts seek to break race barriers.

A teacher-friend—in severe criticism of the uprising—scoffed: "It's just some good-for-nothing, nosy busybody with nothing else to do but stir up trouble. It's jealousy too, you can bet. You've established a precedent here at Neah Bay that no one else has ever done or could do. You have the support and prestige of the National DAR."

Not reacting to the defiance—as strongly as my friend—I rejected the conflict as the tongue of a busybody or from jealousy—just a dedicated white community asking equal recognition for white students.

During the interim, staff members shifted regulations to include white students. With ease and harmony, the smoldering embers scattered.

From the ashes walked mystical footsteps leading to a monument that squelched an eruptive undercurrent: DISCRIMINATION.

From the list of graduating seniors, submitted at the May staff meeting, one boy and one girl were chosen. Over a four-year period, these two had exemplified highest traits of good citizenship: RESPONSIBILITY, LEADERSHIP, ATTITUDE, BEHAVIOR

Academic ability not ignored—but citizenship qualities superior to grades.

Winners' names engraved on the DAR trophy. Each received the distinctive pin—emblazoned with the National DAR emblem.

Senior graduates on edge. Tense. They waited. Excited. I announced names, presented pins. One moment of personal glory. Then it's over.

Honored students may never see the trophy again. It will be kept at school in the trophy case. But the pin—worn over the heart—belongs to each one. Like a Spirit Guide—a star guide—it leads the winner into adult life: to uphold, to invest in the principles of good citizenship—a totem of inspiration for a lifetime.

~

CITIZENSHIP
(written by Bill Kallappa)

Citizenship is abiding by the law, doing your duties and having your own rights and privileges, as a citizen. But citizenship is not only doing your duties, having rights and privileges, but always being fair in games or in contact with anyone or anything. A good citizen cannot always do as he is told, but he must help make a good school, community, and his state and nation into the kind of place where he would like to live among his neighbors.

Citizenship is showing your friends that you're trying to make them understand the importance of getting an education.

When a student quits school, he or she is throwing away a great privilege. Yet most students do not realize it until it is too late. But sometimes it is not too late, and when this happens the student is very lucky.

The future means a great deal to us, so I think that most of our class will try and do our best in the coming of the next four years.

Thank you.

~

And now, on the Reservation, Makah Tribal Council members speak in school assembly: " . . . remember the good and valuable things of all living . . ." Councilmen urge high school students: ". . . learn to be a good citizen—to practice laws of good citizenship: At school. At home. In community affairs."

Lifting his arms as in prayer, this leader of American Indian heritage pleaded: ". . . take advantage of education . . . work for a Tribal scholarship . . . it's here . . . waiting for you."

So few students care about scholarships.

But why?

Did scholarships replace the old ways? Spirit quests—physical endurance tests—visions—legends—guardian spirits—sacred dances—chants to the rising daystar?

Ingrained in their childhood teachings, how can they reject their cultural traditions? Ignore their unwritten laws?

Did white man's education replace the mystery of a loon's call? Wisdom of Earth-Mother? Might and energy of Father Sea? Song of Whale Spirit?

Then again, this is Indian country. Did these young natives even consider living today in the white man's way or old Indian way? Are they caught up in a whirlpool of confusion—frustration—torn this way—torn that way—reaching out?

What do they find?

I recalled a Makah-girl student whispered in anguish: ". . . oh dear God, not another brother . . ."

Alcohol—like an adder's tongue—reaches out to strike and kill . . .

What is wrong? What is missing? Balance? Transition?

. . . the message on the bus spoke to me again: ". . . AN INVISIBLE MYSTICAL SOMETHING . . ."

SOMETHING? Something great? Strong? Mighty? Dominant?

A NEED? A vigorous source of power?

Where will it come from? Indian Christian churches? Dedicated teachers? Makahs themselves?

Memory jogged: Ada spoke direct—without emotion. "You have education—not because you are better than anyone else—but because it's your way . . ."

Faster than the raindrops fell, days followed one after the other. Seniors attended classes for the lunch count. But when I turned to speak to Lissa, she had vanished. So had Scott. So had they all. SENIOR SNEAK!

For three summer months, Neah Bay kids camped on the ocean beaches, built bonfires, roasted hot dogs. Free as sea winds, kids rode horses over the Ocean Prairies—down the middle of Front Street. Forest trails led bike riders to wild huckleberry bushes and strawberry patches.

From a cliff top, the daring shinnied down a rope to Shi Shi Beach. Summer heroes were branded at the "shinny-up."

Flippant summer storms frisked beaches, leaving glass balls, hunks of hemp, old rubber tires, and pieces of old canoe paddles. While strolling on the breakwater wall, beachcombing kids searched for devil fish.

The last words I heard were "Come back for Makah Day!"

And the last days of summer zoomed into Makah Day celebrations: Salmon bakes, tribal dancing, canoe racing, tugs of war.

1955-1956

AI ZANTUA 96

Clasping me in her plump brown arms, Ada laughed, "You're browner than we are!"

After summer school, tanning lotion and relaxation in the sun darkened my skin tones.

"It's wonderful to be back in Neah Bay," I beamed. I loved the light mist on my face—the feel of sea breezes—the sun casting a golden haze.

"Is Robert Kopellah home? When I saw him at the hospital in June, he said he'd be back in the fall."

"Robert back all right. He look real good. You see him in hospital?"

Ada buzzed my visit to see Robert all over the village.

That's a day I'll never forget—in June—right after school.

~

Since last March I had known Robert was ill.

"I've just heard Robert Kopellah has TB," Jule sadly informed me. "They've sent him to the Indian Hospital near Tacoma for treatment. If whiskey doesn't do it, TB will. I hope he comes back." Jule voiced heavy doubt.

I recalled Robert as a typing student. His long, quick fingers practiced drills with precision. Reserved—quiet—Robert walked alone. His slight build—narrow shoulders—baggy jeans—thin sad face—spiritless black eyes—etched in my thoughts. I never realized he was ill—just tired, maybe? Hungry?

This was frightening to me. One of our own school boys with tuberculosis. I never realized it was a threat. I couldn't believe it. But the Indians could. TB was a reality they lived with.

Robert knew he was seriously ill. Three months ago had he thought he might die? That he might not be back?

~

My plans to see Robert began with a telephone call. The Tacoma transit dispatcher gave directions to the United States Cushman Indian Hospital. "You'll have to walk a couple of blocks—but you'll get there," he informed me.

Two blocks! It was two miles!

The city bus driver dumped me in some woods—near a substation—out in the middle of nowhere. "The Indian Hospital is over there." My eyes stared beyond his pointing finger to grim buildings—far, far in the distance.

"You'll have to walk the rest of the way." And off he drove—leaving me holding the sack of apples, bananas, grapes, oranges.

I started to walk. I'd worn white patent heels. I wavered over scrubby grasses and menacing sticks. I side-stepped ruts and holes. Sticker bushes grabbed my sheer summer dress—snagged my nylons. But on and on I trudged. The stifling sun of June wilted me.

From side to side, I shifted the sack of fruit. A slithering movement in a clump of Oregon grape terrified me . . . if I stepped on a snake and dropped the sack! . . .

"You'll get there," I heard the dispatcher say.

And so—at last—I did.

A hospital attendant preceded me—announced, "You have a visitor, Robert. Your teacher has come to see you."

Setting the sack of fruit on a table, I exclaimed, "You're looking wonderful, Robert—strong and healthy. Wait till I tell everyone back in Neah Bay."

Surprised—but glad to see me—his first visitor in three months.

His shy, happy grin boosted my dragged-out spirits.

"You'll never believe it," I rattled, "but that wild prairie out there is crawling with snakes—every step of the way I wondered what next. I stumbled over a root—tripped on a discarded bottle—caught my heel on a rambling vine—turned my ankle on loose stones—missed stepping on a snake by just a wiggle."

The chuckles of Robert and his Indian and Eskimo companions brightened the sterile atmosphere of the TB ward. In a white man's sanitarium, white instructors taught ancient Indian crafts: weaving, basketry, beadwork. Robert sat cross-legged on the bed—threaded beads into fabric—his therapy. He listened while I chattered—while I reviewed the hectic last days of school:

"The whole building was one wild, hilarious mass of confusion. Everybody happy and affectionate—none of us ever knew where the seniors hid on their sneak day. Poor Mr. DeLong drove bus load after bus load of screaming school kids out to the ocean—to the river—even to Twin Creeks for class picnics. For days the hallways reeked of hard-boiled eggs and potato salad."

Robert threaded his beads—grinned and nodded—but said nothing.

After a deep breath, I began again: "Seniors gave out annuals Thursday morning—nobody could wait. Kids snatched and grabbed—an absolute mad house." I shifted on the chair—remembered to add, "Signing annuals—memory books—exchanging pictures—went on harum-scarum until the last potato chip on Friday.

"Oh, I nearly forgot the fruit. Have some, Robert—and your friends too." While they crunched apples and peeled bananas, I jabbered on: "The graduation exercises were beyond description. The band music was the best yet. Your brother Galen sang in the chorus. Did you know?

"Reverend Dale-Smith gave the graduation message. Kirk Hall, as valedictorian, gave the valedictory speech. Mr. Perkins awarded athletic trophies and letters. Knees knocking, I gave the citizenship speech and awards."

Robert beaded and beaded—smiled and nodded—chuckled now and then—but said little. I chattered on. "You know Galen was awarded a Tribal scholarship and will go to college in the fall?"

Robert looked up quizzically. "He did?"

His jaw clamped tight. "I'll be back home by fall but he'll be gone."

I looked around the bustling sanitarium. This time it was not from white man's whiskey—but white man's disease.

"Summer school at Oregon State controls my vacation hours—but I'll be back in Neah Bay by fall too."

~

I told the office about the bus trip. Their response: "Just walk across the highway in front of the hospital and climb on the Valley bus."

Why didn't the city transit dispatcher inform me in the first place! Oh, my poor, beautiful, sheer dress, my nylons, and my twisted ankles!

I will never forget the fogs of September: soft—white—whispy. Last night great billows rolled in. By morning the village hovered under shadow and mist. Patches—like fluff—hugged treetops—brushed Olympic peaks with ghostly stillness.

Fog created timelessness.

Our school building closed out the world. Only us—banded together—shielded by protective fog— faced a new school year.

At our first teachers' meeting, the fog horns on Tatoosh Island sounded a lonely call: a warning.

"Burt is back on the Reservation," our Principal, Mr. Perkins, announced.

Stern lines creased his forehead. "Burt will be in classes Monday." Through locked teeth and tight lips, Mr. Perkins grimly warned, "Burt will try anything. We can only hope for the best."

"A real terror. Hard. Tough. Gangster type," commented the coach. "Older than the other kids. Always in trouble. In and out of reform schools since he was ten. Smoking and drinking at age four.

"Even rumors of a State Penitentiary sentence," added Rick. "No data on it though. Burt's known for his dangerous temper and murder threats."

I listened. Threatened. How could I take one more incorrigible?

On this question of sure-fire doom, the first school meeting adjourned.

Alta and I walked through the double-entry doors into an Indian summer. The comforting fog-rolls had been burned away. Sun splashed on wooded hillsides—striking maples in gypsy colors of gold and scarlet.

Returning to our apartments, I groaned, "Burt. One more incorrigible."

"Oh, you'll get along with Burt all right," encouraged Alta. "You're young and good looking." Optimism rising. I could do it.

~

Monday morning: Burt swaggered up to my desk for English assignments. Snickered. His black eyes darted this way—that way.

Before me stood an Indian youth of average features—of sturdy stature—dressed in worn jeans and matching jacket. His front teeth knocked out, his hands dirty, his fingernails embedded with black grime. What lay behind his dark eyes—his deep-furrowed brows? What brooded in his thoughts?

Despite his brash airs, Burt's first days instilled promise. Temper held in check, he stood polite, courteous, willing. He was trying.

Within a few days though, I sensed anger brooding beneath his stoic exterior. Controlled by mood swings, he teased one minute, turned ugly, ill-tempered the next. At times, his anger flashed out at me in rude hatewords, "Shut up! Don't tell me what to do. Make me! I dare you!" Black eyes glared distrust. Lips curled in derision.

To intimidate me? To threaten?

"This is a stinkin' rotten class. I can walk out anytime I want to! And don't you forget it!" (An enforced reminder: "I'm Indian. You're white. I don't have to take anything from you! And don't you ever forget it!")

Did it stiffen his backbone when I just stood and took his snarls and insults? Did it spur the braggart within? The bully? Did it strike a mark against those who had hurt him?

Burt's actions suggested that authority ranked with brutality: crack ribs, knock out teeth, blacken eyes. Was brutality, then, the only authority he understood?

And I? I determined to be an authority in reverse—sneaky like the fog. After all, fog as spirit-power taught the seeker how to evade and outwit enemies. I turned into the fog.

~

On a later Monday morning, Burt shoved Jesse against my desk. Started fights. Called names. Sidney, sassy and smarty, shouted across the room, "Catch Miss Conly's purse." Before I could grab him, my purple purse sailed into Jesse's head. Jesse jumped to his feet, scuffled with Sidney in brawny reprisal.

To attract Burt's attention, Lorna grabbed his jacket. He whirled, knocking her sideways. Then Christine slapped Joey and screamed in triumph.

Helpless. Thwarted. I walked out . . . the first time I'd ever walked out on a class.

Subterfuge? Escape? Cunning like the fog?

The thought of fog spirits sent me to the Principal's office. Here was escape into the fog . . . "This is the day!" I tantalized. "I've had it! Those obstreperous freshmen warriors need a pep talk. It's your turn, Mr. Perkins. Here they come! Ready or not."

Tramp! Tramp! Tramp! Down the hall they came to defend themselves and tell on me. The stance of the Principal halted the warriors. They respected Mr. Perkins. His calm, understanding response led to a Principal pep talk.

Herded back to class, no one said a word. No one but Sidney. "We like you. We like you. We like you." Pangs of regret shone in his black eyes and shy grin. I learned to accept those teasing black eyes and shy grin—just learned to love them and take it in my stride.

~

Leaving oral-reports class one day, Burt snickered, "Could you tell when I was drunk for two weeks?"

"You mean the days you put me in shock by your winning ways?"

~

One day, a few weeks later, Burt was absent. So was Christine. Eloped with Burt? Lorna stomped into class, flopped into her desk-chair. "Burt and I had another big fight over Christine. He popped me," she sobbed. Lorna scrutinized me through red swollen eyes. "He said he was going to Forks. I hope he never comes back," she wailed through drenching tears.

But Burt came back. This time with his foot bound in a walking plaster-cast. Arrogant and sarcastic he snapped, "I wrecked my foot at basketball practice."

Lorna told a different story: "Burt hurt his foot in a knock-out fight at home. They were all drunk. Poor guy. I feel so sorry for him." (So did I.)

After school, Burt came to my room for make-up assignments. "I'm gettin' out of this monkey-cage," he snarled, looking at the cast.

"You'd better let the doctor decide when to take the cast off. You'll be sorry if you take it off too soon," I reprimanded.

"Says who?" snorted he, and walked out.

~

Burt. Absent again. Hospitalized in Port Angeles. "He took his cast off too soon. Hurt his foot real bad—but he knows it all!" informed Lorna. "He got in another big fight and had to have his foot put back in another cast."

Burt again. Kelly confided: "Lorna bawled and howled all last night after another fight with Burt." Kelly handed me his special-cooking assignments. His goal: to flaunt a *chef de cuisine* cap. "Lorna made so much noise I couldn't sleep. My sister has a terrible temper. So has Burt," admitted Kelly. "It's a wonder they don't kill each other." As Kelly stood in the doorway to leave, he added, "I heard, after a family quarrel, he went to Sappho to look for work—his foot still in a cast."

So . . . Burt was not in school for a while. Will he be back? Oh, yes! He'll be back for the Christmas Tea!

~

Later—riotous and relentless—the wind and rain never eased all night. An invincible force . . . as in Freshman English—an invincible force of pagan savage wildness that I cannot conquer. Each class a barbaric ritual of mockery—falsity. Feeling non-existent, I shifted between the known and the unknown.

Sidney was out and beyond! He pounded his desk. Threw his book on the floor. Hit Simon with an eraser. At the same time, Burt—who had returned for the Christmas Tea—shouted, "Who says so?"

Sitting on his desk—he continued to shout: "I don't have to! You can't make me! Kick me out! I don't care! White trash teacher!"

Brutality was all Burt knew—all he wanted—all he understood.

. . . go into the fog again . . . I did.

. . . I found Jesse in this fog—a strange mixture of Whale-hunter, spirit-power, and problems. Day after day I faced insurmountable barriers—deep, hopeless barriers often tainted by whiskey.

Misunderstood—my approach fumbled—did not conform. Washington State Freshman English classroom: a place to giggle—to gossip. Had white man's system of education failed Reservation children? But persistence, patience, and understanding led many eager learners to seek higher standards.

~

I did not forget that verbs, pronouns, sentence structure proved no cultural rite. English grammar rules—the very last things on earth Sidney or Burt or Jesse could care about.

White man's tragic abuse of the Indian now hit back at me. Did these kids rage at me for circumstances beyond their control? For situations they did not understand?

I took it. I didn't kick them out of class or have them expelled from school or say, "Just for that you can't come to the Christmas Tea."

I took it. I turned into the fog—again and again—to survive.

But I could not ignore feeling crushed and beaten—corrupted and devastated by Burt's insults and Jesse's thoughtlessness. And yet, one day Burt's hands and fingernails were so immaculately clean that it startled me . . . his first sign of response. Optimism rising. I could do it . . .

And now, to my horror, all four kitchen sinks plugged up—the day before the Christmas Tea!!

~

Rain. Rain. Rain. Sloshing, slopping, mud puddles kept the kids in after lunch. The freshman English class and I waited in the library for fifth period bell. By some freakish stint, I pulled a desk drawer out too far. It clattered and clanged and banged to the floor with a crash. Pencils, erasers, paper clips, pass slips, library cards all streaked in a million directions.

"Oh, no!" I cried in dismay. In rueful laughter, I threw up my hands. "That's it, kids. I'm leaving."

Burt—rough, tough, incorrigible—fell to his knees. Without a word, he collected the scattered items and replaced the drawer. I murmured a humbled, heart-touched, "Thank you."

Immediately my murmur erupted into an un-uttered blood-curdling screech. Too late. I remembered my purple purse—concealed on an inner shelf of the library table. With fiendish glee, Burt snatched. The bell rang. Off we trod to class. Burt led the way—a splash of purple clutched under his arm.

Ignore it? I could. Perform as an English teacher? I could not. But who cared? Not Burt. Not Jesse. Not Sidney. Not when Burt pirated a purple treasure trove. To hoot, to loot! A lipstick, a compact, a perfume vial. A real blast. No dynamite concealed therein—but it's an idea. I should have kicked him out.

Misbehaving? Unruly? Yes! The room in an uproar? Yes! Then whack! "Burt, you will report immediately after school in Room 210!" Christy, a student deputy in the high school disciplinary court, had arrested Burt.

But what an unexpected jolt! A sting to Burt's pride. In this rare play-ful mood, he meant no offense. Burt believed he had as much right in my purse as I did. So grim, so serious, so deadly. Teasing was a relief.

I knew, instantly, student courts wouldn't help. Burt was different. He had faced charges so much more serious than plundering my purse. After judgment in stern juvenile courts, a high school court would seem silly and childish. I could see Burt sitting before those kids—not taking it seriously. Laughing at them, smirking in derision and rebellion. Finally, getting mad. Then, in a rage, storm out, quit school, chuck all he had gained, and, foot still in a cast, stomp into more trouble.

When I met Christy after class, she accepted my decision to rescind her charge.

Burt did not report to Room 210 after school. Instead, he came to me for English grammar help. After explaining my withdrawal of Christy's charge, Burt growled, "I wasn't worried. I wouldn't have done anything they asked me to anyway. It wouldn't have worked."

Scuffling and shoving, Jesse and Helmer knocked shy, petite Sara against the wall. Sidney raced in, threw open the window, swung his legs over the sill, stared into the fog.

"You darn dope, Sid," screamed Dolly, "shut that window. You're letting in all the fog, and I'm freezing."

TODAY: Classes in conflict—classes in disruption—nobody listened—everybody fidgeted. Something sets these kids off . . . and away they go. Holiday time? Hangover? Full moon?

TONIGHT: Discouraged and ready to quit, I looked into the darkness—white man's whiskey degenerated my Indian friends—reduced them to blobs of drunkenness—to blobs of slovenliness.

She sparkled! She radiated a joyous vitality! An aura of charm—elegance—wonder—enfolded her. Glistening black braids wound around her head created a halo effect. Her skin tones glowed like bronzed silk. A shimmering black-satin tunic enclothed her. She sat erect—head held high—an aristocrat!

I stared right at her. Our eyes met. I turned away—mesmerized.

Something about this magnetic Indian woman stirred my spirit. An allusion of mystery touched her. Who was she? Where did she come from?

My attention shifted to Jule. "Who is that Indian woman sitting by the door? Four black-haired children huddle on the floor near her. The older girl, June, I recognize from my classes."

Jule glanced away from the Makah dancers to answer with an air of nonchalance. "Oh, that's Lucy Millholland. She's here—she's there. Village people gossip about her—just jealousy—she rarely attends the Community Hall affairs. Too ritzy. I guess."

Chatter stopped. Drums beat to the tone of a War Dance. Costumed—faces daubed with red and black war paint—eight or ten little Indians stomped and lurched.

Above the war cries and beat of drums, Jule briefed Lucy's genealogical history: "Her father was Makah. Her mother is Suquamish. Through her mother's line, Mrs. Millholland traces her lineage to Chief Seattle—great Chief of the Duwamish-Suquamish tribes—later elected Chief of the Allied Tribes of Puget Sound. She is great-great-grandniece of Chief Seattle. That sets her apart. She's ROYALTY! Like Helen, Mrs. Millholland's not just ordinary."

So intent on listening to Jule monitor Lucy's background, I forgot the dancers . . . and there was more to come: "Mrs. Millholland's married to a white man. Lives off the Reservation. She's not always at Neah Bay. I've heard she lives part of the time at Marysville. That's where her mother is. Mrs. Millholland and her children give authentic Suquamish Indian programs in Seattle. They're outstanding singers and dancers."

Jule paused—glanced toward the great Chief's descendant. "She's quite striking in that black-satin outfit—just her style—nobody here ever dresses that way."

I shied away from the war cries—the painted faces—the pound of drums.

Lights dimmed. Guests scattered. Time to go home.

Jule touched my arm. "Mrs. Millholland and her daughter June are coming this way."

"This is my mother." June spoke in soft monotones. "She wants to meet you."

Stunned. Tongue-tied. Within me an intuitive power awakened my inner self. A voice—low and musical—said, "I'm so happy to meet June's teacher."

We stood face to face. Only us. Touching hands. Touching hearts.

I knew we would meet again . . .

 History had marched through the drum beats. A vivid history-book picture had jolted my memory: THE CHIEF SEATTLE MONUMENT! A bronze statue portrayed the mighty Chieftain. His hand outstretched, offering peace and friendship to the white settlers.

A stalwart man—over six feet tall—broad shouldered—deep chested—he stood as a dramatic statesman and orator. A peacemaker—representing the Indian Nations in treaty signing—in treaty breaking—in receding tribal lands—in loss of camas fields—hunting rights. A man of vision, Chief Seattle saw the futility in resisting the white invaders.

Despite lies and deceit—false accusation and misunderstandings—Chief Seattle and his daughter, Princess Angeline, were powerful influences in the settlement of the Puget Sound territory.

INTRODUCTION
FOR MRS. ERNEST MILLHOLLAND AND FAMILY

(by Lillian Smarts at a Zonta Club meeting in Seattle)

Deep within the hearts of men, be they primitive or civilized, there is hidden a certain spark which responds to a rhythmic beat of the Tom-Tom . . . to the rhythmic shuffle of moccasined feet . . . to the rhythmic singings of a chant . . . and among many people these have been the means by which they have their religious beliefs.

These ceremonials are in truth not dances but prayers to the gods for prosperity, for fertility, for beautiful crops, for rain, and for a better life in the world to come.

Unless an Indian trusts you, and you have won his confidence, he will never reveal the interpretation of his various ceremonies and customs.

Mrs. Millholland, like her great-great-granduncle, Chief Seattle, has always been a good Friend to the white race.

Mrs. Millholland her children—June, Ernest, Lylia, and Rita—will do Suquamish Indian Songs and Dances.

 Football schedules linked Sidney's English classwork to his tackles on the football field. His impish grin and snapping black eyes followed me everywhere—and dared me to flunk him. "I dare you!" And his eyes snapped brighter!

Over his head, I cracked the cat o' nine tails, day after day.

At game time. At the last minute. THEY WAITED: the principal—the coach—the team—the school bus, with motor revved.

WILL SIDNEY GET TO PLAY?

And wouldn't you know, there he stood before me. Hesitant. Scared. His helmet clutched to his chest. Beaming innocence, he barely breathed. "I can play? Huh? Can I?"

. . . AND THERE I STOOD BETWEEN THE RED DEVIL FOOTBALL TEAM AND ONE IMP WHO SMELLED LIKE FISH . . .

"Sidney, you flunked the spelling test. You forgot your make-up work. You hit Jesse in the head with a paper wad. You won't work in class nor let anyone else."

Bright eyes dulled. Head drooped. Grin vanished.

I turned away. My responsibility. My freedom of choice.

How could I let him down? How could I say a cold "NO!" He trusted me . . . or manipulated me . . . sometimes I wondered which.

I groaned. Shut my eyes. Turning back, I faced him. "Well, just this time!"

Ecstatic! In wild joy, he threw both arms around me and kissed my cheek . . . and I yelled at him because he knocked an earring to the floor.

That fish-smelling, bright-eyed Red Devil will be the end of me yet!

~

I may as well become resigned to Sidney and Jerry. I may as well quit dreading that abominable period—HOMEROOM! I may as well peacefully sit with one on each side of me.

And then Sidney for the 1000th time:

"Gee, you have pretty eyes.

"Gee, you have a cute chin!

"And the way you toss your head. Gee!"

Flatterer! Just buttering me up for the next game. Behind those honey-dripping words, I heard an old war chant: "I can play? Huh? Can't I? I can play? I can play? I can play?"

Sidney! Lovable rascal. How he exasperates me! I have to leave the room sometimes to get away from his teasing, pestering, and fishy smell!

Shall I kick him out of class and have him expelled?

A splendid idea! But smacks betrayal. There's been enough of that!

No, I'll transcend—reach beyond the median—adapt to what is: Sidney likes me! Sidney trusts me! Just love him and take it in your stride.

~

A scraping sound. A familiar sound. A body—shimmying up the side of the school building into the Home Ec kitchen. I closed my red grade book—looked toward the open window—bound to the inevitable—no escape possible.

First, a head appeared—black hair bristled on end. Padded shoulders followed. Hard-muscled arms hoisted head and shoulders and body over the window sill. Elements scrambled together formed SIDNEY IN FOOTBALL UNIFORM!

Before I could screech "Not you again!" his irresistible teasing grin silenced me. "Fix me a peanut butter sandwich and some milk," he demanded. No time to object. I was shoved toward the refrigerator. "Hurry up! Right now! I hafta get back. Hurry! Hurry!"

While I put peanut butter and bread together, Sidney grabbed a carton of milk—poured it into a glass—slopped milk on the floor—stepped in the puddle.

Gulping milk, he snatched the sandwich, grinned "Thanks!" As he disappeared over the window sill, I shouted, "Sidney, you are a Red Devil!"

The strong, penetrating smell of fish stayed behind. Ever present, it permeated his hair, his clothes, his skin.

Sidney didn't know *is* from *was*—and he didn't care. But he cared about peanut butter sandwiches and milk . . . and game practices on the football field.

. . . Through my gift of food, he knew I cared about him. In return, he accepted me, he liked me, he trusted me. I was his friend.

~

Seconds before the bus took off with the Neah Bay Red Devil Champions—right in the middle of a Pizza Pie demonstration, Sidney crashed full blast into class.

"I gotta have the kneepads sewed in my football pants. Right now! Hurry up! They're waiting for me. We're playing Forks. Hurry!"

I had ceased objecting to Sidney's "right now" demands.

In placid resignation, I threaded a needle, slipped on a thimble, sewed in kneepads . . .

What did they do in the old days?

~

A lovable, mischievous, black-eyed tyrant: SIDNEY!

Behind his sparkling eyes—his fetching grin—he terrified me with black spiders—disrupted Freshman English (which he had to repeat a few times)—watched me with bewilderment and suspicion.

Will I kick him out of class? Will I flunk him?

His exuberant energy—curbed only by fear—fear he'd flunk English. To flunk meant a hard set on the bench with no chance to play. A Red Devil Champion, he'd rather die than be denied game privileges.

Game after game I slipped Sidney through each crisis.

Day in and day out Sidney pestered, tormented, infuriated me . . .

~

. . . and then one day the sparkle in his eyes divined a message . . . the imp in his grin masked a secret . . . from a chain, held in his hand, a tiny gold cross dangled.

"This is for you. I got it in Victoria. Here, take it. It's yours."

Blankness swept over me. My heart spilled over with forgiveness—with affection.

For my Medicine Bag: a tiny gold cross—a touch of spirit—of power—of trust . . .

 My mood, dull and oppressive, matched the dank and sunless evening. I struggled to claw away the whiskey fumes that smothered me like spider webs in a bad dream.

At morning lunch-count, I missed the Blane sisters. "Are Kitsy and Christy absent or just late?"

Rose Mary whispered, "Their dad got drunk and wobbled off the porch and broke his shoulder."

Unable to comment, I heard Cheree chime in, "Their dad's in Forks' Hospital. He claimed somebody pushed him."

At coffee break, Deena looked up from the hamburger stew, hesitated, and then asked, "Have you heard about Helmer?" Deena put a lid on the stew, shook her head—sighed—wiped her hands on a towel. "He was crazy drunk. He drove his car down Front Street—zigzagged from one side to the other—hit Zeke, a member of the Makah Tribal Council—brutally thrown against a parked car. He's in Port Angeles Hospital and may never walk again."

After school, I stopped to see Jule. "This village is reeking in whiskey," she berated under her breath. "You've heard about Helmer? A senior—in line for a Tribal scholarship—sure blew his chances. And that's not all," Jule said, walking into her kitchen. "At Church Circle last night, I heard that Susie found her uncle on the beach in an alcoholic coma. He never regained consciousness. Stay and have some spiced tea before you go home. It's very relaxing."

"I need a relaxant. I'm totally stunned." Leaning against the gold velvet cushions, I began, "Wes came to my room after school. He needed extra help with spelling assignments. At 4:00, I suggested it was time to go home."

"Home? Where everybody's drunk?"

"But your mother will worry about you."

I'll never forget the look on his face.

"That's a laugh," Wes smirked. "She doesn't worry about me. She's drunk all the time." As he walked away, he smirked again, "I've never seen my mother sober."

Living with parents who drink! What chance do these Reservation children have? After a while, I learned to accept that the taste for whiskey came easily even to the very, very young.

Night winds screeched—shrilled and whistled through the village. Iced rain stabbed windows—storm spirits rattled roof shingles—and out in the dark: strangeness—in shapes of village scare-frights—WATCHED!

~

Twisted and tangled thoughts brushed away sleep, but I couldn't brush away the fear-strained faces of the girls . . .

Yesterday, around the study table, voices—low-toned and cautious—spoke of strange tales in the dark: eerie noises—flicker-lights on Waadah Island where nobody lives—wail sounds in old houses—shadow beings and ghost shapes wander about in the dark—all unexplained happenings—supernatural phenomenon . . .

To the village people the supernatural is very real . . .

"Ghosts and strange shapes wander about in the dark," Lissa murmured. "And we never walk by the old house back of Washburn's Store after dark." Silently the girls nodded their heads.

Sliding her chair closer to Cheree whispered, "My grandmother Ada tells that long ago, before the lighthouse on Tatoosh, hundreds of sailors died in shipwrecks."

"And we've heard many old people believe that when we see ghosts they are spirits of dead sailors who died on the rocks near Tatoosh," Cheree chimed in.

Jacqui, an unbeliever, mocked, "Ghosts, goblins, witches and werewolves!" Tiptoeing around the table, she flapped her arms, bobbed her blond head. "T'hoot! T'whoo! See that werewolf out on the breakwater! He stamps his hoofs, flashes his bloodshot eyes, bares his sharp yellow fangs. And he's gonna grab you if ya don't watch out!" Giggling, she pointed a finger at me.

I was amused. The girls were not.

"Oh, knock it off, Jacqui. It's not funny," berated Mary Lynn, spitting verbal arrowheads at the skeptic.

"No-o-o-o. Not funny at all." Wary voices denied Jacqui's ridicule of the unseen—the unknown. But Jacqui continued to scoff. She hunched her back, high-stepped around the table, lifted her voice to a high-pitched squeak: "Hob-goblins and witches slink down the back roads—whistle and howl. Ghosts flutter in the graveyard and float down Main Street. Black ogres, dripping pale green slime, whoosh through the dark and then skedaddle into the forests!"

Ignoring Jacqui's antics, Becky confided, "The man who swings the lantern scares me the most. He walks through the village at night. He's tall and humped over and wears a long overcoat. It sags and flops loose." Becky folded her arms across her chest and shuddered. "No one sees where he comes from. He's just there. Then he's just gone. It's spooky. I'm afraid to be out alone after dark."

"The burned house is really haunted," spoke up Bonnee. "Before the bell rings, I want to tell what Shana and Dock heard. They were down on the beach—near an old shack—not far from Ruth's little red house. They heard horrible moans and chopping sounds. The noises came from the dark old shack. They were so scared they couldn't get away fast enough."

Bonnee stretched her arms across the table and shuddered. "The old people say someone was murdered there years ago."

"The old deserted house behind Skeleton's Bridge is the one that scares me," one of the girls admitted. "Gives me the creeps just thinking about it. My grandfather said even on hot days the air around it is ice cold. There's always ground-fog and swishy-whisper noises and a really mucky smell."

"Every time I think about it, I get shaky and dizzy," another girl stammered. "And I remember when old Jenny told about picking berries near the upper creek. She told that the underbrush began to rustle. Strange sounds came up from the ground. Jenny was scared to death. She vowed a gray shape swooped up all around her. Nobody goes there anymore."

From Jacqui: "Jenny can't see very well. She probably just imagined it."

Daphne sighed, grasped the edge of the table. "I know one thing for sure. Since the loggers cut the forest down in front of the school buildings, Ada and Natah walk over here more often. I guess the old people still believe and fear demons that lurk in the woods. It's scary in the dark forests."

"If this keeps up," laughed Jacqui, "we'll all be too scared to go home—even me. I have to pass a patch of forest to get to my house." . . .

Out in the dark—a place of hidden terrors—ghosts, witches and unknown monsters—lurk—unfolding bone-chilling fears. Whether on the breakwater or on Waadah Island, manifestations of the supernatural—with magic spells and icy undercurrents—belong to the secret plane of their own.

. . . BUT TO THE VILLAGE PEOPLE, THE SUPERNATURAL IS VERY REAL . . .

Gathering at Clallam Bay, Neah Bay teachers met with Clallam Bay teachers for a Salmon Bake.

Ada told this story as we sat on a log on the beach in the brilliant October sun. I pivoted toward her—greedy for more stories:

Lowering her head, Ada paused. "I tell story of famine among Indians. Long ago—tides not right—run all wrong—no fish—no food—people hungry. Indians pray and pray to Great Spirit for food. One day big noise in sky. People saw great Thunderbird—in claws great Whale." Ada swung her arms in flying motion. "Thunderbird leave Whale on beach—Indians have big feast—they praise and praise Great Spirit—gave thanks for Whale."

"I saw him die. I was in the car. It happened so fast . . ." Above the fog horn's mourning, Annabelle's voice faded to a shudder. The tragic message stilled the room. Sober-faced girls quietly set their lunch trays on the table . . .

That morning at coffee I had flippantly greeted Deena, "It's Monday morning! What's new?"

Her reply was not flippant: "Jerry Hardke wrecked his car Saturday night. There was an accident. A boy was killed. It's all very hush-hush."

By lunch time the school kids felt the grip of tragedy. Huddled in the lunch line, they compared rumors:

"I heard a boy was killed . . ."

"I heard his chest was crushed . . ."

"I heard he was drunk . . ."

"I heard somebody bled to death . . ."

"Oh, knock it off," Lester drawled. "Everybody tells a different story. S'pose we change the subject. Smells like corn fritters for lunch."

Silence smothered the usual squeals and chatter, giggles and gossip. A fog-shroud of sadness hovered. But they all needed to know about the accident. Last year's graduate, Jerry was one of their own.

Staring at her corn fritters, Rose Mary spoke first. "All morning we've heard wild rumors. What really happened?"

"Who was killed?" interrupted Christy, opening her milk carton. "Do we know him?"

"Joe Pendlebury, a friend of Jerry's." Annabelle stifled her tears. "Bob Owen raced us coming back from Port Angeles. At a curve near Twin Creeks, Jerry gunned the motor, missed the curve." Annabelle lowered her head and wept—wiped her eyes—blew her nose. "Jerry's car jumped off the road—crashed into the brush—hit a tree or something." Crossing her arms, Annabelle placed her hands on her shoulders, twisted her lips, winced. With an anguished sigh, she mumbled, "The police at the accident believed Joe's neck was broken. His head had hit the windshield."

Girls gasped. Pained. Shocked. Fingers tightened around forks.

The awesome silence broke with Cheree's question, "What happened next?"

"The police ambulance took us all to the hospital in P.A." Vaguely coherent, Annabelle fumbled for words: "Jerry was really shook up—trembling—spooked out . . ." She paused. "Bruised and bleeding, Jerry passed out when he heard Joe was dead."

Appearing far away in thought, Annabelle absently wound strands of her long black hair around her finger. Then, as from a distance, she pulled her thoughts back to her listening classmates. "We were taken to emergency. They said Jerry had badly smashed-up ribs, some cuts, and bruises. The doctors want to keep him in the hospital for a few days. He's really messed up though. But he'll be okay."

No one interrupted—only listened—or munched on corn fritters or muffins.

I watched Annabelle press her hands against her temples. "My head still throbs and aches. I was riding in the back seat with Scott. When we crashed, Scott and I were thrown against the front seat. The doctor said I could have a slight concussion." She touched her right hip and shoulder. "My muscles ache from bruises on my shoulder and hip."

"Was Scott hurt?" Becky hoped to conceal her fears.

"Just some bumps and bruises—some swelling over his eye where his head hit the back of the seat."

Once hot and crisp, the golden corn fritters on Annabelle's lunch tray turned cold and soggy. "I can't eat. I'm too upset." Trance-like, she ambled to the window, stared into a massed bank of fog. Dense. Bleak. Menacing.

. . . Shocked. Stunned. The details of the accident flashed my thoughts back to last year's typing class: To Jerry—to his brags and boasts: "I've made it through nine auto wrecks—three totals!" He had thrust back his head and roared with laughter.

Horrified, my pulse raced as I watched Jerry exhibit the traits of a car-speeding demon. Shoulders hunched, he grabbed an imaginary steering wheel. Gritting his teeth, his black eyes glazed, he uttered demon growls to mimic an engine running at high speeds. He topped an imaginary eighty-five miles an hour, ninety, ninety-five—raced around curves tipped on two wheels—tires screeched—he jumped road dips.

"Haw! Haw!" In raucous guffaws, Burt gloated. "That ain't nuthin'." He sprawled his legs into the aisle—flapped his arms above his head. "I've skidded around them Neah Bay curves one-hundred miles per!" he ranted. "I can count fourteen wrecks." Totals? Unremembered.

I couldn't believe it! This recklessness of misdirected energy staggered my mind. The approval of drunkenness—the excitement of smashing cars—the thrill of unlimited speed. The risk of a broken neck, a twisted back, or death only stimulated them.

I knew that in the old days—before white man—whiskey—and cars—young men Jerry's and Burt's age had already quested their Guardian Spirit . . . The search urged boys to follow purifying bathing rituals for cleanliness of mind and body—tribal laws of proper behavior—tests and training sessions for physical endurance. Success of the quest earned boys tribal status—self esteem and spirit power to help and protect them all their lives.

White man's culture and teachings excluded the Spirit Quest—left an irreplaceable void—a need unfulfilled. So now, instead, boys drank whiskey and wrecked cars and died.

~

In class the next day, Annabelle slumped into a chair, nibbled at a piece of cornbread. "I just can't take much more."

Elizabeth gently placed her hand on Annabelle's shoulder. "We understand. We want to help. I'll bring you a cup of hot chocolate." Elizabeth offered to ease—to soften—the razor edge of Annabelle's nerves.

In this way, Annabelle's circle of classmates nourished her emotional and physical needs. Embraced by ritual bonds of friendship and love, Annabelle endured.

Still uppermost in Annabelle's thoughts: Jerry's accident. "Last night the Tribal Council held a meeting about the accident. We all had to be there. The FBI was there too." Fidgeting with her olive-shell necklace, Annabelle sipped the hot chocolate. "The Council members and FBI men kept asking questions. They had to know everything: the names of those in the car—Joe's position in the car when he died—if anybody moved him—who called the police. Just everything." Covering her face with her hands, her voice muffled, she sobbed, "It was awful. I'm so scared. They may take the trial to Federal Court."

~

By now the darks of November engulfed us. No sun. No moon. No stars. Just rain and fog. Ghosts and goblins and black-cat costumes left over from the Halloween dance were packed away and forgotten. Autumn's leaves of yellow, scarlet, and orange—sullied by mud—lay discolored and sodden. But the Junior Class girls bubbled with excitement.

"We've never had a Thanksgiving Breakfast before. What fun!" they shouted in agreement. "It's holiday time! Party time! Let's do it!" Daphne urged.

"What shall we have to eat?" chirruped Mary Lynn, reaching for a cookbook.

"Oh, I know!" teased Jacqui. "Roasted wild turkeys and bog cranberries and pumpkin pies, baked squash, and orange Kool-Aid!"

"Let's string Pilgrim and Indian paper dolls across the windows—like we did in grade school," tittered Rose Mary.

"Of course, we'll invite the Junior Class boys," giggled Kitsy.

"Of course," I groaned—and any other boy who wandered in.

⌒

Home Ec spirits rising high. Holiday happiness threaded through the girls—touched all but Annabelle. Grim faced, she uttered, "I've been subpoenaed. I have to appear before the Makah Tribal Court versus Jerry Hardke."

The girls' excited chattering became murmurs. Annabelle lowered her voice to bitterness. "No one knows what will happen. Nothing's in Jerry's favor. He was driving without a license. He'd been drinking. He raced to beat Bob to the curve." Annabelle pressed her palms against her temples. "I'll be glad when it's over . . . I can't take anymore questions . . . anymore explaining . . . over and over, again and again."

Annabelle's bitterness infected the Breakfast plans—dragged them to doom—pulled us all down, down . . .

"Let's take a break," I prompted, hoping to revive their happy spirits. "Rose Mary and Cheree, mix up a batch of Indian fry bread. Serve a jar of Annabelle's gooseberry jam—a zippy treat on a dull November day. How about it, Annabelle?"

I felt her tension ease. A shadow lifted. She smiled. "I really would like that. I haven't eaten all day, but fry bread and gooseberry jam sound good."

⌒

". . . Jerry's unconscious muttering gave way to his guilt and suffering," Zettah recalled. "He didn't know I was in the hospital room—but I believe he remembered tribal laws learned as a child."

⌒

Jerry lay in dark silence on the sterile hospital bed. A Spirit voice whispered, "Racing Wolf . . . Racing Wolf . . . I, Spirit Guide, sent by Grandfathers, speak: You erred in the ways of your people."

"Jerry! Jerry! Wake up!" Jerked from sleep, Jerry divined a white blur in the nightlight's glow. "It's time for your pain medicine."

Between lips—bruised and swollen—Jerry sobbed. "R-a-c-i-n-g- W-o-l-f . . ." Strong arms lifted his shoulders. "Swallow this, Jerry. Then go back to sleep."

Back in the realm of sleep, Jerry brushed his hand over his face, as if to brush away cobwebs—as if to brush away the sharp curve—the car out of control—the crash—Joe's instant death—the death that had ripped ugly gashes of pain and guilt in Jerry's mind and emotions.

His thoughts, drugged by medication, drifted back . . . He was twelve years old. Jerry recalled the naming ceremony. RACING WOLF. Totem name of runner. Given by ancestral Grandfather.

Darkness enfolded him. In pain and anguish he groped to understand the Spirit Guide's next words: "You erred—broke laws set by Great Spirit—by Tribal Elders. Purify your body and mind in ritual waters . . ." Jerry struggled to follow Spirit's instructions. ". . . fast in mountains—seek energy in mystical breathing rites."

Jerry's drugged mind drifted—boyhood beliefs and teachings emerged. He heard the Voice again: " . . . chant old songs to redeem prayer power—praise Great Spirit for healing and protection—follow laws of your people—face your own identity—face truth of your own spirit being—your spirit power . . ."

Jerry believed ancestral Grandfathers knew the harsh edge of his fear—his confusion—his suffering. He felt their love—their understanding—their forgiveness.

In a flash of clarity, he let go of the darkness. Jerry's mind opened. Under the white hospital sheets, Jerry's clenched fists gave power to his thoughts: "I, Racing Wolf, know what I must do—as taught by Grandfathers."

Bound to the spirits of his people, Jerry drew their powers into his own spirit body for strength—for protection. Whatever the decision of the Tribal Court—his fears ebbed—his tension eased. He could face the charges.

~

The day after Jerry's trial, Annabelle returned to classes. In typical languid style, her movements appeared almost fluid. Her drawn thin face, her dull sunken eyes, mirrored her sufferings.

"It's over." Annabelle breathed a long, deep sigh reflecting her relief from anxiety—her worry—her nights without sleep. She pulled the cover off the typewriter. The foghorn mourned in the background—sounded across the breakwater and into the classroom.

"They couldn't prove he was drunk. The Tribal Judge sentenced him to fifteen days in the county jail for reckless driving and a year's probation."

"He was sure lucky!"

 Girls! Boys! Food!
They mixed. They stirred. They spilled.
Whose idea was it in the first place that kids do the cooking? Oh, no! Not mine!

My blood pressure soared to 450 degrees.

"Come on, you guys! Take it easy!" admonished Jacqui. "I'm trying to make a cheese-green pepper omelet."

"A what?" smirked Chet. "Never heard of it. Do you eat it? Not me!" He turned his back and walked away.

"Look out, Champ!" screamed Cheree. "You're spilling the orange juice all over the floor."

"Hey, Kitsy! If you don't watch it, you'll burn the eggs," yelled Simon. "Looks like you'll have to scramble them now." Laughing, he grabbed a pancake turner.

"You're so smart. Come on and help me. I need a platter."

Food releases excitement that invites fun: fun in relationships—fun in preparation—fun in choices. A known: Indian bread. An unknown: cranberry bread.

"What's this?" snickered Jesse.

"Pineapple, raisin, walnut relish," giggled Rose Mary. "We made it in cooking class. Try some. It's good."

"Nah. Not me." He turned his back and walked away.

"What's that?" quizzed Lonnie, pointing to a reddish mixture.

"Tomato preserves," answered Dolly. "Have some. It's really delicious. This is my second helping."

"No way," he snorted. "Thank you, I'll have a piece of Indian bread." Lonnie too walked away.

"This is a dish of gooseberry jam, Genevieve. Try some," I offered.

"Nah." She wiggled her broad Makah nose. "Looks funny."

"Oh, come on, Gen," coaxed Kitsy. "It's yummy. Try a drop on a piece of Indian bread. It won't poison you."

Genevieve shook her head in stubborn refusal. None of this white-man stuff for her. Unwilling to try foods different in color or different in taste.

Does a cultural collision begin with food?

Bold and bossy Genevieve, with her friends Erma, Molly, Sara—shy and withdrawn—just stood around and watched. Fun—just to watch!

And Sidney. Always Sidney. He followed me around—stepped in my way—pushed me into a chair—shoved a plate of food under my nose. I looked into those impish black eyes and pleaded, "Sidney, you tyrant, only some coffee, please."

Better believe it—there had to be time out for horse-play: muscle testing—snap the dishtowels—gobble up the leftovers—then, tug of war.

Feasters—stuffed and hilariously happy—faced the inevitable: CLEAN-UP! Stacks of dishes—piles of forks, spoons, knives—heaps of pots and pans. The boys hoped I'd forget them, but the girls were too smart.

"Come on, Champ. You're not getting out of this." Cheree marched him toward sink #1.

Chuckling, Simon grabbed Kelly's arm. "I'll take this sink. You take the next."

Annabelle shoved her brother into place at sink #4.

Hunched over sinks, boys scrubbed pots and pans. Faucets turned back and forth. Hot water steamed. Cold water splashed.

"Get a mop and wipe up the floor," bossed Genevieve from the sidelines. "Hurry, before somebody slips."

. . . but it was too late. "Oh, no!" wailed Jacqui. And away sprawled Jesse into a slide—a tray full of silverware skidded under sinks, against baseboards, and under tables.

"Whoops!" shouted Sidney. In a scramble of arms and legs, he and Jesse scooped up the assortment of utensils—covered with floor oil and dust. The pieces were heaped back on the tray.

Above the clatter and clang, Lester groaned, "Oh my aching back!"

Sharp-eyed Kitsy giggled nervously, "Now you have to wash them all over again."

"How so? We just washed them."

"Oh, no! My back is killing me," agonized Lester. "Let Kelly do it this time."

"Come on, Gen, help me dry dishes," urged Jane.

"I got no time," retorted Genevieve. "You do it."

When the revelers ran out of dry dish towels, they used the wet ones over again. When sopping wet, towels were hung to drip dry.

BANG! CRASH! Pots and pans stacked to a mounting Eiffel Tower collided in crescendo to the floor.

"It's all your fault, Sidney," shrieked Becky. "If you hadn't tried to pile that last iron skillet on top."

THANKSGIVING in bedlam!

A zesty, merry mix-up of kids and food—a new experience—a break in routine. They loved it! I rejoiced. A staunch breath of success overpowered me: "SHE'LL NEVER LAST UP HERE."

My thoughts—pierced by the bell—chased away SHE. "Run to your fourth period classes. You've done a wonderful job," I praised. "I'll put the pots and pans away."

. . . and out they staggered, calling back, "That sure was fun! See ya."

Quietly beside me stood Elizabeth. "I have Study this period. If you'll write a pass, I'll stay and help."

I tingled. Indian-Spirit-Power?

～

Later, in the library, exhausted after his workout over the kitchen sink, Lester mumbled, "If a teacher or Perkins comes in, let me know." And he buried his head in his arms to sleep a la radio.

"Oh?" I questioned. "Just what am I supposed to be in this establishment?"

"OH, I TRUST YOU!"

Guess who piped up? Sidney. "Ya. All the freshmen trust you."

Lester is a senior. Four years with that Freshman Class? Four years with Sidney?

～

Brief remarks from a Makah elder concluded our Thanksgiving Assembly:

"When I was a boy, we learned our lessons outdoors. Either our grandfather or an uncle was our teacher. We began our bathing at five years."

Smiles deepened the wrinkles in his cheeks and under his twinkly black eyes. "We called it *ducking*. Early every morning we took our *ducking* in the ice cold river. Shivering and naked, we ran home where our mothers had hot soup ready for us."

The old Makah paused, spoke slowly. "I remember Thanksgiving after the white man came. But my mother's soup—cooked with dried deer meat or Salmon or dried clams and potatoes, carrots, onions, and wild herbs—was better than the turkey dinner," he chuckled.

~

Later, after the Thanksgiving Breakfast, in my spot away from the world, window shades blocked out the night. A twist of the key snapped out the dangerous, treacherous eyes of SHE.

I gloried in another victory over Rega Buckthorn and Lola. Every Home Ec achievement—sooner or later—reached their ears.

SHE: dominant—critical—ready to pounce—to discredit every attempt—until each project of the school year evolved into a survival test.

But why have I allowed SHE to plague me? Annoy me? Irritate me? Disturb me? Scare me? Because SHE called me a witch? Because SHE hexed me by declaring I'd never last up here?

"Up here" in the ceaseless span of sky and sea, SHE and I are only names—disconnected from past, present, future—from needs to survive.

"Up here" in the vastness of isolation do we lose our identities?

"Up here" do we all become one?

Or . . . will the shadow of SHE forever hex me?

After school—a week ago—Kelly drifted into Home Ec. "We're having a winter ceremonial Friday and Saturday." His statement stirred a childhood memory: Kelly remembers when he was four years old. Three-hundred Indians crossed the Strait of Juan de Fuca from Vancouver Island. They arrived in huge war canoes paddled by slaves. They paddled through thick heavy fog. It was real spooky. Kelly shuddered—a blankness clouded his eyes.

He recalled the ornate, the elaborate, carvings on the canoes, the brilliant colored images painted to represent legendary animals. The tribe came to attend a Makah potlatch—a winter festival of feasting, dancing, singing, gift giving. Kelly remembers the Indians as being very tall and heavy. Dressed in formal tribal costume, their ceremonial robes and ritual capes gave them an aristocratic and awesome appearance.

"No one dare touch a part of the costume, or death would follow," Kelly declared. "I sure was scared of those Indians." Once again, blankness clouded his eyes. He whispered, "They don't come anymore."

I listened. Asked no questions.

But after Kelly left, his story disturbed me. Why? Something didn't fit. But what? Then it hit me! Of course! Kelly's description of the huge war canoes paddled by slaves fit into the 1800s, not the 1900s. A fleeting mysterious glimpse into childhood's imagination?

Had his impressionable child's mind devoured an old story—told over and over—by grandparents and elders?

Had the vivid story-images been locked forever in Kelly's four-year-old mind?

As years passed, had Kelly fantasized that he had stood on Makah shores watching a pageant of power, wealth, grandeur—the last of the old potlatch days?

~

Yesterday I wore THE DRESS. When barriers towered insurmountable, bleak and desperate, I wore THE DRESS. Textured fabric. Tiny gold metallic threads outlined patterns in red, black, and dawn gray. Annabelle radiated approval, "Oh, gee! I sure like your dress. It's real cute. Real sexy." S E X Y! Wow!

~

SIDNEY AND HIS BLACK SPIDER! Of course, I squealed. I'd always squealed at black spiders. Then Christine squealed. Then all the girls squealed. Horrors! "A teacher screaming at a black spider!" giggled the girls. Lost dignity.

~

In the midst of holiday confusion, AN ETHNOLOGIST, A CULTURAL ANTHROPOLOGIST, scheduled for a meeting. We all had to go. Woe! Woe!

~

Time out for football games. PLAYERS FROM PORT ALBERNI flew in by hydroplane to match skills with the Red Devils. Sensational. Big time. Whole school in a Medicine-Man-Dance whirl—rushing, twisting, spinning.

Girls: wild—in a trance—ready to fly into outer space! Trembling with excitement—nothing but boys on her mind—Cheree cuddled up to me, "Let's ask the team to stay over for the Christmas Tea."

Speechless. Rescued by Rose Mary's admonition: "Don't even think about it. Too many complications, rules, and regulations. Stop dreaming, Cheree!"

~

Lester, tall, lanky Makah—sauntered into Home Ec—sixth period—after the bell—after the girls . . .

Perched on a table—shoulders slumped—long legs dangling—he grinned—tore a note into tiny pieces.

"Geez—these girls! Geez! I try to be friends with everybody and look what happens. Guess I'll have to be friends with just boys, eh? Speak to somebody—somebody gets mad. Geez!"

He strolled to the wastepaper basket—tossed in the torn bits. "Geez!"

This morning Karla called me Miss Lester! What's that supposed to mean, eh? Geez!

 "Tell Art there's one more garbage can. He's loading the truck for a trip to the dump. Hurry," I called.

Truck loaded. Engine fired. Art slammed into gear and drove off. Cans clanked in metal discord. Boys—sent to help—waved and shouted: "See ya later!"

In sarcastic jest, I shouted back: "At the garbage dump?" Everybody in the village had been there but me.

Then one Saturday afternoon Debra and Tuffy stopped by in a pickup.

"I'm taking trash to the dump. Come along," she invited.

"Am I—at last—going to this mysterious, intriguing, garbage dump?"

"Well, it's not exactly mysterious or intriguing," Debra explained. "But it's a dropping-off-place for everything from mouse traps to rusty tea strainers. Let's hurry while the sun's out."

I climbed into the pickup and we were off.

Beginning at the village, the garbage-dump road wound to a cliff crest. From here, the universe changed, becoming a mighty arc of cold blue skies and startling forested greenness. Once spotted, this magnificent crest that rolled a thousand feet to the sea now posted a sign: GARBAGE DUMP.

"This is it!" Debra announced. "Let's get out."
High in the sky squawking seagulls dip-dived. On the ground quarrelsome, greedy gulls gorged on edible trash.

Walking toward heaps of rubbish, my eyes centered on flashes of color. Incredible! Color emblazoned a garbage dump: orange peels—lemon rinds—bright spots like exclamation points—red and gold coffee can labels—earth-brown potato peelings, withered. I squinted at sun sparks glinting off sardine cans and glass jars. Scattered egg shells—half buried—gleamed ivory against scorched coffee grounds. Ashy gray, a slender forked bone—for wishing—poked up from debris . . . and someone <u>had</u> wished . . . The wish . . .?

So fascinated by color, I had forgotten bad smells of garbage. But now the smells lifted. My nose twitched at spoiled meat swarming with flies. Through putrid, moldy stuff, maggots crawled and wiggled. Among heaps of dirty old rags, a turkey carcass. Enough smells. Enough of the garbage dump . . .

 It rained and it rained and it rained. Steady torrents slashed hour after hour. I do believe this Sunday afternoon Neah Bay met its annual quota of 122 inches.
A sun flash razored through cloud drifts—sky-streams dripped to a stop. Hurrying into waterproof jackets and boots, Alta and I rushed out with bags of trash. We followed the slushy oozy path past the school buildings—past an evergreen thicket—into a clearing where stood BURNING BARRELS. And—to my horror—HORSES.

Five monster, rain-slapped, beasts fed on winter grasses. Lifting shaggy heads, they snorted disapproval—and stared. Bulging eyes impaled me. I felt doomed.

"Let's go back before they step on us," I cried.

"Oh, nonsense. They're not going to hurt you," scolded Alta.

Exasperation, disgust, and amusement played over the lines on Alta's cheeks. Lips—a firm straight line—eyes—in fierce hardness—Alta glimpsed the soggy ground. There—mixed with twigs, dead leaves, sloppy weeds—a broken branch with Medicine Man powers? A power stick? Shaking the sturdy crooked power stick at the horses, Alta shouted, "Shoo! Shoo! Go on! Go on! Shoo! Shoo!"

With heavy-hoofed stomps—with one last defiant glare—the horses headed for the woods. Not for naught had she taught for forty-five years—not even horses dared to question Alta!

I'll never forget how their ears twitched—their heads hitched up and down—their whiskered lips dangling dry long-stemmed grasses!

"Oh, Alta, thank you. You're always rescuing me from something."

What a comedy! Great balky horses clopping in clumsy dance steps to Alta's stick! Power stick, indeed!

We dumped our trash and started back—even in drenching rain the burning barrels smoldered.

With her usual sputters, Alta complained, "It's a pity this town doesn't have refuse service. Having to walk over here in rains—blizzards—on slippery ice—is ridiculous." Just in time, she side-stepped a puddle. "Watch out! Puddles—puddles—everywhere." Not dropping the refuse subject, "If they had a service, the Tribal Council would probably charge an arm and a leg."

"What do the village people do with their garbage?" I questioned.

"Oh, I don't know—burn it in cookstoves—or toss it out the back door—or throw it under the kitchen sink, if they have one. Why, I've seen garbage thrown right out here in the bay. And, of course, there's the old garbage dump out of town aways. If they're not too drunk or lazy, I guess they haul it up there and dump it for the seagulls," Alta added in sarcasm.

I ignored her censure and relished the keen rain-washed air and winter sun. Then—like a burst of magic—a rainbow! "Oh! Look!" Alta was unimpressed.

But I stopped to glorify the rainbow arch—"Heaven of the wild flowers," sang the poet. "When on earth they fade and perish, blossom in that heaven above us . . ." I remembered too the Rainbow Bridge of the Gods, the Bridge that connected mankind to the celestial home of the mythological gods.

Alta had walked on—now opposite the school building. I hurried to catch up. Suddenly a rocking jerk—a violent earth-shift under foot—a shuddering building—EARTHQUAKE!

Today—on the edges of an earthquake.

A night of blackest black. Silent. Mysterious.

Destination: Presbyterian Church

On foot, Alta and I trod streets—muddy—squishy—from rains. Eerie sea mists brushed our cheeks. We felt lost. No lights. No cars. No people. Was everyone already at the wedding?

"Are you sure we're going in the right direction?" I whispered. "It's so dark I can't tell which way's which."

Alta snapped, "This whole thing is ridiculous. I'd never be out here in the first place if it weren't for you." Grumbling, she shoved stray hair under her yellow and brown plaid head scarf. "I can't see one foot ahead of me. This old flashlight doesn't help any." Alta grouched and sputtered with every step.

My first Indian wedding! And I was going to get there—even if I had to crawl on my hands and knees—even if I had to drag Alta all the way.

"Look out!" she warned. Too late. I stepped on horse manure.

"Oh, no!" I blurted—cleaning my rainboots on soggy weeds. "It's better than stepping on a horse." Those huge creatures that roamed the streets terrified me.

At last—following the dim, frolicking dance of the flashlight—we found the church. Greeters opened ornate doors of cedar. Alta and I entered—shutting out cold and darkness. I sensed an aura of warmth and friendliness.

Quietly we slipped into center-aisle seats. I looked around—wondering . . .

My vision skimmed thick clumps of sword ferns bunched against the altar wall. Makah cedar baskets filled with kinnikinnick, mistletoe sprigs, and bright holly berries splashed on the piano and on the steps leading to the altar. Wedding tunes flowed from a violin and piano duet.

Soon, Kelly eased in beside me. Pleased and flattered, I turned toward him. Always gentle and soft spoken in class, he whispered, "No matter where you are, France or China, I'll invite you to my wedding."

"And even if I'm in Timbuctoo, I'll come to your wedding."

"You might still be here." And we laughed.

Sanctuary lights dimmed—whispers quieted.

A stream of happiness and contentment rippled through me. The presence and influence of love-guardians hovered. I remembered strains from *The Indian Love Call*.

Then, in pale yellow gowns—shimmering like moonbeams—Kitsy and

Christy carried candlelighting tapers down the bridal aisle. Graceful and poised, the dark-haired sisters lit yellow candles set on window sills and candelabra on the altar.

The bride's sister Wyleena, matron-of-honor, glanced happily at the best man, Jeff, her husband. Jeff's flicking black eyes sent a message, "You look gorgeous in your new dress—like a drop of blue from the sky."

Luke's rich, full-toned tenor preluded the ceremony with *The Lord's Prayer* and *At Dawning*. Flushed with pride, Lissa and Cheree smiled at their tall handsome father. Glowing within an aura of rose-pink chiffon, the daughters stood as bridal attendants.

Lorrene waited at the altar—a picture-bride of mature elegance. Candle-light toned her snow-white bridal gown and trailing veil. Pearl-strings, twisted into a headband, edged her raven-black hair. Steady, grave eyes spoke her tradition. She possessed a depth of soul, a quality of being, true to her race and to herself.

But this Indian maiden's love call was not answered by one of her own race. A white man wearing a sailor's uniform entered from a side door to stand beside her.

A WHITE MAN! Inwardly I jumped straight up. I expected a bronze Makah warrior. What a disappointment!

But why not a white man? We lived in a bi-racial community.

Lorrene had reached beyond the Reservation and brought a white man to the misty forests of her ancient Land. And now, tonight, man and maid stood before a tall, black-robed clergyman. Candlelight beams—like bright blessings—showered over them.

. . . I, Lorrene, take thee, Clark . . .

"NEVER TRUST A WHITE MAN" erupted in my mind. So riveted by my own feelings to the beauty and charm of the ceremony, I had forgotten the expletive of prejudice.

The romantic splendor of this moment—the flowers, the vows, the exchange of rings—stood not to be desecrated by prejudice. I felt a strong, powerful presence of love that flooded the sanctuary—reached into all hearts—burst into the night—spreading throughout the universe.

But how did I know what others felt? Was I carrying my Hiawatha romanticism too far?

Now, I wondered. Was Lorrene's family pleased? Did anyone object to this inter-cultural marriage? In a flash, I recalled a school girl's previous remark:

"My father tell me . . . don't marry white—don't marry black—marry Indian."

What about Clark's family? I thought of village white families. Would the Merediths accept Indian brides for their boys? What if the Griffins' sons brought home Indian maidens?

. . . "I now pronounce you man and wife . . ." ceased my wonderings.

Chucking aside his stiff, fixed, clerical manner, Reverend Dale-Smith clasped the bride's hands in his. Blessing her with an affectionate smile, his heart spoke, "Lorrene, I'm proud to unite you and Clark in marriage and wish you both happiness in full." Soft young lips smiled. Looking into his kind, deep, blue eyes, she knew he understood.

Lorrene brought thousands of years of ancestral heritage and customs to her marriage. Would her sons quest their guardian spirits? Would her daughters weave cedar baskets and cut Salmon the old way?

What would this white sailor bring to his marriage? Would he bring understanding, tolerance? Would he permit his children to carry on totem dances and spirit songs? Would Grandmother still tell the old legends: Destruction and Tatoosh, Thunderbird and Whale?

And so I pondered as we stood to leave. Kelly nudged me. "I'll see you in class Monday." Then he slipped away to join his friends.

Moving with the other guests into the vestibule, I glanced at faces of tribal elders. How could I know their feelings? What did grooves across foreheads tell? What did wrinkles down brown cheeks and crinkles under aged eyes reveal? I looked into faces stern and staid. Then, the booming laughter of Perry Idea shattered my wonderings.

"You made it, I see!" he sang out—clasping my hands in welcome.

"I sure did!" I beamed. "Alta and I waded through mud and dark streets—but we made it!" Perry's rolling mirth filled the church. I felt his strong, brown hands release mine as others crowded between us.

Helen's shy, friendly greeting embraced me. "I'm so glad you could come." Before I could answer, Ada grabbed me in a hard hug.

"Lorrene's going to throw her bouquet!" screamed Kitsy. We all turned toward the outer door. Standing on the threshold, Lorrene whirled, flung her bouquet ceiling high. Kitsy squealed, jumped, caught the cluster of white roses and baby's breath. Would Kitsy be next?

Shouts, laughter, and showers of rice followed the newlyweds into the night.

"I hope he's good to her," Rick said in serious comment. "Some white men treat Indian girls like dogs. In the old days, only white trash married Indian girls—good ones and bad ones. But now, servicemen have brought a change. We have the Air Force station here and the Navy base at Bremerton."

Rick looked over my head to wave at Mrs. Dale-Smith. Turning back to me, he commented, "You may have noticed. The Indian boys bitterly resent all servicemen who attract Indian girls."

Before I could respond, Ada chuckled beside me, "My husband say it easier the old way. The maid follow her man when he call 'Come'."

"That's right, Ada," agreed Mrs. Dale-Smith who had joined us. "In the old way, two in love just walked off into the wilderness. They lived with nature in secret seclusion for several days or weeks. When they returned to the village, they were accepted as man and wife."

"Then big Indian party," grinned Ada. "Everybody come. Lots of presents. Lots to eat. We dance and sing all night."

"The Indians still celebrate with a wedding party for the newly-married couple," said Mrs. Dale-Smith. "In a few weeks, Lorrene will have her Indian wedding in the Community Hall. Be sure and come—both of you."

THE MATING WALK

No stiff collar, no formal robe
no words by clergy,
spoken in rigid ritual,
just "come."
The trail leads sharply down
to the pebbled beach.
She follows him
along the crescent shore
past sea towers
into the wilderness.
They walk the spirit path
to the Indian Paintbrush
blazing orange-red flower
totem of primitive love.

A story written by Karla, one of the Makah students.

At one time the Sea completely covered the Earth. After millions of years, the Great Spirit made the Earth and the Sea separate. On Earth the Great Spirit put forests and oceans—rivers and lakes—towering cliffs—and huge rocks. The Sea beat against the rocks—grinding them into Sand.

Sand covered the beaches. Sand covered the bottom of the Sea . . .

Sand went out with the tide, but the Sea brought the Sand back . . .

The first life on Earth came from the Sea. The first animal came from the Sea. The first animal living on Earth ate from the Sea—ate clams buried in the Sand.

The Sea and the Sand are the Great Spirit's most beautiful creations . . . so old—so wise—so brave—and sometimes so afraid.

Have you ever sat on the Beach—on deep soft Sand—and listened to the Sea or Ocean? I have. One day when I sat on the Beach, the Waves seemed to talk to me. They seemed to call to me. They told me a story about the Indians of long ago:

When there were Whale hunters, many whaling canoes went out in search of Whales. Now, the Ocean told me it was very sad because the whaling canoes never went hunting anymore. The Ocean told instead the Whale hunters went fishing with big nets—catching all the fish in the Ocean—and taking all of the little ones.

The Ocean told me it was very very sad and wished that the fishermen would leave the little fish so they could grow up.

The Ocean said it was sad that the White Chiefs and the Red Chiefs could not get along . . . and the Ocean wished they would quit fighting over the fish and share equally.

. . . even if the White Chiefs and the Red Chiefs never quit fighting, the Sea and the Sand will last forever and ever . . .

 Were Karla's fears and tears—her hysteria—her frantic worries for her mother just beginning?

The series of events that ended with the bride that wore black flashed in my mind. One day in October a new girl skipped into Freshman English. "I'm Karla. I'll be in Home Ec too," she beamed. New, only to me, Karla renewed friendships formed in elementary school.

Like a bright spirit, this light-skinned Indian girl drew her classmates to her—charmed by her friendly smile—her twinkly eyes—her bouncy dark brown hair—her playful ways. Karla's friends followed her everywhere.

Karla charmed me too. I enjoyed her delightful personality, her willingness, her enthusiasm.

Soon a droopiness in Karla's energy descended—squelching her bright spirit—snatches from incoherent muttering revealed anxieties: "My mother—I'm so worried—she talks about getting married again. My mother—what will happen to me—to my younger brothers and sisters? Will we be safe?"

Between tears—sniffles—sobs—Karla had written *The Sea and the Sand* for an English assignment. Does she think of herself as the Ocean that wishes the Red Chiefs and the White Chiefs would stop fighting? Does the conflict relate to her own life?

In class today—out of class tomorrow—back in class—her eyes swollen and red. She wipes away tears. Her anxieties continue.

A presence in Karla's days of anguish, I listened to her uncontrollable crying—her fears—her hysterical worries over her mother's unpredictable marriage plans: "My mother keeps changing her mind. She'll marry tomorrow—then sometime—then in two weeks. Yesterday she called the whole thing off.

"If my mother does marry again," Karla wailed, "how will it affect my future—my security and safety—and the younger children. What will happen to them? My stepfather now threatens to take away my brothers and sisters."

In this after-class interval, Karla pressed her palms to her temples— shook her head. In dismay, her Ocean of troubles continued to spill out: "Where will he take them? Where will they live? Who will take care of them? Will they have enough to eat? And my mother. What will happen to her? Will she be safe? I can't sleep at night. I can't eat. I can't do my class work."

Then, one day, all obstacles—delays—uncertainties—anxieties—untangled. Her bright spirit back, Karla threw her arms around me, "I'm so happy! They were married in Forks." I sighed with relief. "Their Indian wedding is set for Saturday. I want you to come. It'll be in the Community Hall."

I was thrilled—but hesitant. Would I be welcome? Only a school girl had invited me. I conferred with my Prop Pals. Their response: "It is an honor the Indians pay you when you are invited—and you honor them with your attendance."

~

Through December's wispy mist, Jule and I trod over Makah Land—drums signaled a welcome to the Indian wedding ceremony of Karla's mother. The throb of drums set my wild Makah blood racing. I love the deep rhythmic beat—so primitive—so NOW!

And I love Indian gatherings. Submerged in this irresistible spell-binding atmosphere, I forget the world outside. I'm absorbed into the laughter—the festival chatter—the shifting and sliding of chairs at the feast tables.

What! No Salmon! Where were all the Salmon People?

Tonight the Salmon People yielded to the King of the Cattle Range: ROAST BEEF.

Disappointed: Jule and I. An exotic treat like octopus or mussels or barnacles would have sufficed.

Feast dishes cleared away—more shuffling, shifting, sliding of chairs—everybody into a semi-circle against the back wall. Jule whispered: "There's a larger crowd than usual here tonight—probably many members from other tribes. I've heard the bride is very popular—kind, sweet, and generous." Jule glanced around the Hall. "There're hardly any white people—a real Indian party—looks like old Tom is starting the procession," Jule observed. "A tradition to honor the bride and groom."

Another prominent Makah elder led. He carried a feather-fan arrangement. "A sacred emblem," Jule explained. More Makah elders followed with chants and drum beats. Jule and I joined in the procession. Perry Ides, Deena, Marta, and Ada greeted me warmly. It was fun to see them.

Inspirited by the power of ceremony—the splendor of the moment—wrapped up in wonder and excitement, I stopped short. I stood before the wedded couple.

The groom—a well-dressed Indian—sat at the end—an older man—gray mixed in his hair—deep lines carved down his cheeks—stern and unsmiling. I shook his hand. It was hard and rough.

Then I faced the bride. That's when I shuddered. THE BRIDE WORE BLACK. Sprays of delicate ferns and mini-flowers in a corsage lessened the blackness. I barely whispered: "I'm Karla's teacher." I touched her hand—and then was suddenly aware that Jule smothered an outcry. Why? "Later . . ." she muttered.

In the background: pulsations of drums—wedding songs—steps of an ancient wedding dance. Primitive power called to the Great Spirit—praised the Great Spirit.

Makah dancers and singers honored the wedded pair with chants from Makah past. Later, two Makah warriors lurched and whirled in spectacular dance.

Whispers began to ripple: . . . The bride has taken her third husband. . . . Will it last? . . . Who will be next?

Jule—the cynic—raised her eyebrows: "Since when did the Indians so glibly dissolve the marriage vows?"

Now Jule confided why she had smothered an outcry in the procession: "I've heard of THAT BRIDE for a very long time."

More ripples . . . many unsavory stories . . . many scandalous rumors . . . many children of questionable birth . . . petite—vital—attractive . . . they say her fun-loving nature appeals to men . . . anyone would find it tough to keep her contented . . .

But this man is different, they say—as old as the bride's parents—in his seventies. He's Quillayute from La Push—very wealthy—timber—has children of his own.

In him will the bride cease her searching . . . seeking for that ILLUSIVE SOMETHING NOT POSSESSED? In him will she find the security she has never known? Are her flighty-flitting days over?

"He the man. He head of house," declared Ada. His determined look—his severe scowl—say so. The true old Indian is within him.

Not back to classes since her mother's wedding—but one day Karla stopped to chat after sixth period:

 . . . not happy at La Push or Forks
 . . . back in Neah Bay—still unhappy—discontented—frustrated
 . . . has heard from her former stepfather—favors him
 . . . her mother's new husband is an old old Indian—believes in old Indian

traditions
... mother dares not speak to another man—dares not be out with
friends
... mother sometimes seems happy—sometimes seems unhappy
... she's not well—I worry about her—Karla confided
... bewildered and unhappy
... lives one day at a time
... what will tomorrow bring?—Karla frowned
... I'll be back in school sometime—she said, as she left.

Then one day—weeks later— Karla brought her tears and fears back to
class—her bright spirit in depression. I gleaned from Karla's wrenching sobs
that the marriage of the "bride that wore black" was in disruption.

"That old Indian husband is cruel. I hate him! He's mean to my
mother. I'm afraid for her life. He's struck her several times." Karla threw
up her hands—weary and weepy—tears flooding: "He accuses her of things
she never did. He's so jealous. She doesn't dare look at another man."
Resting her head on the desk, she cried: "I have nightmares. I can't sleep.
I worry so. Now my other stepfather wrote a twenty-two page letter to some
social service. He threatens to take away the younger children again."

And then, a few days ago, Karla confided that her mother had reported the old Indian to the Makah Tribal Council. They escorted him off
the Reservation. He's forbidden ever to return.

In wild joy and relief, Karla threw her arms around me. "He's gone!
We're rid of him!" She urges her mother to divorce him.

In other moments, more of Karla's stories spilled out: "This old Indian
killed one of his wives—he's had five. The wife was pregnant and he beat
her." Karla sighed: "I feel so sorry for his own children. A relative told me
that during the Christmas holidays one of his sons drowned."

There is a bridge at La Push. THEY SAY:
> "Superstition and fate
> claim a drunkard's body
> if he falls from the
> bridge when drinking."

"... all our money goes for whiskey, wine, or beer. Without our free
school lunches, we kids would starve."

". . . home? Where everyone's drunk. No food most of the time. Just crackers and potatoes."

". . . drinking among school kids is getting worse and worse."

~

My thoughts returned to a scene. On my way to Cerena's room, I passed a group of school kids. A quick scan focused on Karla. With two or three students, she shielded a school boy—in the hall—after school. He leaned against a radiator. Sick. Vomiting. Wretched from whiskey? Protective arms held him—kept him from falling.

On today's absent list. Why did he return after school? For support? For comfort?

Karla's tender humane tolerance—her bond of concern—for a Red Devil basketball warrior—a champion—snared by whiskey—gripped me.

Unnoticed, I walked past the group. Silence overcame my impulse to interfere—my urge to help. No one needed me. Karla—like an Indian Medicine Woman—held Spirit Power to heal . . .

~

They say Chet's mother is a prostitute—and drinks like crazy. I discredit what they say. They didn't say she weaves Makah baskets with primitive skill—mixes her own dyes—displays her basketry in gift shops.

~

They say a Tribal Council member is a skunk—drunk most of the time—picked up in Seattle. They say his kids are the worst offenders on the Reservation. Wow! Strong words—not believed by me. They are my friends.

Reject-frowns on fallen warrior faces. Muttering and grumbling, "These girls. Who do they think they are? What's their big idea anyway? Just playing cat and mouse games."

"What do *you* think of the girls here at Neah Bay?" asked blue eyed, blond Stephen. "Do you know what they did? Yesterday at the Clallam Bay-Quinault basketball game they yelled for Quinault."

Champ, parked on the table, interrupted, "You'd think we were back in the old Indian days with the Makahs and Clallams at war."

"Neah Bay didn't play, but our team was rooting for Clallam," explained Stephen. "Then those crazy, stupid girls betrayed us and yelled for Quinault. They even made faces at us. Stuck out their tongues. I don't get it."

"I went down to Home Ec yesterday. You sweetly offered me a cooky, and the girls grabbed me and made me wipe the dishes," complained Champ.

"They're so darn stuck-up. They won't go out with us," Lester lamented.

"When we see them at a show in Clallam, they won't speak to us. Just turn up their noses like they never saw us before. Sure beats all," sighed Stephen.

"They'll go out with the Air Force guys or out-of-town guys, but not us," deplored Champ.

Lester, with his funny slow drawl and clever wit, remarked, "We hear the Navy's moving into Bremerton in January. Three cheers for the Navy! Good-bye, Neah Bay girls."

The bell rang. The boys stomped out. The girls flipped in.

"Those dumb boys," snickered Cheree. "I suppose they were talking about us. They're mad because we don't rush them off their feet and beg for dates."

"For one thing," agreed Jacqui, "they don't have any manners."

"You can say that again," quipped Mary Lynn. "The first time I went out with an Air Force guy, I nearly died I was so embarrassed. We were in a movie. He was helping me with my coat. No one here ever did that. I got all shook up because I didn't know what he was doing. I thought he was being fresh. It was really embarrassing."

"The Neah Bay boys won't do it. They think it's silly," Dolly scoffed. So did Rose Mary.

Of course, they will pass up Champ and Lester and Stephen. Neah Bay girls want dates with class and know-how. Boys label girls as frivolous and fickle. Girls earmark boys as jealous and ill-mannered.

I loved their bickering—set on a stage of conflicts—a battle zone—a hilarious play of cut-throat rivalry—warrior/maiden conquests!

~

"The Indian girls here at Neah Bay have their heads in the stars," observed Jule Craggs. "They're demanding better things. They want lovely homes, electric refrigerators, washers and dryers, and pretty clothes. What do the boys here have to offer? Any old black dress out of the church attic would be good enough for their wives."

Neah Bay boys—drunk—race their cars around sharp Neah Bay curves and flip upside down over an embankment. Next day, smiling and happy, they come to class with only a few scratches and bruises. What does the future hold for these Reservation youths of today?

Reservation maids of today see only emptiness ahead. A void that frightens, tightens, and crushes. White civilization intrigues and tantalizes these black-eyed girls.

An airman offers a way off the Reservation. Escape.

A sailor invites a new, exciting life with social standing and security. If a girl can catch one, she grabs him and clutches. Hoping . . .

One day in class, as Becky demonstrated Indian skillet bread, she softly sighed, "There isn't much future for us Indian girls." Reaching for a spatula, she added, "There's too much intermarriage now among the Makahs. If we marry white men, the only ones who want us are the white trash."

 Mrs. Roberts—Makah—spoke at Forum (PTA) Tuesday night. She began: "I speak three languages—my own Makah, my husband's from a Canadian tribe—and this *foreign English.*"
In brief statements, Mrs. Roberts interpreted the meaning of the old potlatch. Then she launched into *The Makah of Today*, describing Karla's mother's wedding. ". . . at this wedding we were honored by the presence of two teachers—two from the Neah Bay School. They were invited guests. They were honored by all Tribal members. I think one was Miss Craggs."

I was the other teacher, but Mrs. Roberts didn't know me. However, she emphasized the importance of our being there: "The Makah of today accept white people at Tribal functions."

Karla wanted so much for me to come to her mother's wedding. I asked if I could bring Miss Craggs. That's how we got invited!

Still in awe of this culture—*far different from my own*—my innermost spirit reacted to this honor with an amazement and wonder.

How exciting for me—living between two cultures—to be "honored" by the Indians of that culture.

Jerry and Dirk—Makah students—served coffee at the refreshment tables—got their kicks in by teasing me about the Wassail Bowl.

~

To the Journalism Class: A letter from the WHITE HOUSE—acknowledged receiving the school paper, *The Chieftain*, from Neah Bay, Washington—the farthest northwest corner of the USA.

～

A Makah June graduate visited school this morning. Dolly has received a diamond from Tom. How handsome he is! Sweet and dear as always, he sent a Christmas card to me: To a wonderful person. May God bless you.

～

Moments of defeat . . . gloom
An island for retreat . . .
A self-sufficient unit of purpose?

～

How can I appeal to the Freshman English class? I cannot reach them. And yet there are moments of gratification . . .

The Journalism Class . . .

Well, anyway Champ is to be editor of the next edition. Mr. Perkins gave them a pep talk! But I didn't tell him Champ did his bookkeeping in Journalism Class!

～

Champ drifted half naked into sixth period Home Ec. "Oh, Champ, you look just like an Indian!" Cheree squealed. And I guess he does!

～

Daphne's frozen meat roll did not broil through the frozen mashed potatoes. Jacqui's parfait pie did not set in time to eat it. We had coffee—set the complete affair in the refrigerator—and with resigned patience waited until next Monday.

 "When I got home from school yesterday, both my sisters were crying. They said Mom was in Forks Hospital." Chet looked down in despair.

"In the hospital!" I gasped. "What happened?"

"The girls said Dad came home drunk and beat her up. My married sister took her to Forks. Mom had her collar bone broken.

"And that wasn't all. My dad, crazy drunk, ran out of the house, jumped in his car, and drove it over a cliff. Now he's in the hospital in Forks too. What next?" Laughing—to cover his concern—Chet walked away from violence and family tragedy . . .

If this had happened to Champ, his bouncing good humor—his light-hearted acceptance of family troubles—would have kept him in balance.

If this would have happened to Burt—arrogant and dangerous—he would viciously strike out to get even. One day he grouched: "My family argue and quarrel sometimes till four o'clock in the morning (most all night). They're all drunk. I can't get any sleep."

I watched this boy of heavy tempers. Troubled. Confused. In hot silence, Burt sulked and brooded. Dark eyes smoldered. Anger cut deep scores into his brow.

". . . and after the Freshman Initiation Party, I got kicked out. They said I stayed out too late."

"Where did you go?"

"I had no place to go. Even the Pool Hall was closed. I slept in my car all night. They'll be sorry."

Inner strengths and weaknesses of an individual determine reactions and ability to meet life:

Champ laughed in defiance!

Burt threatened to kill!

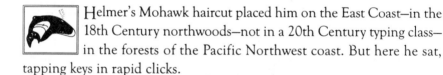 Helmer's Mohawk haircut placed him on the East Coast—in the 18th Century northwoods—not in a 20th Century typing class—in the forests of the Pacific Northwest coast. But here he sat, tapping keys in rapid clicks.

Class dismissed—typists turned in their papers as usual. But not Helmer. His paper—ripped from the machine—was crumpled into a ball—tossed into the wastepaper basket. In stoic silence, Helmer stalked out.

M-m-m, I thought. How come? Today's typing lesson: industrious practice? discarded love letter? confessions of a whaler? Why fling his classwork away?

Curiosity led me to research: the crumpled page . . . a piece of creative imagination or a revelation of the truth? "To see ourselves as others see us . . ." (Robert Burns)

HELMER'S RULES FOR TYPING

Always type slutched in your little old fannie holder. (In other words, your chair.) If you make a mistake, just try to make as many more as you can as are teacher taught us to do last year. In a test try to make as many mistakes as possible because the teacher will not count them as mistakes. (Soft Hearted Soul.) When you crumple up a piece of paper throw it at the nearest person near you. If he throws it back, go and show him who's boss by pounding his brains out or else to a pulp.

When you don't feel like working and the teacher tells you to get busy just frown at her and tease her to pieces. If she tries to send you to the office just sit and laugh her pieces. Ha-Ha.

Always look at your work while you type any assignment — it will help you bring your grades up if the teach don't catch you. (That's the chance you have to take though.) If theirs a hard worker in your typing class bother IT as much as possible because if you don't it might make you and your comrades look bad.

When you get all the class roudy then that's when the fun begins. First you assassinate the teach then start a brawl between your selves. If you don't find any fun in that then take the whole school on - starting with the principle. Spill his brains (what brains he has) all over the hall to show that you were their —then after that slice him into little chunks. If the blood doesn't flow down the halls sling his chunks into a bucket and throw it all over Shabang. After you get through with the school take the town on if you/still in one piece. If your not in one piece, take the deep six by cutting your wrists. The person who did this is last year's Charlie Brown —

Writer

Namingly Helmer

~

A shocker? A weird piece of Helmer humor? A piece for a psychoanalyst? Whatever Helmer's reasoning . . . he earned an A-plus for his creative imagination!—his out of mind travel!

 "This doesn't make sense!" exploded Becky. "How can the sun all of a sudden just stop? It says here that *SOL* means *sun*. *STICE* means *to stop*: Sun to stop. I don't get it." Exasperated, she slammed the dictionary to the floor.

"I'm supposed to write a theme on *Winter Solstice* for science class.

"Forget it," she blurted, picking up the dictionary.

"Oh, Becky, we're in the shortest, darkest days of winter solstice now," I explained. "It means the sun has traveled across the sky as far north as it can—stands still for two seconds and then starts back."

"What difference does it make anyway?" In disgust, she poked a pencil behind her ear—lowered her head on the table—mumbled, "It pours down rain day and night. Even if the sun did stand still, we'd never see it."

Hearty guffaws from Burt and Jesse. Sitting up, Becky yelled, "Shut up, wise guys. You don't know anything about it."

I ignored their tiff. "Remember, Becky, ancient people didn't understand the earth's revolving around the sun. In winter when the sun hung low in the sky—rising late, setting early—people were terrified. They believed monsters at the edge of the world were swallowing the sun."

Shivering in mock terror, Burt and Jesse grimaced—pointing at Becky. "Monster eating the sun. Guess who?" they chortled in unearthly sounds.

"Unless the monsters were overcome," I added, "the ancients believed the sun would die and powerful spirits of darkness would destroy the earth. To help their gods bring back the sun, the people celebrated with magic, religious rituals, and ceremonial dancing. Stories of winter solstice give play to the imagination. Meet me in the library after school, Becky. I'll help."

In the library, we pulled "S" volumes from book shelves to begin an adventure.

"Here's something," reflected Becky. "This encyclopedia tells that the ancient Chinese believed dragons ate the sun at winter solstice. People beat on gongs and made horrible noises to frighten the dragons."

"This will interest you, Becky." I handed her the volume. "Solstice dances—celebrations in dance form—were created to aid the changing of the sun's course."

"I can't believe it!" Becky exclaimed. "Listen to this. It says the Sioux, Pueblos, Hopi, Zuni and others all observed solstice ceremonies with a Sun Dance. We Makah have a Sun Dance. I wonder . . ."

Words broke off. Puzzled, Becky closed her eyes. "You know, Miss Conly, I remember . . ." Dark brows puckered. Mysterious full lips parted as to speak a cryptic tongue . . . she seemed to lift into another time . . .

"I remember Grandfather told us kids old tribal stories. They don't seem important anymore. But the one about Sooez . . . I remember he said

Indians danced at night and in wintertime."

Sooez: Makah ceremonial site, facing the ocean.

"Grandfather told that Indians at night ceremonies gurgled Whale oil from seal-skin bladder bags on burning logs."

Night fires blazed. Jagged flares flamed yellow-orange and magenta-crimson.

"He said they used fire-brands to see by when they ran up the beach. Indians made howling sounds and danced wild and crazy around log fires to frighten away evil spirits."

Torches of oiled cedar shreds with flaring pitch knots stabbed the black sky. Shrieking howls streaked through demon darkness. Natives danced in frenzied rituals . . . when the sun stood still . . .

Out of Makah past, Becky led us into happenings of today.

"We still dance the Sun Dance! You were at the Community Hall last week. I saw you. Remember how the dancers lifted their arms and swayed to drum beats? How they turned from north to south, east to west? All the time they were chanting praises to the sun." Becky giggled. "It wasn't the way Grandfather told it."

I reminded her, "Since the time of your grandfather's story, many Makah have become Christian. Think of Whale-oil flares turned into fragrant candlelight. Shrieking crazy howls have become songs honoring the Nativity. Blazing logs at ritual fires represent the Yule log of long ago."

Art poked his head in the door. I waved. "We'll have to go."

Through the double-entry doors, we stepped into misty darkness.

Like a secret spirit, Becky whispered: "Now I know why it's so dark and spooky at four o'clock."

 THE CHRISTMAS TEA! First festivity in the new building! Final touches: Kitsy stood on a stepladder—stretched to hang the last holly wreath over the door. Lester's long arms reached the tree top and wired the golden star in place. Weaving popcorn and cranberry strings among pine branches, Becky and Dolly stood back and exclaimed, "Oh, how beautiful!"

"This tea has been the most fun," Kitsy rejoiced. "Before you came, Miss Conly, we'd never heard of a Christmas Tea."

So traditional in my culture—so unheard-of in theirs. I loved their enthusiasm.

"I'd never heard of winter solstice either," admitted Becky. "Today,

December 21, is the first day of winter and the shortest day of the year. To-morrow the sun starts back and the days begin to get longer."

"I can hardly wait till June to graduate," chimed in Kitsy. "Even after we graduate, I hope you'll still have a tea at Christmas time. Just look at the tea table! Loaded with fruit cake, chess pies, Banbary tarts, bonbons, and cookies."

"Yes indeed. Here we wait," I moaned, "sozzled in with rain. We need icicles and jingle bells and snowdrifts ten feet high."

Peering through windows, I stared into stone-gray obscurity. No jingle bells—just fog horns. No snowflakes—just vaporish wisps of fog twisted around evergreen branches. My hopes for icicles turned to clobbering drops of rain.

Shouts interrupted my thoughts. "It's two o'clock! Here they come!"

And in flooded the kids—like a high tide. Drenched—they clumped through the entrance. No kid could dash or sprint or dart between build-ings fast enough to beat rain and wind storms. So, boys dumped sweaters and jackets to puddle the floor.

Boys at a tea? Whales in a fish bowl?

"They're always hanging around begging anyway. We might as well in-vite them," decided the girls. "Why not invite boys from Shop classes. They never get in on any of our fun. And Mr. DeLong too."

First time for boys at a tea! I expected the usual shoving and pushing—shouting and bumping—but no . . .

Blinking tree lights signaled a path to the tea table. Rose Mary and Mary Lynn—holly sprigs clipped to their hair—lit fragrant red candles. Deep-woodsy scents drifted from centerpieces of pine cones and red-rib-boned cedar swags. Scattered among tinsel, tiny silver stars glittered like diamonds. Ooh's and ah's bounced back and forth among the excited kids.

Kitsy, Daphne, and Cheree mingled among hesitant tribal classmates. Boys from Shop classes: the leery ones—unaccustomed to me—eyed me and white man's food with hostility.

"Come," the girls coaxed. "Come to the tea table and punch bowl." Mistrusting black eyes scrutinized me with furrowed brows. White man's food—even party food—was under suspicion. Standing by Genevieve, I smiled encouragement. They trusted her.

"C'mon, Terry." She handed him a red paper plate. "Have some cookies." Grinning, he accepted.

"Willy, here's a green plate for you." No grin, but he took the festive plate.

Genevieve was succeeding.

Wary—strong brown hands reached for dainty star cookies and sassy gingerbread boys. Strong brown hands, I thought, shaped for boat-building, canoe paddling, harpooning Whales—reached into the white man's culture: Food—Cookies and Kool-Aid.

"Now have some punch," suggested Mary Lynn, leading the way.

"PUNCH? What's that? Never heard of it!"

"Well then, Kool-Aid. You've heard of that!"

A holly sprig pinned in his black hair, Champ held the dripping ladle. "Come, come to the Wassail bowl," he chanted.

And joy, joy! Burt and Jesse—in rollicking moods—gobbled goodies and sniggered over some secret joke.

Sidney beamed. Black eyes squinted mischief: "I brought you a glass from the Wassail bowl."

"Thank you, Sidney." It's Christmas, I remembered, and forgave his many torments.

Burt, standing on a chair, waved candy canes and shouted: "Everybody come 'round the Christmas tree. We're gonna sing."

Swinging a long red taper for a baton, Cheree vigorously led off with *Frosty the Snowman.*

Genevieve and her followers stood back—unwilling to join. The leery boys from Shop classes just watched and listened.

Inherited family prejudice still heavy across their shoulders, these boys and girls felt uncomfortable. More time is needed. Next year will be better.

~

An old Chief once said: "We offered them the peace pipe. They gave us whiskey."

We offered punch with cinnamon red-hots and cloves and called it Kool-Aid."

 Deserted, broken down in decay, an old church rested by the village roadside. Weather-faded, the unpainted cedar-planked building had grayed to a silvery sheen. Arched windows, vacant and staring, listened in silence to echoes past. Ghost voices whispered in dark angles of the crumbling bell tower.

Once, long ago, Indian voices chanted songs to praise a new Spirit Guide . . .

Ringing bells called all to come. Will they come back? The chanting voices? The ringing bells?

~

On our way to the post office, Alta and I glanced quizzically at this dilapidated structure. Passing by on tippy-toes, we never spoke. Did SOME-THING hidden, SOMETHING not seen or heard, exude from the arches and bell tower? We thought so!

"I believe this old building is an abandoned Indian Shaker church," Alta said.

"It's spooky," I whispered. "What does *Shaker* mean?"

"From what I've heard, an Indian Medicine Man held a stick. Some member would grasp the stick, and if the person started to shake . . ." Alta, for once, groped for words, "Well . . . like the shaking influenced or gave power to receive . . . in white man's terms . . . the reception of the Holy Ghost . . . or something like that."

Alta believes the *ghost* church was deserted by a sect of Indian Shakers. "I'm only guessing," she concluded.

Alta was only guessing . . . but some day I am going to find out!

 David P.: "You'll be back next year? We like you."
Bender: "You're splendid!"
Blanchard: "You're incorrigible!

"What *does* incorrigible mean?"

(Had he heard me say it a million times?)

"Bad—bad—beyond reform!"

Scream! Scream! Hilarious roars!

"You're a good teacher!"

 Lucy Millholland—the Indian mother that sparkled—faced me: "I'm forming a Camp Fire Girls' group. I'd like you to work with me as helper."

Once again I stood tongue-tied. I couldn't believe it. ME! What a privilege! What an honor!

"I would love to . . ." At my humble acceptance, pleasure beamed in Lucy's black eyes.

"I will teach the little girls beadwork," she smiled. "You can teach them charm."

Oh, Lucy, I thought. You have more charm, poise, grace than I ever dreamed of . . .

Asked to work with Lucy filled me with tremors. How could I ever forget who she was: ROYALTY! Descendant of Chief Seattle, a great Indian leader. Lucy carried the power and majesty of her race into the present. It seeped into my senses. Just to look at her—just to be with her—filled me with awe.

~

"You have brought AN INDISTINGUISHABLE SOMETHING here," Cerena once told me.

An indistinguishable something . . . I can bring to Lucy's culture.

An indistinguishable something . . . I can take from her culture.

And yet, Jacqueline had urged, "Next year you should teach among your own kind of people." My own kind of people? An intrinsic part of me accepts these "Cape People"—the Makah—as my own kind of people.

I long to move forward from the dream-time sequence of some deep past into a new sense of being. Away from the classroom—away from city life—to where the new system meets the old system at some invisible crossroad?

~

Today I slipped into the Principal's office.

"Mrs. Millholland has asked me to work with her in a Camp Fire Girls' group," I beamed. "I'm so excited!"

Mr. Perkin's face mirrored my own excitement: "That's a nice compliment," he smiled. "I like teachers to become involved with Indian people. It's good for the community and helps strengthen relationships. Working with Mrs. Millholland gives you an opportunity to become a part of this biracial community."

Mr. Perkins leaned back in his desk-chair—looked up at me: "To my knowledge, Mrs. Millholland has never asked a teacher to work with her before. You must be at the top of her list." We both laughed.

It rains and it rains.
. . . where can I run?
. . . where can I hide?
". . . I WILL NOT LEAVE THEE DESOLATE–I WILL COME TO THEE . . ."

But I feel desolate. I am desolate. Corrupted, ravaged, demolished by Burt's insults and Jesse's thoughtlessness.

. . . and last year Alta had said, "You'll get along fine with Burt. You're young and good looking."

. . . and the next day Alta deflated me when she vilified: "Oh you're just nothing. SHE considers you not worth bothering about—you are so utterly insignificant and worthless."

~

"THEY are not with us at all. THEY only put up with us because we are here."

I never at any time felt that way about the Makah. Is it only "in the eye of the beholder"?

Silent and speechless for two years, William finally spoke to me. "You should see the eels we brought back from the beach!" Ugh! I thought. Eels! Creepy crawly—long slimy snakelike fish. What do they do with eels? I decided not to ask. But to William, a catch of eels was a catch that proved he possessed powers. He was a hunter—hunter of eels.

Unlike his classmates, William was shy, reserved, mannerly—an elite carving of today's Indian youth.

In a casual slide, he had perched on my desk. Others gathered and perched too. Questions and answers followed.

"You ask about Whales," William replied. "Yes, Whales come in. My grandfather has a harpoon from the early days. Whale hunters went out in whaling canoes—seal hunters in sealing canoes."

Bantering among the boys led to boisterous arguments: "Whales and sharks fight to kill each other."

"'Tain't so. Never heard of such a fight."

"Sharks don't come in these waters. Anyway, sharks eat people."

"Blue sharks aren't man-eating," William declared.

"How do you know?"

William changed the subject. "Once my grandfather told about canoes full of hunters. They went to Alaska. He told about a man who died. The hunters covered him with salt until they could bring him back for burial."

So intent and interested in William's comments—serious, thoughtful, informative—I ignored Helmer and Forbes and Gerald and Kelly—all full of nonsense. Like clowns, they teased—playfully punched each other—poked through my purple purse—salvaged a vial of perfume—passed it around for sniffs—WHISKEY!

Helmer stopped his jumping-jack clowning to perk our attention with "Once there was a woman who was s'posed to be dead. But later she came back to life. My grandfather told about that—and he has seen spirits walking around too."

In a sly movement, Helmer tweaked Kelly's ear—scooted to the other side of the desk for protection and then added, "Some people have seen Indians dancing at night on the beach around a big bonfire. *Devil Dancers*—my grandfather believes. What about all that? And spirits that walk about Neah Bay in the dark—and the ghost-man who walks swinging a lantern. Do you believe all that?"

Helmer, restless, walked around the desk—continued to question: "Some old people have seen the Devil. What about that?" The tone of his voice revealed an uneasiness. Did Helmer's questions originate from his own cultural and spiritual background? His inherent belief with his Indian spirituality? He searched for answers beyond teachings of tribal elders and medicine men. His quizzical eyes probed mine for an answer: "Many people believe the Devil suggests or represents evil forces—not in the flesh-and-blood sense," I volunteered.

Kelly stared at me, and in a quiet positive statement declared: "But if you saw him, then you would believe he is a person. Jesus saw him."

Their silliness subdued—a solemn type of silence—a closeness—covered us. The bell rang. My clowning boys picked up their books and left the library.

William slid off the desk—smiled. "You're a good little Indian."

I tingled with emotion—Indian Spirit Power? A warmth of victory flooded through me. I had won their trust, entered their spirit world, entered realms not understood: death, burials, spirits that walk after dark, devil dancers on the beach. All because William had caught eels—giving him power to speak to me.

WHAT ABOUT ALL THAT!

~

Later, I returned to the library. Four or five senior Makah boys—their study books unopened—joined in serious discussion.

By listening, I learned Bret was disturbed by restraints of Catholicism—its demands upon marriage—confessional requirements—not eating meat on Friday. Why punishment for that?

He stared at me. His questioning eyes demanded an answer—one I was not licensed to give. How could I explain that tutorial restriction? How could they understand?

They waited. I hesitated. They were drawing me into an inner place—reaching out—seeking answers. Finally, I issued a feeble reply: "You must understand there are many churches, many religions, many governments. They all set up their own special laws or decrees. Members are expected to live by these rules—the same as American Indian tribes. Each tribe sets up a different code of laws—cultural rites—traditions . . ."

Was my answer understood? Did it help bridge the differences from one faith to another—from one culture to another?

Bret shifted restlessly. "At a church meeting last night one of the leaders said he'd seen angels. Another guy said spirits spoke to him."

"Yah," interjected Dick. "Our old people here have seen angels and spirits too. What about that?"

Their choosing to discuss spiritual concepts amazed me. Drawn into the aura of their trust, they wanted answers. To these eagerly searching teenagers could I give them the answers they wanted? In spite of Christian invasion into their culture, parents and grandparents still praised the Great Spirit—they still believed that spirit-beings lived in the unseen world. Did this result in confusion? In skepticism?

To cope with Dick's question, I began: "Angels and spiritual beings have been seen by people throughout the ages. It's a divine gift of the Great Spirit. Some people have powers to see invisible beings. They believe the unseen world is alive with spirits."

More from Dick—scrunched down in his seat—his hands clasped behind his head—insolent and scornful—he spoke through twisted lips: "Last night they talked about the crucifixion. I don't think Christ was so great.

He was crucified for us—but anyone could have done that!"

Was this to shock me? To challenge me? Did he want to force me into an opinion? To agree with him? To press me into an answer leading into an unwise dispute?

Unsure of an adequate reply, I ventured: "It was Jesus' teachings while He was here on earth—the laws He gave us to live by—that set Him apart."

The last-period bell rescued me from further questions.

I REJOICED AND I WAS GLAD!

 Last night after school—instead of compiling the history of the 1956 graduating class—I listened to Ruth:

. . . once she killed a devil fish. "It was very large. I found it on the beach. I threw rocks upon him until he was dead." Ruth smiled— leaned on her broom handle. "The devil fish was too heavy for me to manage alone. I left him ashore and went for help."

Ruth's killing the many tenacled octopus created excitement—stirred doubt . . .

"Did she really kill the devil fish?" her friends questioned among themselves.

. . . and she laughed. "I did kill the devil fish—even though my friends doubted my story. I love to eat the meat. It tastes like clams. Many are found in Neah Bay waters—most often at the breakwater. I like to go down to the rocks at the beach—just to sit—look out over the water."

Ruth swept floor dirt into a pile—as if preoccupied. She began again.

. . . once she belonged to the Indian Shaker Church. "But about nineteen years ago a group of us broke away—soon after the Shaker religion in Neah Bay collapsed . . . and even today I wonder if we did right. Was the Lord pleased with that cleavage?"

. . . the Shaker Church was divided into two groups . . . "One group wanted to live by the Bible—by the Word of God. The other group wanted to keep some of our primitive spiritual ideas of the *old way*. That's why we split."

At the time of the split, Art and Ruth joined the Assembly of God— and there have found great spiritual rewards.

. . . last year Ruth had told me about the shaking—the messages—ringing bells—chanting . . .

Art and Ruth—devout and dedicated to the Word of God—to Bible teaching . . . their religion brought a *new love*—a new way. Ruth is happy, radiant in her acceptance—illuminated by inner renewal the new way has given her.

All this began when she mentioned: "You like our Indian dancing. My friends tell me how much you enjoy it. I do not go very often anymore—since I have found a *new love*—the Christ way. I fear the old Indian ways will hinder my spiritual progress."

Ruth declared Indian dancing was not religious dancing. A contradiction . . .

". . . I used to dance all night—but now my ways are different."

The Indians believed in a higher power—the Great Spirit—but the Word of God, as Ruth has learned it, was not taught.

SCHOOL FLYER ANNOUNCED:
BROTHERHOOD MEETING AT COMMUNITY HALL
SATURDAY, 6:30 P.M.

(Speakers will discuss race prejudice.)

RACE PREJUDICE! I'd forgotten about IT.

. . . but all week the village a-buzz—prepares to feast and entertain members of a BROTHERHOOD group Saturday. The Makah Club is in charge.

Champ strolled into Home Ec after school. "Are you going to the BROTHERHOOD meeting?" I asked.

"Thursday night there was a dress rehearsal," he said. "Sounds like a big deal—costumes, masks, chants, and dances." He turned to leave. "I was asked to dance—but I can't be in Neah Bay Saturday."

"Oh, no!" I groaned. "The reason I'm going is to watch you dance." He just grinned and walked out.

At six o'clock Deena picked me up. Flattered and delighted by her thoughtfulness—and feeling smug because I knew SHE watched.

On our drive to the Community Hall, Deena remarked: "I'm so glad you could come with me. Luke went early to help set up tables. He'll be at the speakers' table. Last week I heard a Negro family will be here. They come as guests of the Rogers' family. We hardly ever see Negroes up here."

I spotted SHE ogling at me. Because I was with Deena? Or because I had *lasted up here?*

An exciting festive evening of food, songs, dancing—the speakers were great. I felt spirit power pouring over dedicated persons.

. . . to bed about three o'clock in the morning . . .

. . . couldn't sleep—too much coffee—too much to think about: the BROTHERHOOD—an ethnic organization—like on an ethnic-spirit-quest—seeks to unite all races—all peoples of mankind.

Champ is so different this year: sweet, willing.

The day last year when he facetiously plunged the huge wooden mallet down within a fraction of my nose—I guess that did it.

I remember peacefully sitting on a chunk of wood in Shop, next to Typing. I was looking up at Champ, watching him, talking to him, when suddenly he lifted an enormous wooden mallet high above his head—to smash my brains out, I supposed.

I smiled, shut my eyes, waited . . .

When I opened my eyes, the mallet had stopped within an inch of my nose.

A beautiful, wonderful smile spread across Champ's face!

I had survived the sacrifice. Or did it prove that I, a white teacher, had trusted him?

February basketball game schedules hit the school calendar like electric shocks.

RED! BLACK! SCHOOL COLORS! A BATTLE CRY!

Red Devil warriors leaped to victory in red and black basketball uniforms.

Warrior maidens—turned cheerleaders—led victory yells in red and black pep skirts—waved red and black pompoms.

Cheerleaders—brisk and snappy—swung into action:

Beat 'em, team!

Rah Rah!

Rah Rah Rah!

BEAT 'EM TEAM BEAT'EM!

. . . and they did! Victory after victory!

Last night we trimmed Chimacum. Speedy and swift—Varsity Captain Tom—bolted, darted, leaped—and in the last quarter led the Red Devils to score 48-30.

Our gym erupted into a madhouse! Screams—yells—stomping feet—flying caps—boys hugged boys—girls kissed girls—hero worshippers leaped and jumped to salute the Red Devil champions.

"WE WON! WE WON! Now we're headed for League championship!"

RAH! RAH! NEAH BAY CHAMPIONS! RAH! RAH!

Screams for my champions last night wrecked my throat—raspy, scratchy—I croaked all day.

Red Devils would do nothing in class but gloat. They bragged. They boasted. They thumped their chests.

"A's for beating Chimacum? Aye, teacher?"

~

Next week we play Forks. A rough tough rival. Husky, hard-muscled Indian boys.

Again, this time during the week preceding the Forks' game:
BEAT FORKS, TEAM!
BEAT FORKS!
RAH! RAH!
RAH, RAH, RAH!
BEAT FORKS!
Red Devil warriors thump-thumped on the gym floor—strut, strutted, in the lunch line—click clacked on typewriter keys.

Each thump—each strut—each click: A BATTLE CRY:
BEAT FORKS! BEAT FORKS! BEAT FORKS! BEAT FORKS! BEAT FORKS!

One day I peeked in the gym during practice. A shrill whistle halted the scrimmage. The coach shouted: "It's action on the floor that counts. Watch your feet and arm positions. Be ready for rebounds if you miss. Wrist it in. WRIST IT IN!" Players flew into a brief huddle and then jumped back into action. Hour after hour they practiced free throws, outside shots, passing, guarding, dribbling.

Skittish players flexed arms and legs instead of pencils and books. "Gotta stay limber to beat Forks," grinned Tom. Lester walked in rubbing out a muscle cramp. Varsity players staggered to classes—in and out of Home Ec—anytime.

Today, Champ drifted into Home Ec. "Come, have a piece of Jacqui's parfait pie," Cheree coaxed.

He bellowed: "Parfait pie!" He wrinkled his Makah nose. "No, thank you, ma'am!" Patted his stomach. "My figure, until after Forks." And walked out.

Speechless, the girls watched Champ disappear through the open door—then turned abruptly to Mary Lynn's excited, "Guess what?" Pulling her long black hair away from her happy, vital face, "I was down in Shop the other day—sh—sh," she whispered, placing her finger over puckered red lips. An impish twinkle in her eyes silenced her quizzical listeners: "It's a secret—b-u-t band members are working on a huge red crepe-paper profile." On the blackboard, she chalked an outline: Tom? Scott? Lester? Champ? Anyone of the Red Devils in profile.

"They plan to nail it over the open double doors to the Gym. Just before the game, the band will strike up, the cheerleaders will rush out, and then the Red Devils will crash through the paper profile onto the court." With a sassy smile, Mary Lynn tilted her head to one side, "Don't tell anybody. Only the cheerleaders are supposed to know."

"Very dramatic," smirked Jacqui. "Sounds exciting though. Sure will make a big splash when the team crashes it. Have some pie, Mary Lynn."

"Just a small piece—my figure!" she laughed and added, "We're working on new songs and yells for the Forks' game."

"Try 'em on us."

But the bell rang and the girls trounced out chanting, "We are from Neah Bay! WE ARE FROM NEAH BAY!"

Passing my desk, Jacqui whispered, "I could be gone before the Forks' game."

Jacqui's father—here on temporary work assignment—had enrolled her in Neah Bay High School. Possessed of arrogant energy, Jacqui moved apart from her classmates. But I sensed a fragile sheath enfolding this tall, fair-haired girl. Behind glasses, deep blue eyes pleaded: "Is there anyone *here* I can trust?" Sensitive lips quivered. Questioning tomorrow and tomorrow and tomorrow . . .

~

Neah Bay crashed through the Red Devil profile. Wild shouts, boisterous cheers, and stamps of feet shook the building. We were off!

The teams bulldozed each other with mighty whacks of vengeance.

Neah Bay scored. Forks scored. Points were made. Points were missed.

Boo's roared. The shrill blast of the referee's whistle called Lester on a blocking foul. But he made up for it. His height, long arms, big hands spurred him to jump shots with unbelievable skill and ease.

Two points. Foul. Free throw. Two more points.

At half-time we tied: 30-30.

Cheerleaders led the fight song:

FIGHT TEAM FIGHT!

FIGHT TEAM FIGHT!

NEAH BAY RED DEVILS!

FIGHT! FIGHT! FIGHT!

Chet fumbled.

Black anger at Chet's fumble dyed Champ's face deep red. To offset the fumble, Champ fought tough and grim. His swift, accurate plays led to a floor shot that scored: 32-30.

YEA! CHAMP! YEA!

YEA! CHAMP! YEA!

Daring and fast, Scott snatched a flying pass. He dribbled, stalled for time, shot from the floor. Two more points.

Furious, Forks fought back.

Lester shoved at Forks' guard, slowing the game on a second foul.

More boo's.

Called out to discuss program plans for the Valentine Dance, I missed the last spectacular play. But I heard the eruptions. Tom injured his back in a twist-throw but made the basket that led to victory: 42-41.

NEAH BAY CHAMPIONS!

RAH! RAH! RAH! RAH!

NEAH BAY RED DEVILS!

RAH! RAH! RAH! RAH!

CHAMPIONS! CHAMPIONS!

High on victory fever, cheerleaders cheer-danced and flip-kicked in a whirl of red and black skirts and flash of red panties. They shouted. They waved pompoms. They cartwheeled into the night.

～

"Come on!" yelled Champ, spotting the cheerleaders. "Get in this car. We'll lead to the dance." One by one the rest followed. Tires screeched and skidded. Victory shouts split the night air over Neah Bay. Horns blared. Red Devil streamers flew. Banners trembled through fog-mist.

Inside the Hall, champions swung cheerleaders into wild and crazy dancing. As on burning coals, their whizzing steps seemed to scorch the dance floor. I noticed Jacqui with an Indian boy unknown to me. Moving in mysterious ways—come tomorrow she would be gone. Elope? Run away? Move again? For tonight, Jacqui and her Indian danced with champions.

"You're free for tonight, Miss Conly. We'll take over the kitchen." I turned to face beaming happy Pep Club mothers and fathers. Mary Lynn's mother offered. "We'll serve the hot dogs, potato salad, Kool-Aid, coffee, and cakes." Crowding around me, they insisted, "Go, enjoy the party."

This stalwart core of excited parents never missed a game.

Cheerleading daughters roused them to boisterous shouts. Tense, they watched warrior-sons toss passes and throw baskets.

So, tonight, not mixed in with mustard and catsup, I watched the kaleidoscope of dancers. In the frenzied flurry of fun and conquest, had anyone remembered Saint Valentine? Had anyone gasped at the red and white balloons bouncing against the ceiling? Was anyone's attention grabbed by the curling Valentine streamers fluttering over the arch? Whose heart had stood still in view of the elaborate arch decorations with ruffled ribbons and frilly lace? Who had listened to the whispering crepe-paper hearts and flowers? Was the enchantment of Saint Valentine's red and white to be stomped over by the black and red of the Red Devils' championship?

But at midnight I watched the patterns in the kaleidoscope change: music stopped—lights dimmed—spotlights hit the arch. Gowned in vivacious red with sprinkles of golden hearts, Cheree stood as mistress of ceremonies. Beaming and glowing, her dimples sparkling, she raised her arms. "Attention, everybody! WE BEAT FORKS! Congratulations to our team and Coach! RAH! RAH! TEAM!" Time out for cheers. "I know you can hardly wait to hear the winners of the Sweethearts' Contest. After I announce them, Miss Conly will crown the winning boy and girl as King and Queen of Hearts." Piercing whistles, clamorous shouts, waving arms acclaimed the contest winners—Daphne and Blanchard.

Honored, I placed a crown of gold and jewels on each royal head and donned attendants with golden headbands.

The Principal signaled: "Time for the Grand March. The procession will form behind the King and Queen." Then began the victory stomp—the stomp of champions—the stomps increased to pounding crescendos that ended this wild and crazy night . . .

Champions, cheerleaders, hero worshippers, and followers vanished into the night chanting:

WE ARE FROM NEAH BAY!
WE ARE FROM NEAH BAY!
RAH, RAH, RAH, RAH, RAH!
NEAH BAY RED DEVILS!
RAH, RAH, RAH, RAH, RAH!

Were they going home? To the Pool Hall? To some rendezvous to laugh and drink till dawn?

～

Monday morning after the Forks game . . . Journalism Class

Eyes swollen, face black and blue, Lester slipped in late.

"Just let me sleep," pleaded his dark eyes.

Ignoring his bumps and bruises, I said, "We're working on the Annual. Write something cute about Kitsy for the *Prochecy*."

"I don't feel so cute today," he mumbled.

You don't look so cute either, I thought.

Kitsy whispered he'd been in a fight.

Because of fouls in the Forks' game last Friday?

Drunk?

~

"What were you doing in the river at two o'clock Saturday morning, Champ? How come?" taunted Jacqui.

Champ erupted into boisterous description:

"I missed that darn curve again. Only this time, I slammed on the brakes too late. Tires squealed and skidded like crazy!"

Violent shuffling of arms briefed the flip-flop squeegeed action of his car. "It ripped sideways, hit a tree, bounced backwards over the bank and plunked into the river!"

"YEA, CHAMP, YEA, YEA!"

"RAH, RAH, RAH!" shouted his classmates.

Gloom spread across the morning sky. Another gray day. It's March! It's time for blue skies and robins! But sinister snow clouds darkened Mount Olympus. Darkened my spirits too. Rejoice! I thought. Deena's fragrant, stimulating coffee will banish the snow clouds and cheer me. But the sight of her troubled face did not.

"Deena, what's wrong?"

She answered in blunt, terse tones, "Harry, Sidney's brother, is dead."

"Dead! I just saw him last Friday at the class bake sale."

Instantly, Sidney's tortured face flashed before me. "This will be rough on Sidney. He worshipped and adored his war-hero brother. What happened?" I poured coffee. Settled myself on the kitchen stool. Waited for details.

"It was at Forks—late Friday night," Deena began. "A group of reckless boys playing Russian Roulette . . ."

"Russian Roulette? I don't understand."

"A deadly game," Deena shuddered. "The gun has one bullet in it. The player spins the cylinder, puts the gun to his head, pulls the trigger." Deena leaned against the counter—covered her face with her hands. "One of the boys dared Harry. They were all drunk."

"Oh, I see. A game of chance: hit or miss—live or die—murder or suicide."

"That's about it," Deena agreed. "The whole family's in shock." She assembled pots and pans. Tuesday was potato soup and cornbread day. Murder or suicide—kids had to eat.

Numbness swept over me. I watched Deena move in routine. "After Harry came back from the War," she reflected, "he was always so restless—wandering, unsettled—away from home a lot and drunk most of the time. He worried his mother so much."

On my way to class, I thought: Russian Roulette. Risking life to play with death. Spinning the cylinder. Pulling the trigger. The one bullet—riding fate sent Sidney's brother to his death . . .

For this one time, English class was quiet. Voices low. Faces somber. They all knew. They all talked at once: "Sidney's absent. His brother Harry is dead."

"Sidney walked all the way to Port Angeles . . ."

"Harry was in the hospital there . . ."

"Russian Roulette. Poor Sidney. I feel so sorry for him . . ."

"Harry died yesterday morning . . ."

They eased each other's grief. So somehow we all survived that class. Later in the day, Sidney came—without his teasing—his fetching grin—his demands for peanut butter sandwiches. He stood. Hesitated. Looked at me.

"Oh, Sidney, I just heard about Harry this morning. I'm so sorry."

His voice strangled. He choked out: "I'm gonna get the guy and flash a knife." With his fists doubled in hard knots, he whacked them together.

"Oh, no, Sidney, you can't win that way. You can't right one wrong by committing another. You'd be the one to get hurt. Come. Sit down," I suggested.

Before me, an Indian youth stricken by an insane tragedy sought comfort. How could I give him the strength he needed? Gently, I touched his arm, "Sidney, you must realize and accept that part of playing the game was Harry's responsibility."

Instant hatred flared in Sidney's eyes. "The guy dared Harry, didn't he? Harry couldn't chicken out, could he?" His bitter rage pierced right through me. My spirits sank to lowest ebb. Heavy hearted. Despondent. Helpless. I offered food.

"I'll make some hot cocoa. Would you like a piece of gingerbread? The girls made it." I hoped to calm him.

"I'm not hungry."

Sidney stared out the window—tears edged his eyes. "Harry was in the hospital in P.A.—I had to get there—my heart pounded so hard—I hurt so bad—could hardly breathe—" he pressed his chest.

He turned toward me. What was he thinking? After a moment of silence, he buried his face in his hands, stifling a sob. "You wouldn't understand," he whispered.

. . . I did understand. He needed to speak out his grief—his mood—his feelings. But instead, bitterness and anger distorted his face.

. . . with an impulsive "I gotta go" he stood—lifted his hand: "See ya."

Did Sidney walk all the way to Port Angeles? I had heard he did. I was told later that part of the time Sidney was running. Did he stumble in the darkness? Did he hear spirit voices? Did the voices help him find his way? Did the voices tell him to hurry? That's what I heard.

. . . then at the hospital, Sidney sat by Harry's bed. Harry knew Sidney was there—spoke his brother's name. That's what I heard.

Shades of sadness followed me home. So did a bitter icy wind. So did the first flurries of snow.

Tonight I pushed aside test papers and lesson plans. My thoughts shot back and forth from Sidney to Harry—from Harry to Sidney.

I recalled plans for the Class Bake Sale at the Community Hall last Friday. "It won't be Saint Patrick's Day, but it'll be March. And we need a theme for the bake sale and party," declared Class President Dolly.

"Great idea!" they shouted. "Let's celebrate Saint Patrick's Day!"

To price pies, cupcakes, cookies and cakes, Sidney and I had come to the Hall early. With marking pen and tags, Sidney's buoyant spirit relished the task. "My brother Harry's back home. He's coming here tonight." A casual remark, but Sidney marked and tagged in restless movements: "Harry drinks a lot. Oh, he's here now."

And so it happened that in honor of Saint Patrick—midst green balloons, green streamers, shamrocks—I met Harry, Sidney's brother.

Harry tottered on the threshold of the back door. HE WAS DRUNK.

Sidney ran to meet him—grabbed Harry's arm—pulled him toward me. "Come, I want you to meet my teacher." The two brothers stood before me. Harry—taller and heavier than Sidney—a bit disheveled—but in identity: Makah.

Sidney twisted his hands—cracked his knuckles—fidgeted—as though unsure of Harry. "This is my brother Harry. He was a paratrooper in the War. He won some medals." Pride, wonder, adoration—and also anxiety—mirrored in Sidney's black eyes.

Harry took my hand—grinned—the same mischievous grin that beamed on Sidney's round face. "We're happy to have you here," I welcomed. "We're hoping you'll stay for the party after the sale." But he was fidgety and restless too.

Harry lit a cigarette. In silence, Sidney and I watched smoke rings swirl above Harry's head. Preoccupied, he snuffed out the cigarette. Was he thinking in some realm we did not understand? A quick dip of his head toward me—a turn toward Sidney: "I'll be back later." Harry raised his hand in salute: "See ya."

Disappointed, Sidney courageously chattered on. "Harry was a good paratrooper. He's a crack shot with a rifle." A brief quiet veered our course. I broke the mood. "It'll soon be time for the rest of the class."

Sidney absently answered, "Yah. Yah. Once he told me he'd been to London and Paris—even to New York to see a War buddy." Opening a box of sugar cookies, "My mother sent these. She worries about Harry. He was away in the War four years. Now he's not home most of the time."

All at once the rest of the class burst in. Noise! Excitement! Enthusiasm! THE SALE WAS ON!

Shenanigans—smiling Irish eyes—lively Irish jigs—marked this evening's madness. Perky green corsages worn atop hairdos—green crepe paper aprons with wildly fashioned sashes—all brightened the girls. Boys donned green top hats—green bow ties—looked very Irish. Happy-go-lucky lads and lassies boxed and bagged goodies for village customers.

"We're gonna make it okay," predicted bold and bossy Genevieve. Chewing on a piece of Indian fry bread, she frowned at the party-refreshment table. "Where'd all that green stuff come from?" Not waiting for an answer, she turned away to join her tribal friends.

". . . all that green stuff . . ." Indeed! On the kelly-green tablecloth, green Kool-Aid sparkled in glass pitchers. Heaped in Makah cedar-basket trays, green-frosted cookies resigned until party time. Leprechauns and three-leaf clovers decorated white paper cups and napkins. Delightful! I praised the effect of tokens from the Emerald Isle.

"Sure enough now, the spirit of Saint Patrick is on strong tonight," teased a voice in Irish brogue. "Will you need the Luck-o'-the-Irish too?"

Without turning, I recognized the facetious brogue belonging to Coach Rick. "For sure," I answered, "a wee bit of Irish luck is always a pleasure."

Rick changed the subject—asked about Harry. "He was here, wasn't he? I met him down on Front Street aimlessly wandering. He reeked whiskey. Mentioned a party at the Hall.

"The draft plunged Reservation kids, like Harry, into an explosive world of bombs and guns." While Rick talked, he set up another table—arranged folding chairs. "Uprooted from caring families, they were thrown into barracks where nobody cared." Arms akimbo, Rick glanced across the Hall. "The kids are doing okay with their sale," he observed. Turning back to me—"From what I've heard, these boys gradually learned self-reliance—found they could make friends—even with white soldiers."

In a rush of enthusiasm, Sidney bounced over, "We're selling like crazy! Gotta go! Have you seen Harry? He might come for the party."

"I doubt it," Rick muttered under his breath. Rick's revelation of Reservation boys at war fascinated me—enlightened me. Eager to learn more, I pursued: "Sidney is so proud of Harry and his War record as a paratrooper."

"You bet he is," agreed Rick. "It was in military training that these kids learned they could excel. Their officers recognized their skills and placed them in specialized units. In Harry's case, he was a natural for a paratrooper.

"I've talked to several American Indian veterans from other Reservations. They're all like Harry—depressed, bitter, restless—more often drunk than sober."

Rick poured a cup of Kool-Aid. I poured coffee—watched the green streamers sway from the ceiling—wondered if they'd last till party time.

Casually, Rick reached for a cooky. "These kids have real problems. Some don't honor their tribal leaders or the old ceremonies anymore. In the Army, Harry grew proud of himself and his unit. He earned *respect*. Back here on the Reservation, he feels no one respects or cares about his War record—no one but Sidney."

. . . and no one but Sidney watched for Harry to come back.

Sidney's voice edged in concern—in disappointment—in hurt: "He didn't come back. I wonder where he went." And I wondered too.

~

In the silence of my dream, night stretched into a long tunnel of darkness. At the end of the tunnel: HARRY. DISTURBANCE. CONFUSION.

As I awakened—an epiphany—a LIGHT that Rick had lit enlightened me.

Had Harry's restlessness—his wandering—his searching—drawn him into a tunnel of darkness. Who would send a light to lift him out?

Sidney? Rick? Or his Spirit Guide?

Like the mighty wings of Thunderbird—that dropped over Whale—Harry's senseless death had dropped heavy wings of sorrow over coffee time. In fantasy, I flew away with this great bird—leaving Sidney's sad face behind.

~

A voice jerked me back. "Harry's funeral is Saturday." Marta filled coffee cups, set out toast and marmalade. "We thought you'd want to know."

"Oh yes. Thank you, Marta." I hesitated. "Sidney wants me to come. But how would the family feel? I don't want to intrude. I saw Harry only once."

"You're Sidney's teacher. It would mean much to the family. They'd feel honored that you cared enough to come," Deena explained.

ME! I was the one honored. ("THAT WITCH . . . SHE'LL NEVER LAST UP HERE!" dropped from the ether.) Did they really understand that I cared for them as a race—as a tribe—as a family. Cared about Sidney's bitter pain—cared about his mother's loss?

"If you want to go, we'll pick you up," Deena offered. Busy with school lunch preparations, she continued, "I promised Sidney's mother I'd bake and decorate a huge cake in memoriam. Luke will sing at the services in the Presbyterian Church. Then we'll all go to the cemetery on the hill for the burial and grave services."

"After that," Marta remarked, "there'll be the traditional funeral feast at the Community Hall. During the ceremonies, songs and dances and speeches will be given to honor Harry."

"It will be a military funeral," Deena began. "I remember one—a military funeral—several years ago at the cemetery." Deena paused—dabbed her eyes—tension touched her brow. "Members of a military unit stood on the hillside." Sudden anguish struck the softness of Deena's face. She faltered. "They played Taps. It was like . . ." Her voice dropped. Her lips quivered. The essence of hidden pain visualized—formed a mental image: in tears—in trembling—in Deena's stricken stare—I sensed this moment of remembrance to be a hard one. As returning from some spiritual connection, she repeated, "It was like, l-i-k-e, the sound of bugles coming from the sky."

Stunned by Deena's strong feelings to a memory urged me to search yonder. But I left my yearning to search—and moved to English class.

~

Harry's funeral day dawned sunny, bright, and fiercely cold. I waited for Deena.

Even in this time of sorrow, this presents a strangely high moment for me. By Deena's inclusion of me with her family, I recognized I am privileged. I am honored. I am accepted. Deena is not just anyone. A notable Makah woman, she is talented, artistic, accomplished, and beautiful! Also a member of one of the ruling tribal families. That she would plan her time—drive out of her way—so that I might be with them all at Harry's funeral—uplifts me—inspirits me.

In secret smugness, I glory in this attention—for SHE WATCHES!

I checked the time—pulled on my snow boots. As I continued to wait, I reviewed the staccato progression of events that led to this funeral:

- After the bake sale
- After the Saint Patrick's party and dance
- After the last green party balloon popped
- After Sidney's fear-loaded question: "He never came back? I wonder where he went?"

Who was to know that, powered by destiny, Harry had hitchhiked to Forks? Who was to know that THERE he tangled with foolhardy daring boys who had been drinking?

In a web of fate. In a game of chance. In risking life to play with death.

"I dare you. It's just a game. It's all for fun."

But the gun was not. The gun with one bullet . . .

Harry took the dare . . . spun the cylinder . . . pulled the trigger . . .

It was solemn—a time of heavy tragedy. Harry: victim of the white man's whiskey.

~

In quiet reverence, Indian and white villagers came together at the church. Over heads bowed in obedience—in resignation—Reverend Dale-Smith lifted his arms to bless—to give solace and understanding. He asked the grieving family and friends: "Trust the one Great Spirit Guide—the one Great God."

Recalling my dream, the prayer brought Harry into the Light—out of the tunnel of darkness—of disturbance—of confusion. Had his Spirit Guide lighted his way—brought him to the Land of his ancestors?

Influenced by the enlightened tone—by the heightened effect of prayer—I was moved, aware only of feelings—of impressions. When Luke sang *The Lord's Prayer*, I felt the Presence flow through and touch each and every one. The same Presence shimmered through me as I passed Harry's casket. Again, did the Presence hover over the church tower as bells tolled for Harry?

At the cemetery on the hill, streams of March sun burst through clouds—to bless the burial site. Bundled in heavy dark winter garments, we all tramped up the hill to the grave. Snow crunched under boots. Bitter-cold, chilled faces.

In an utterance of bereavement, Reverend Dale-Smith committed Harry's body to snow-encrusted Earth-Mother.

Makah Elders, Tribal Chiefs, old Medicine Men, and family members stood in last salute to Harry. One old and shriveled elder swayed and moaned—sobbing out his grief. Another old one—with sunken cheeks and straggly gray hair—lifted his cedar power stick over the grave: A blessing? A protection?

Sidney stood beside his mother. I recalled his threat: "I'm gonna get the guy and flash a knife." His words attacked with rage and hatred.

As if to erase the threat, streamers of sunlight in rainbow-bright colors passed over Harry's grave.

At the same time, the clear pure bugle notes sounded Taps signaling a respite. During this pause, I could believe Harry's soul was called up the spirit path—through the spirit gate—to the Land of his ancestors.

. . . bugle notes faded—wind currents carried echoes out—out—and far away. Deena stood beside me—tears filled her eyes . . .

Now—time to leave the grave—time to leave the cemetery on the hill—time to leave for the ceremonial burial services and feast at the Community Hall.

Here—at the ceremonies—Makah prayer chants answered by prayer songs from other tribes—filled the Hall with vibrant power of the Great Spirit. The soft throb of deer-skin drums gave essence to sacred dances.

Deena whispered, "It's traditional to meet members of the family. They are seated at the back of the Hall."

Again, Sidney stood beside his mother. "This is my teacher." His mother touched my hand. "I always worried so much about Harry. I don't worry anymore. I know where he is."

Still aware of feelings and sensations, I felt as one in mind and spirit with my Indian friends. I reached out and sensed a universal pull with all moving figures around me . . . and last year I wailed in distress because I felt so many failures.

～

For days and days—again and again—I relived Harry's funeral: I entered a Christian church—bowed my head with Indians—tramped up the hill through snow and bitter cold to the cemetery. At the ceremonial feast, I received within myself the sorrows of them all.

What had prompted Harry to take such a foolish risk? Will any of us ever really know? Will the Great Spirit that Harry believed in free him from his distress: his living in two different worlds—greed and injustice of the white world—the darkening dangers of the Indian world?

I remembered Deena spoke of *reincarnation*. Could I have been with the Makah in some past lifetime?

Once Dotti amazed me when she exclaimed: "You're speaking Indian spirituality! You were with us in another lifetime."

Does this define my feelings of closeness to these People—my yearning to understand—to effect such distress and concern over their tragedies?

Once again a weekend away from classes and kids. Once again I'm the lone passenger between Port Angeles and Neah Bay. The rickety old bus rolled into the Olympic wilderness.

Hit by a stiff but brief blizzard the night before, now bright snow dazzled on cedar and fir boughs. Slush, part snow, part watery ice, covered the road. But in the *going down of the sun*, I slid into RETROSPECTION—IN-TROSPECTION.

My eyes shut. My thoughts drift. At once they link with Sidney—a Makah teenager sky-rocketed into inconsolable grief. To Sidney, Harry stood as an image of power, of courage, of honor. One bullet shattered the image. The shattering bullet left a boy outraged—belligerent, bitter, vengeful. *"I'm gonna get the guy and flash a knife . . ."*

Before Harry died, did he breathe "Spirit Guide"? To grow out of this wretchedness, need Sidney seek his own Spirit Power—his own Spirit Guide? To find the power the elders believed in, need Sidney practice ancient disciplines of tribal laws and codes of behavior? Need he emulate—develop—the qualities he esteemed in his brother?

The bus screeched to a near stop. Ripped out of my drowsy retrospection—my voice quaky—I asked, "What happened?"

"A deer jumped out of the brush," the driver answered. "Don't want to hit one of them big fellers." He turned toward me, "Where there's one, there's usually more—a whole family maybe." He turned back to concentrate on his driving.

Again, composed in mind, my thoughts trickle in bits and pieces to this ancient Land—its people, hunters of the Whale, once a strong tribe—now reduced to a few hundred—customs, traditions, language near extinction.

A sharp jog in the road jerked me out of my composure. My trickle of thoughts violated, I opened my eyes to dots and dashes of snow—to the swish of slush spraying out from under the wheels.

The bus lumbered on. Over the long years of settling down, the old road has tipped dangerously toward the chilly waters of Juan de Fuca's narrow sea. It's very scary. I always held my breath. Would we make it—driving so near the edge? What if the road gave way—tumbling us down, down into the icy blue waters? The Indian kids flip around these treacherous curves—near the edge—speeding at ninety or ninety-five miles per. . . . They don't always make it!

Often during sodden sopping rains, earth rips from the hillside sliding to a muddy mass across the road. This blocking heap of upturned earth twisted roots, uprooted broken trees, and rocks—just squats. Like a foreboding spirit—the mass defies anyone passage—coming or going—until road crews dig a trail-way.

Does the Great Spirit send protection over this precarious unstable track of land travel? No traveler—the Old Ones say—has ever been stuck in a mud slide.

My head bobbed with the rhythm of the curves and bumps. When the bus skipped a beat—or was it my heart?—I thought: How can anyone here possibly understand how I feel? Do I understand myself? No one can understand WHY I am HERE.

Still dozy, I recalled Jerry's remark. He leaned back in his typing chair—squinted his black eyes—quizzically wondered: "Why are you HERE? You don't find somebody like you every day."

I'm sure of THAT, I thought facetiously. Jerry's next remark puzzled me: "Do you know any jujitsu or karate attacks to protect yourself?"

When I answered his strange question with a NO, he immediately demanded, "WHY NOT?" Innocent and ignorant of martial arts techniques, I never related their defensive skills to me. I—baffled—concluded the discussion: "I've never thought I would need them."

Still touching memory cells: A new teacher, Rhonda, and I walked home after a party at the Community Hall. Uppermost in my mind—on this dark street—HORSES! Feeling very insecure and shaky, I voiced my fears: "I hope we don't meet any horses. I'm scared to death of those roving monsters!"

In quick response, "Aren't you afraid of the people?"

"It never occurred to me to be AFRAID OF THE PEOPLE!"

Then one day Jule remarked, "People in the village ask this about you: 'Why is she teaching in Neah Bay?' I snapped back, 'Why NOT Neah Bay?' You'll never guess the answer, 'W-e-l-l, I should think she would go some place where she could find a man.'"

This reminded me of my first year—of Annabelle's ridicule—three necessities of life: "OH, NO! NOT FOOD, CLOTHING, SHELTER—BUT MEN! MEN! MEN!"

The village people all wonder. Indian? White? They cannot understand . . .

Little do they know. The fate-steps of Destiny beginning long ago—that led to my being here.

All happenings, not understood—all phenomena, not explicable.

Once, a friend, indirectly, said about me: "She needs to give of herself to fulfill a great need." An awareness—a consciousness within me?

That first bus ride—the mystical SOMETHING pulling me to this rocky Cape.

I could believe I am here because I was SENT here—that the Great Spirit planned my life in such a way that I was BROUGHT here.

 I learned to identify Forks with *trouble.*
A logging town south of Neah Bay, it stood at the forks of the Bogachiel, Soleduck, and Calawah Rivers.
The town became a cauldron—brewing misfortune.

Bitter enemies on the basketball court—Forks and Neah Bay players carried vicious grudges off the court.

Lester shuffled into class—face bruised—eyes swollen. Kitsy whispered, "Got into a fight with Forks' players because of the fouls at the game, I guess."

"Scott's all banged up—got in a fight at Forks."

"After the accident, Jack was taken to the hospital in Forks."

"Coming back from Forks, Chet wrecked his car on Burnt Mountain."

"Burt and Lorna had a fight. Burt's gone to Forks to look for work."

Sidney's brother died—a loser in a game of Russian Roulette in Forks . . .

". . . LET THE TALENTS DIE. THERE'RE ENOUGH CRAFTS IN MUSEUMS . . ."
At a school assembly last fall, this remark from Ada—like an expletive of denial—phased Helen not one whit. Neither did the month of March: cold, blustery, snow predicted.

Helen visualized a Craft Shop!

Down on the waterfront!

What a high-spirited adventure!

What a factor to keep talents alive!

What an enlightening retreat to lure summer tourists!

"We'll set up a small frame building . . ." Helen happily dreamed. "We'll put in shelves, counters, show windows. This way we'll display Makah crafts."

Caught up in Helen's enthusiasm, I too visualized. My thoughts drifted away. I left Helen behind . . . shifted, in fantasy, to the beach. Sharp

March winds rumpled my hair—stung my eyes. Incoming—the tide hissed and spit. A sun streak shot through storm clouds. I heeded neither winds nor tide. Tangled among sand and sea shells, kelp ribbons and sea grasses, a glass ball in purple hue glistened: a power gift for Helen's Craft Shop.

Swells, breakers from the sea, splashed and crashed upon the shore— left strange irregular shapes of driftwood, sea shells in curlicue forms, barnacle-crusted rocks, legendary sand dollars with mystic marks, distorted twists of dried kelp—inherent items, from sand and sea—all belong on display shelves.

. . . and who would believe these indigenous totems held spirit power!

. . . and who could pass by the Craft Shop—down on the waterfront— set in a background of great forests—rocky shores—with summer-spirit breezes whispering: "Come see! Come see! Follow me! Follow me!"

If I followed the spirit breezes, I'd look for novelty pieces—like a tightly woven cup and saucer set—a carved Thunderbird and Whale emblem attached to a key chain—a doll crafted from cedar strands. I'd stuff them all into my Medicine Bag with all my cherished charms—my favorite things.

If tourists followed the sea breezes into the Craft shop, what would they stuff into their tote bags? A carved oil dish? A tiny replica of a whaling canoe? A beaded medallion? A headband crafted from olive shells? . . . all take-home items from Neah Bay.

. . . back from fantasy . . . back to Helen . . . her black eyes snapped. "We'll string olive shell necklaces, bracelets and earrings on jewelry racks. We can show beaded headbands, beaded medallions—worn as charms— with strange designs."

Before Helen spoke again, she appeared to move away from the Craft Shop. Her happy, cheerful mien turned serious and thoughtful. "We can't use our family crest on crafts sold to the public. Our culture forbids this. Family symbols and totems are often guarded in secret. Sacred ceremonial robes are hardly ever worn in public."

Like legends, talents will never die . . . not as long as one Makah weaves a basket—carves an oil dish—strings an olive-shell necklace, native crafts will live on.

 A pair of deep, dark, snapping black eyes of one school girl puzzled me. The Oriental slant—not inherent to the Makah— caused me to wonder.

"Every time I look at Mary Lynn, her eyes stand out more Oriental than Makah." This chance remark to Cerena induced her to uncover a vague bit of history:

"More than one-hundred years ago a Japanese ship capsized right out here in our bay. The story goes that the few surviving Oriental sailors—jerked about in the rowdy sea—struggled in terror." Cerena paused. Was she feeling the cruel winds, crashing waves, and icy waters?

"Then what happened?" I asked.

"Courageous Makah paddlers canoed to the tragic wreckage—pulled the half-frozen survivors into the canoes—wrapped them in cedar-bark blankets—paddled back to their village here at Neah Bay."

Cerena had opened a spirit gate to the shipwreck—to the survivors—to their acceptance by the Makah—to the natural-smooth blending of cultures. Now the descendants had become part of family and tribal history—facts and circumstances—long forgotten—no longer important.

But long ago, did the spirits of the lost ones—swallowed by the sea—travel back to their village in Japan?

Did spirit messages cross the waters to those who waited?

Was one who waited—a maid—fragile, delicate, with almond eyes—with ivory cheeks—with tender words—with a love song?

And now, today, do spirits of the lost seamen walk the secret sea?

Cerena whispered, "Many old people claim they have seen spirit lights flicker over dark waters—on stormy nights—near the scene of the shipwreck."

~

And why does Dane Brooks wear his hair to his shoulders?

One day after school, Jule called my attention to him. "Have you noticed Dane's unusual outfit? His jacket, pants, and hat—all decorated with fringes and feathers—and that long hair!"

Smashing originality, I thought. "But why the individualistic attire?"

"For some reason—who knows—Dane aspires to belonging to an Indian tribe in Montana. I believe it's called LONG GRASS," Jule said. "The only qualification: long hair. His aunt told him to let his hair grow long so he could belong to this tribe."

To belong has become Dane's dream—his motivation in life—even as a fourth grader . . .

Is he living in a fantasy world? In imagination does he live the life of a romantic adventurer—a world of color and dash—a Spanish sea-captain who charts the seas?

In admiration of this strikingly handsome boy, I noticed the strong characteristic features of the Makah were missing. Instead of the broad Makah nose, Dane's was straight and slender. Instead of full lips, Dane's were thin, but well shaped. In contrast to the Makah's wide-boned facial structure, Dane's face was refined—sculptured in narrow outlines. Dane's body also showed slighter lines than the sturdy, robust Makah.

Do Dane's features allude to Spanish ancestry? Who knows?

~

The Spanish built a fort at Neah Bay in 1791. Did some of the seamen stay behind—to be absorbed into the tribe—just as the Orientals?

~

SPANISH FORT—NUNEZ CAONA—1871

I stand on the rough-pebbled beach
mesmerized by vibrations
of conquistadors from across the sea
Breezes shimmer with Spanish energy
Spanish voices echo, re-echo
I watch at the edge of the same
wave-rippled strip of shore
where Spanish footsteps marked the sand
washed away—long ago—by distant waves
I breathe the same salty-tangy-misty air
feel the same drippy-drizzly-ghostly spill
of raindrops across my cheeks
gaze into the same darkly-green
mysterious cedar forests
I behold Makah children hidden
behind tangles of silvered driftwood . . .
THEY STAND—THEY WATCH TOO!

Kids huddled over desks—pecked at typewriters. Every minute counted.

Kitsy's scissors snipped around heads and legs for the

snapshot pages.

Champ concentrated on paste and labels—licked paste off his fingers—twisted and turned to stick labels at correct angles—whistled and sputtered at mistakes.

Chewing the end of his pencil, Lester finished class *Prophecy* and *Athletic* write-ups.

Cheree—lips squeezed tight—dimples determined—typed the final drafts and *Class History*.

Prodded by Stephen, Jacqui wrote the *Dedication* and checked final sequence of pages.

⌒

. . . and then today, March 18, 1956, the ANNUAL—boxed, weighed, stamped—was sent to press.

"US" Indians—six graduating seniors and me—just sat and stared at each other and sighed: "Isn't it wonderful! The Annual has gone to press!"

"The big spring push is over at last. Now we can sit back and relax the rest of the year," rejoiced Rose Mary.

"I'll never forget when Champ pasted a whole page of snapshots upside down," drawled Lester.

Champ howled, "And I wasn't drunk either!"

"And I dumped glue on my new wool skirt," giggled Cheree.

"It's a super-deluxe edition—the best ever put out at Neah Bay High School," spoke Kitsy, pride glowing in her eyes.

"LET'S HAVE A PARTY TO CELEBRATE!" shouted one and all.

. . . and so we did!

To my horror, Jacqui set before me an enormous piece of pecan pie topped with mountains of whipped cream.

"OH, NO, Jacqui," I groaned, "not pecan pie at ten o'clock in the morning!"

"OH, YES! You've got to eat it. I made it especially for you."

With grim determination, I ATE IT.

Lester and Stephen opened cans of mixed nuts. Kitsy's chocolate chip cookies soon vanished.

"My sister stayed up all night to bake this Red Devil's Food chocolate cake for our party," announced Champ. Wielding a knife above the cake, he yelled: "Come 'n' get it! Who wants whipped cream?"

"It's so yummy with gobs piled on top," Cheree encouraged. "Sprinkle some nuts on too."

A rush to Champ's expertise soon demolished the cake and whipped cream.

Champ has a picture in his wallet: MY PICTURE!
Tom has one in his wallet.
I DO NOT LIKE THOSE KIDS WITH THAT PICTURE: It looks rowdy, wild, hilarious. Undignified. Unprofessional. Not an image to transcribe to my fellow teachers, principal, or district superintendent!

The picture was snapped last year: TYPING PERIOD.

Class over: Typewriters covered. Books put away. Kids wait for the bell: play time!

Waving a camera, Champ—with a wicked grin—shouted: "Let's snap Miss Conly!"

"Great idea!" vigorously agreed the class.

"Oh, no you don't!" I snapped back. In protest, I turned my back—hid my face—only to be grabbed by Diana—pounds heavier—inches taller. Protest overruled. Her greater strength—in a quick flip—to her astonishment and mine—landed me unexpectedly in her lap!

Riotous! Boisterous! Hilarious howls from the class! In the midst of all, I still tried to turn away, but Jerry grasped my lower jaw, forced me to stare at the camera. Beside him, Tom towered over all to aid and abet these culprits.

Not until this year did I see the results. Still protesting a year later—to me the picture was humiliating—I hoped they would let me tear it up. I begged for mercy—understanding—from my point of view.

PROTEST DENIED! Just unsympathetic smiles and Champ's coy remark: "Well—if you had smiled pretty in the camera, they wouldn't have done it!"

Webster defines *catastrophe*: an *event* overturning the *order* or *system* of *things*.
Event: Test of Pronouns
Order: Procedure—paper and pencils—thinking caps on
System: I
Things: Pronouns—him, her, she, it, they

The event overturned the system all right—crashing into calamity: A violent and widely extended change in the system.

After the overturning—disbelief, shock, numbness

Teacher failure?

Time to go home?

Curricular change?

Never, never anymore tests. There must be a better way.

Cultural fault? Indian kids just aren't ready for the mechanics of pronouns. But the white kids flunked too.

I wailed and moaned.

The class had been so thoroughly drilled: upside down, crosswise, backwards.

But the whole class fell flat on their faces and flunked.

. . . never heard of a PRONOUN . . .

. . . what's that? . . .

From school days, I recall:

Her has went

Her has gone

Her has left I all alone

It could never was.

BUT IT WAS!

1956-1957

Black clouds darkened the sky over Makah Land—flickers of lightning spit through the red-cedar forest—thunder rumbled in the Olympic Mountains.

When Storm Spirits took over the sky-lanes, I thought of Thunderbird and my first plane ride over Puget Sound . . .

THUNDERBIRD: majestic bird of Indian legend. Described by some storytellers as a gigantic feathered creature that dwells in a cave—in the Olympics—near a great glacier. His power and energy come from meat and blubber of Whale. When restless and hungry, this giant bird flies to the Ocean in search of his food.

In flight, his mighty wing-spread darkens the sky. Thunder crashes from his rushing wings. His speed stirs up violent wind and rain storms. Whenever he opens and closes his eyes, lightning flashes.

When Thunderbird sights Whale, he dives—straight as a spirit arrow. In his strong fierce talons, he seizes Whale. With a whirl of his out-stretched wings, Thunderbird flies back to his mountain cave. There he squats. With grunts and clucks, he devours his prey.

Watching those black clouds thicken, my thoughts squirmed in doubts:

Did I really want to fly over Puget Sound tonight? Did I really want to miss the Makah party and all the fun? What if there really was a Thunderbird out there in that black sky—swinging his mighty wings? Legend or no legend, I could change my mind and stay in Neah Bay.

"Don't let old Thunderbird scare you," my Prop Pals urged. "Marta and I will drive you to Port Angeles," Deena encouraged. "From there you take the night plane—you'll love it! In no time you'll be in Seattle."

That's how I found myself at the airport in P.A.

Damp air moved in from the Strait of Juan de Fuca. Chill blasts off the Olympics struck me. Shivers twisted down my spine.

Excitement? Fear?

I decided not to risk Thunderbird's take-off for the Ocean. What if his time clashed with my plane's take-off time—and there I'd be high in the sky with winds and lightning and that giant bird? No way!

Too late! Too late!

Lights flashed—engine revved for flight—from the loud speaker: "Passengers now boarding for Seattle."

"Great Spirit fly with you—take care of you," Deena whispered. I snatched my scarf from mischievous winds—turned to wave—boarded the plane.

In my forced excitement, I forgot about Thunderbird—adjusted the seat for my first plane ride . . .

"We're taking off for Seattle in a few minutes," announced the pilot. "Please fasten your seat belts for our short flight over Puget Sound."

Relaxed—I closed my eyes. In fantasy—I winged up with the winds of the world—listened to the song of the stars—flew into a night rainbow fringed with yellow and azure-blue edges . . .

Then—an unexpected WHOOSH! In sudden anxiety, I felt the small plane lurch into the storm sky. With a jarring yank, the slight craft began to rock—jerk—whirl—skid slantwise. It swerved—it swooped. Bouncing up—it bounced down. Tempest winds zigged the plane forward—now zagged the plane backwards.

Was this violent disturbance in the sky caused by Thunderbird's flapping wings? Was I living the legend after all? Was Thunderbird flying to find Whale? Had the plane confused him? Was he flying blind to the Ocean and taking the plane with him? On this wild ride, I could believe in legendary wings and fantasy flights . . .

How did the other five passengers feel, I wondered. How were they managing the jolts and jumps? I glanced around. Faces blurred before me in shades of greenish-gray. Stunned. Sick.

"How are you doing?" the flight attendant asked me. His lean, freckled face, and curly copper hair wavered before me.

"Just thankful I'm not throwing up," I choked. "But this is rough."

"It's rough, all right," he agreed, shaking his head. "The roughest flight I've had." To avoid head collision with the ceiling, he grabbed a sturdy black strap. "Usually takes about twenty minutes. But tonight, fighting updrafts and downdrafts, it'll be an hour or more."

A swift plunge—down, down to the bottom of the world! Terrified, I covered my eyes.

Far away and a million years ago, I heard my Makah friends predict, "You'll love it! In no time you'll be in Seattle."

A shattering wrench returned my thoughts to the airways. Winds gusted and twisted. In spirals, like a tornado, the plane funneled up the sky. I gripped the armrests and squeezed my eyelids to slits. Expecting the plane to crack against the roof of the world, my mind dizzied into nothingness.

Then, as from a far-distant sky, the pilot's voice droned, "We're flying into Seattle. Keep your seat belts fastened for landing."

I heard a whirring as if feathered wings hurtled the plane into a wild downward loop. I panicked. We're in a crash dive! But no! With a bump and a thump, the landing wheels hit the runway. The pilot braked, and the plane rattled and shook to a stop on Great Earth.

My shaky fingers fumbled with the seat belt. Still reeling between the world of fantasy and reality, I slung my brown paisley raincoat across my arm and clutched my lizard-skin purse. Knees wobbly, I smiled at the pilot.

"Do I look ashen and scared?" I asked.

With a broad grin, the pilot replied, "That was a rocky ride tonight. We flew into strong winds. One of the worst storms I've flown over Puget Sound. It can be rough riding in a small, local plane."

"It was a fantasy flight for me." I faked a laugh. "For a while I thought Thunderbird had flown right out of the Olympics and took control. My Makah friends said he was getting restless."

The pilot's amused chuckle lifted my spirits. "If you're flying back to Port Angeles Sunday, Thunderbird forecasts calm skies."

 In and out of Home Ec with Shop passes, *drifters* made my day: Totem pole carvers, boat builders, canoe makers arrived with wounded fingers—splinters driven deep in Makah flesh.
A first-aid needle—long, sharp, sterilized. I gently probed, squeezed, coaxed until the evil spirit erupted.

Brave warriors: No blood-curdling howls. Nobody faints. No blood-pools on the floor.

Emergency covered with a Band-Aid.

Drifter-patient returned to Shop.

What did they do in the old days?

～

Later in Home Ec:

No one liked the Peanut Butter Squares.

CHAMP drifted in—took off with the whole batch. We never saw the cookies again—or the pan!

"Time for a joke on the basketball team. They'll never know we forgot the spices and brown sugar!"

"RAH, RAH, RAH! WE ARE FROM NEAH BAY!" chanted the girls as they dashed off to their own basketball practice.

 "WE MADE IT!"

"We're Seniors! We're Seniors! We're Seniors!"

They chanted. They shouted. They strutted.

Giggly and frisky, the Freshman Class of 1952 began a trek to mighty senior standing. Esteemed by lower classmen, they were looked up to. Senior status lifted heads, widened shoulders, firmed footsteps. It was BIG TIME being a Senior at Neah Bay High School.

~

Over after-school coffee, Alta, Senior Class Adviser, began:

"Not all students that started as freshmen stayed on a four-year course to reach senior standing. Out of a class of eighteen, only seven will graduate. Seven dropped out and four moved away. But oh my! These graduates must out-do every class since Year One! They have such high and mighty plans. Right now the Senior Ball is the most important event of their lives."

"That's all the girls talk about," I interrupted, filling cups with steaming hot coffee. At this point there is no past or future—just today—just the Senior Ball—just a sky full of stars and dreams—and a night of MAGIC!

Today the girls zeroed in on formals: "Shall I wear angel blue or shocking pink? Shall I dance in a gown of chiffon and lace, or lace and satin, or rustly white taffeta?" Cheree, Kitsy, and Annabelle sketched designs for an original dream gown. But if they want originals, they'll have to cut and stitch their own!"

"That'll be the day!" Alta threw up her hands. "I can just see THAT! Waiting until the night before the Ball."

Leaning back in her chair, Alta said, "Oh my, in Library, first period, the chatter was about dates. Who's going with whom? Will Tom ask Dolly? Will Champ take Annabelle? Who will Mary Lynn go with? And Bonnee? A lovely, beautiful girl, but she doesn't run with the others."

Preoccupied, Alta plucked at the shell combs in her hair. "As far as dates go," Alta added, "there'll be some disappointments. Some girls may sit and wait—then go with a group from their own class. The Senior Ball is not an exclusive senior-class affair as in city schools. Every girl in Neah Bay will be chasing rainbows to the Senior Ball. Am I taking too much of your time?" Alta asked, glancing at the wall clock.

"Oh, no! I love it! All day I listen to Senior-Ball talk. Besides, as Girl's Club adviser and Home Ec teacher, I'll be at the Ball—waiting for water to boil in those huge granite coffee pots and standing guard over the goodies. Any THING could come c-r-e-e-p-y crawly—like octopus tentacles—over the breakwater and through the backdoor!"

As if thinking to herself, Alta continued, "Decorations for the dance theme—CARNIVAL OF VENICE—are due any day. Nothing would do but that they order decorations from a school-supply house in Chicago." She fussed and fumed and twisted in her chair. "I tried my best to convince the Planning Committee to settle for Seattle. BUT, OH, NO! Their minds were dead set. There's one consolation. Decorations come complete in one package. Crepe-paper streamers of every color from A to Z." Alta swung her arms in rhythmic demonstration.

"I can see streamers swoop and swing across the ceiling just as the seniors will swoop and swing over the dance floor. There'll be carnival balloons, fancy dance programs, and memory books. All we have to do is wait until the package arrives."

Did I sense a trace of anxiety in that last sentence?

After a deep-felt sigh, Alta added, "It was quite a trick to find an orchestra willing to risk Neah Bay roads in November. Cheree's clever dealings and pretty dimples did it, I guess."

"Why the Senior Ball in November, anyway?" I asked. "Seniors don't graduate until next June."

"No other time. December's out. Basketball tournaments begin in January. From then on it's full schedule till school's out." Alta shivered—reached for her sweater. "It's getting late. I must go."

"If you'll wait until I clear my desk, I'll walk home with you."

We pushed open the double-entry doors—walked into gray gloom and fog—watched skies over Neah Bay darken. I watched worry-lines darken over Alta's strained face.

Her voice—in whisper tones—betrayed her fears of doomsday . . . "We sent in the order for the decorations the last of September. I only hope they arrive in time."

~

SUSPENSE . . . ANXIETY . . . ANGUISH . . . WAITING . . . UNBEARABLE . . .

With excruciating speed, days leaped closer to the Senior Ball.

"No decorations came today either. Maybe tomorrow," Cheree agonized.

"This waiting gives me the jitters," said Rose Mary, lapsing into despair. "Days go by and nothing comes. What'll we do?"

To vanish fear-thoughts, girls chattered Senior-Ball talk. "Have you heard about Cheree's formal?" exclaimed Kitsy as she spooned cranberry preserves on Indian bread. "Her mother bought it at a boutique shop in Seattle." With her mouth full, Kitsy mumbled, "Nobody has seen it. It's a secret!"

"You guys always want to keep everything so secret," grumbled Genevieve. "I'm not even gonna go to that old Ball."

"Nobody asked you to," snapped Dolly. "You're not a senior anyway."

"So what!" snorted Genevieve. "I got no time!"

"I wonder what June will wear," Mary Lynn mused, reaching for a sponge to mop up spilled jam. "Gee, you're messy, Kitsy."

"June will look like a princess. She always does, no matter what," added Rose Mary.

∽

I recalled Jule Cragg's comment as we walked the crescent curve one day last spring: "These Indian girls step out of unpainted, fish-smoked, broken-down shacks looking like Cinderella at the Ball. I don't know how they do it. I've taught here five years, and they do it every time."

∽

Sixth period dismissal bell jerked my thoughts back to class. The girls scurried down the hall to their lockers and out the double-entry doors.

Before I could catch my breath, June's mother stood in the Home Ec doorway. "I'm so much excitement!" she chattered. What now, I wondered. Lucy was always "so much excitement" but I loved it! "My sister in Marysville sent money for June's formal—her graduation present."

June's Senior Ball formal: a vital mark in family history—a totem of Spirit Power—a portrayal of elegance—a tribute to an Indian princess . . . but all girls' formals were just as important to them . . .

"How wonderful! Tell me about it, unless it's a secret. Kitsy just made coffee—a new brand, YUBAN. I'm sure you'll like it."

"It's not a secret," beamed Lucy, savoring the new coffee brand. "We found a specialty shop in Bremerton. The formal is white. It sparkles with sequins, and it's beautiful!"

~

I remember the Senior Ball decorations DID NOT arrive when expected. Senior Home Ec classes fell apart. The whole building fell apart—collapsed—no one could think or walk in a straight line.

"It's the first of November."

"The decorations didn't come in today's mail either."

"What'll we do? We've only a week. We won't have time to decorate the Hall," wailed Cheree.

Anxiety attacks. Tormented days. Sleepless nights. Like stampeding horses on the Ocean Prairies, senior hearts stampeded in panic. Desperate, Alta clenched her fist, called for action: "Enough of this nonsense. Only a miracle can save us. And I have a source . . ."

When I wanted Storm Spirits chased away, I summoned a primitive Makah Medicine Man. When Alta wanted to divine the missing decorations, she summoned her Christian Science practitioner.

And sure as fate, bewitched arrows darted in every direction. The search was on . . . and by some *divining* the missing package was found . . . delayed in some midwestern warehouse.

"Can you believe such carelessness?" Alta sputtered. "I declare I never heard of such a thing." Twisting her hands in disbelief, she continued her incredible story: "Miraculously the package was rushed by plane non-stop to Seattle. Then it was trucked to Port Angeles. Of course, it had to be Saturday and no deliveries were coming up here."

Her bright eyes snapped. "Thought transference!" I guess. The truck driver left the package with the owner of the Shell gas station. Mr. Something-or-Other knew Teddy Choppensawh from Neah Bay was in town . . . but where?" Throwing up her hands, Alta exclaimed, "Magic! I declare it was magic! A flat tire brought Teddy to the station."

Alta leaned against the tapestry cushions of her couch. "This is the first time I've relaxed since we sent the order in. Everything magically materialized at the right time in the right place. Teddy brought the package back to Neah Bay and delivered it in my hands. Praise be! I was never so thankful in my life! You can have your old witch doctor. When I need miracle power, I'll call my own mystic helper!"

~

But over it all, hovered NOVEMBER–DARK AND DREAR AND DANGEROUS. How we watched the charcoal skies! What will the winds do? Blow foul or fair? Will frost-spirits ice roads and blow sleet and snow? Will storm-spirits block traffic with a rock slide or a sliding hillside?

In secret, I pleaded with my old Medicine Man: Magic Spirit, cast a heavy spell to bring us a night of unclouded skies for the Senior Ball.

And sure as fate . . . he did! As slick as you please. Not a cloud in sight. Only sparkles in the black–diamonds, stars, flashy jewels.

~

C-R-E-E-P-Y crawly, the pace of the days changed.

New haircuts for the boys! New hair styles for girls! Mysterious packages arrived by special delivery from Seattle or Bremerton. Last-minute shoppers to Port Angeles zipped around road curves: Ray's necktie was the wrong color. Kitsy's slippers were a size too large. Lucy rushed in for new dancing sandals for June. (But I knew kids danced in stocking feet!)

Seniors sparkled in their own galaxy: ALL STARS.

Tension smoldered and rumbled through halls. Air crackled and snapped. And now, at last . . . TONIGHT! A night erupting into a rhapsody of color, music, dances, and wild enthusiasm.

~

At the Senior Ball, before I reached the door of the Community Hall, I was grabbed: "Shut your eyes," ordered Simon. "Don't look till I tell you." Pitch black . . . I stubbed my toe on a rock, but Simon caught me, guided me up the steps into the Hall. "NOW!" he exclaimed.

I stared. Streamers wavered and fluttered down the walls and across the ceiling. Shimmering purples, luminescent blues, vibrant Venetian reds . . . the streamers transformed the Hall into a multi-color splash–like sunsets over the Danube.

So too were the boys transformed. No crumpled, rumpled jeans and T-shirts tonight. No rhinoceroses' wild roars as when fingers struck the wrong guide key in typing class. Champ–Jack–Ray–looked sharp in dark suits. Curt–Lester–Kelly–smooth and suave in pale blue jackets.

Exhilarated, radiant, beaming happiness. Girls with their dates moved toward the musicians' platform. Cheree's gown, no longer a secret, enfolded her in a glow of flaxen yellow. Gold sequins sprinkled down the skirt glistened with every step. In contrasting shades of pink, Mary Lynn bloomed in a gown of wispy chiffon . . . tucked in her long black hair, a tiny rosebud corsage.

"Oh, look!" I exclaimed to Alta standing beside me. "June's formal is white . . . it sparkles . . . it's beautiful . . . just like Lucy described." June's royal beauty glittered in shimmering white taffeta with sequin bodice . . . a princess!

Among the dazzles—the sequins—the shimmers—I spotted Kitsy, vivacious in a gown of atomic blue satin—her rhinestone earrings and silver-lace scarf added startling accents. Mary Lynn swished in changeable shades of luminous green taffeta. Contrasting shades of green ribbons held a wrist corsage in place.

"The Seniors gave me this dainty orchid corsage," Alta beamed. She sparkled too. A new dress of pale peach-colored crepe and crystal earrings and necklace enhanced her pleasure and pride as Senior Class adviser. "The girls DO look lovely. It's their BIG NIGHT. Oh my!" Alta exclaimed. "Look what's coming. Lorna's tricked out in bright red!"

"Lorna's in bloom too," I laughed, "like a blossom from an Indian Paintbrush." Looking around the ballroom, sprinkled like Ocean Prairie violets and wild roses, other pretty maids waited for the first beat of drums. They all waited. Waiting bore an allusion of mystery. Suspense. Tension began to build—ready to burst—then erupted into claps and shouts as the band leader signaled players to the platform. Musicians tuned instruments, shifted sheet music. Fingers of the organist tripped over the keys and dancers moved to choose partners.

"Isn't the band leader handsome?" whispered Cheree.

"I'm just as handsome," smirked Lester.

"He looks too old for me," sighed Mary Lynn.

"Look! They're getting ready to play."

Lifting his baton, the band master swept his players into a snazzy rhythmic beat that rolled like syncopated thunder. Drums tattooed a razzmatazz boogie woogie tribute to Seniors. Class president, Tom, whirled Annabelle into the swift catchy steps of the jitterbug.

Fascinated, I watched Ernie spin Daphne into whips and turns. Scott and Dolly kicked and rolled in full swing. Happy and breathless, Champ and Kitsy bounced and beboped in lively breaks.

Jitterbug dancers of today have been described as " . . . tribes of youth spinning and turning and burning with that snazzy beat . . ." And we lived it that night. When a trombonist slid into Glenn Miller's *Chattanooga Choo Choo*, the kids' whizzing feet all but disappeared. Only the deep-velvet voice of the organ echoing *Moonlight Serenade* tamed their wild-panting pace.

At intermission, Clare, a new teacher, asked, "How did they ever get an organ past those twisting curves?"

"Magic!" Alta smiled whimsically. "Just magic!"

Magic was everywhere . . . over the Carnival of Venice . . . over the skies of Neah Bay . . . over the Seniors . . .

Seniors led classmates in vigorous whirls and turns until lights dimmed at midnight. Tom—leading—formed dancers into single file for the last dance of the night: THE BUNNY HOP.

Hop to the right—hop to the left
Jump forward—jump backwards
Three jumps forward—quick, quick, quick
Thump. Bump.
Hop. Hop. Hop.
The thumping shuffle of *The Bunny Hop* stomped in my head all night!

 Today we talked about a common variety of herbs:
. . . sage and bay leaf—used to flavor soups, meats, casseroles
. . . cloves and cinnamon—used in pies, cakes, cookies

At the mention of licorice, Daphne piped up, "Oh we know about licorice. We buy it at Washburn's Store."

"That's right, Daphne. Licorice flavors candy. It is also an important ingredient in cough syrups and cough drops," I added.

A colorful chart pictured herbs as derived from roots, plants, leaves, tree barks—even flowers and seeds. "Herbs coming from natural sources must be processed before they can flavor or season foods," I explained.

"You all know about onions." In my hand I held a garlic bulb. "This onion-like bulb is GARLIC. Garlic is added to soups and other foods. It's known to have powerful healing qualities. In fact, herbalists claim garlic as the herb with *miracle healing powers*."

"Now I know what you're talking about," interrupted Annabelle. "My grandfather's eye was hurt in a firecracker explosion. He ran out in the woods and dug up something. I don't know what it was, but it saved his eye from blindness."

Annabelle's story reminded Daphne of another story. "My mother knew an old Indian who understood roots and herbs to cure every disease—even cancer. He's dead now—and she doesn't remember anything he told her."

"There's a village family that knows secret herbal combinations to prepare the mother for birth—during birth—and after birth," contributed Elizabeth.

"No one else knows how to make these combinations," added Cheree. "They won't tell anybody else—just keep it secret within the family." Cheree paused. "My grandmother knows a lot about healing herbs and things. Once I had a bad sore on my arm. Ada made a poultice out of some leaves that healed it."

"We've all heard of village elders who wear a bag of dried rose hips and secret things around their necks. They believe these prevent sickness and protect them from evil spirits," added Rose Mary.

"We all remember Natah's telling us about an old Indian woman. She came down with pneumonia. Someone fried onions—tons and tons of onions—put them in a cloth—put it on her chest—and she got well." Becky, remembering, enhanced the power of healing herbs.

Once Helen Peterson confided: "The white doctor's medicine doesn't heal my cough or make me feel better. I'm going to make some Indian tea and drink that instead."

. . . not recorded . . . many secret formulas will never be known . . . long lost . . . long forgotten . . . long buried . . .

 Puzzled—bewildered by algebraic symbols—Sara sat aloof. Disappointed—defeated—Alta cried in despair: "What can I do with this child? She just sits—shy, timid, withdrawn." Barricades set by language differences—answered Alta's distress: "I just learned from Ruth that Sara is being raised by her old Makah grandmother—who understands English—but refuses to speak it. I'm afraid Sara's one of those I can't do very much with."

As little Indian girls learned long ago—Sara sits quietly, listens, watches—but doesn't do. In most of her classes, there is no response—no participation—no interest—only rejection of the system. Forced against her will into the white man's school, Sara enters a dream-world of her own.

. . . drenched in old Indian ways—Sara escaped complete assimilation.

. . . did she also escape the elementary grades and junior high?

. . . did Sara's age place her in high school?

Sara's family bitter—resentful—still resists the white man—leaving Sara lost—frightened—to question:

WHY AM I HERE?

WHAT CAN YOU DO FOR ME?

In Freshman English, Sara just sits and giggles with Josie and Genevieve. In Home Ec—hesitant—Sara follows instructions—if coaxed. I coax.

Language difficulties are rare in high school. Most Indian students speak fluent English. The *bilingually disadvantaged* are still among us though. Champ once confided, "I spoke Makah until I was six years old."

⁓

SPEECH CLASS
HEAR YE! HEAR YE!
ATTENTION HIGH SCHOOL STUDENTS
EXCITING NEWS!
JOIN A SPEECH CLASS
MASTER THE ENGLISH LANGUAGE
LEARN WORD SKILLS
IMPROVE VOCABULARY
SPEAK WITH CONFIDENCE
WRITE A SPEECH
BE FIRST TO SIGN UP (ROOM 210)
SIGN UP TODAY

⁓

Elizabeth stepped forth each morning—from her Makah home—leaving the old culture behind. When she pushed through the double-entry doors of the school building, she stepped forth into the white world—the new culture.

Juxtaposed to Sara, Elizabeth was shy, timid, withdrawn also. But Elizabeth's willingness, her eagerness, set her apart from Sara. Elizabeth possessed an intellectual curiosity—an urgent need to learn from the white teachers.

A strong, patient girl, Elizabeth aspired—with an ardent desire—to adventures off the Reservation. Attracted—persuaded—to join Thomas B's Speech Class, Elizabeth enrolled. Here, she dropped her shyness, her timidity—

withdrawn no longer. She stepped forth from class self-confident—determined—*a self-sufficient unit of purpose.*

Conquest of self placed Elizabeth as valedictorian of her graduating class. Courageous, self-assured, she gave the valedictory, graduation speech.

Awarded the DAR Citizenship trophy and pin, Elizabeth stepped forth from the platform to conquer her new world—the white world.

 Dinner ready. But no Zettah.

At last—a knock.

I opened the door.

THERE STOOD THAT MAN! MARRS HENRY!

. . . the man who shouted: "Never trust a white man . . ."

. . . the man behind: "Kick out all white teachers—hire Indian teachers."

. . . the man who terrified me . . .

Zettah cowered beside him.

I didn't gasp. I didn't scream. I didn't faint. I left my body! A Spirit Power took over.

From somewhere, I heard myself joyously exclaim: "OH HELLO, MR. HENRY! How wonderful to see you. Please come in. Let me take your hat and coat. Please sit down. Dinner is all ready. It's so nice to see you. It's so nice of you to come." So overwhelmed by his presence, I forgot Zettah.

. . . but in a quick flashback, she materialized. Yesterday—Zettah—our coffee chat—"Marrs will be out of town until Sunday," she said. I invited her for dinner. "We'll go to the school band concert together . . ."

Marrs' surprise attack changed all that! What was he doing here? Why had he come?

DINNER! I must serve dinner.

I rushed around—invited them to be seated. Mr. Henry—a big man—squeezed in between the small kitchen table and the cupboards—barely fit. Where did I fit in this cataclysm? Did I too barely fit?

Nerves on edge—raw and frazzled—I chattered incessantly—fear I'd make a Makah social blunder—fear I'd inadvertently insult him—fear I'd make a devastating impression—fear he'd send me to the chopping block.

In silence, they ate—finished their dinner—left the table—put on their wraps—thanked me (I guess. I don't remember.)—walked out the door toward the school.

I wished to faint dead away—but didn't have time—scurried around—

flung a jacket over my shoulders—dashed out the door to attend the band concert.

Still in shock—still feeling torn to bits—shell ravaged—still wanting to hide a dark secret—I told no one but Lucy. "Why on earth did Marrs Henry show up uninvited—unexpected? I nearly died."

Lucy's reply: "He just wanted to find out what was going on. Knowing him and all that goes on in the village, I'm sure he expected to find men and booze. He'd never trust a white woman—not even a teacher."

Marrs Henry would never trust a white man either.

Thinking back to my first year—to Jule's gossip stories of immoral behavior and drunkenness. Were all those tales true?

. . . and did Marrs Henry really believe I was one of those *riffraff women?*

. . . did he think of ME as just another immoral white woman? In his mind *immoral*—until proven otherwise?

. . . Lucy once said, "Corrupt—immoral—drunken—*riffraff* women . . . and they think *we* Indian women should look up to *them!*"

Ada came for dinner.

Valentine's Day: hearts and flowers—ribbons and lace—adorned the table. Delighted—Ada clapped her hands: "Before white man—no Valentine Day!"

I behold Ada in distinguished wonder: a Makah matriarch—a tribal potentate—a sovereign power—a spirit messenger from a great Indian nation.

Family members held positions on the Tribal Council—were leaders in village affairs—prominent in church activities—arrogantly proud of family name and heritage.

When we are together, Ada creates a state of mystery—excitement—as from unseen sources? I never know. Her stories always amaze me.

Today's theme began with a startling comment: "In WWII we fear Japan bomb Neah Bay. We cover windows with black cloth—everybody thought Japan strike through Neah Bay." I shuddered—Neah Bay too close to Tacoma. "Once, Japanese uniform found on breakwater—Indians sight submarines from Cape Flattery—subs all around Neah Bay. They tell me cement pill-box—a lookout—on Cape Flattery—men look down on water—watch for submarines."

Ada jumped from submarines to Siam: "American missionary—once teacher in Siam—came to Neah Bay—teach Makah children. Teacher use yards and yards of my calico cloth—drape around children like Siamese." Ada chuckled, "I'll never forget that year! End of school—teacher and children in program for village."

I waited. What will Ada talk about next? She cleaned her glasses on the corner of her apron—nibbled on Valentine mints. "I tell about people come to Neah Bay—they ask about Makah culture. I tell about old ways . . . anthropologist pay me twenty-five cents an hour. Cheapskate that one—skinflint. For lecture—anthropologist get more than twenty-five cents—you bet!"

Did Ada's derogatory statement tell something? Reveal underlying resentment? Did she begrudge telling of the old way—of how the Makah lived before white man?

"I tell," Ada chuckled to cover any doubts. "White man take culture away—now want it back."

A scowl replaced Ada's chuckles: "I give headdress to anthropologist—with promise to give it back—now won't give it back—broke promise." Discouraged—she sighed. "It mine—it belong to me—got no right to keep head-dress—belong to family."

An ancient headdress! Left to deteriorate on an Indian Reservation? Oh, no! Safe in museum. Safe for posterity. So anthropologists clutch—grab—steal . . .

Ada regained her poise—but her heavy cheeks drooped. She dipped cookies in creamed and sugared after-dinner-coffee. Silent. Burdened over memories. "I tell about smallpox epidemic. Hundreds of our people die—Medicine Man not stop it—made it worse—people just die and die—sick people sat in sweat baths—then jump in cold river. People cry and cry for dead ones—hardly anyone left—no one talk about it anymore."

Ada backed away from fear of Japanese bombs, teacher from Siam, lost headdress, smallpox epidemic to the eleven-million-dollar inheritance.

FACT? FANTASY?

Since coming to Neah Bay—by a word here—a sentence there—I learned of the inheritance. Myth? Vision? Reality? Like a spirit-promise, it threaded through the village—created rifts among friends—clashes of opinions—hostilities—mind-boggling tensions.

WHO WAS ELIGIBLE? WHO WAS NOT?

Tribal Council members disappeared on mysterious out-of-state meetings. To verify inheritors? Or just to talk?

. . . AND THIS FROM ADA: "That hurted me," she despaired. "I may not be one . . ."

Ada's despair pointed to the legal distribution of the inheritance (a government settlement). Makah ancestry must be established—traced back four or five generations—to the signing of the 1855 Treaty of Neah Bay.

I listened to Ada—pieced fragments together—asked no questions. Like a spirit voice, the fragments spoke an irrevocable message: direct blood lineage must be proved. No adoption acceptable.

Why Ada's despair? What's wrong? Is something missing? Direct blood line?

What a bombarding blow! Inheritance denied! Ada and her family?

Ada's origin? Hidden in some secret recess? On Vancouver Island? In mysterious Alaska? Only a guess. I didn't ask.

Ada: Makah by adoption? Ada's husband too?

Dispirited, Ada inferred: "They (we) cannot sue the Government—it is the final authority."

. . . AND THIS FROM JULE: "Ada's family left out of the inheritance? One of the Tribe's ruling families! No proof of direct lineage? That's discrimination!" she jested. "But no one can change blood lines." Not even a Spirit Guide or Medicine Man, I thought.

"Hatred, envy, jealousy, bitterness flares as it is in this village," Jule interjected on our way home from school. "The *would-be-upper-class* who have sailed so high and mighty could stub toes and fall flat on their faces. Some tribal families are deliberately scorned and snubbed—consider *lower-type-Makah*—but *they* can prove their ancestry."

Cynical Jule: "I expect the big fuss will just fizzle out and never amount to anything."

. . . AND THIS FROM A SCHOOL GIRL—vented hostility toward a tribal classmate: "There she sits—just as dumb as ever." Implying *her* family's included, while *I'm* not.

. . . AND THIS FROM MINNIE: "The Tribe's now split into two factions—one group or the other has strong followers that thwart and hinder opposition wherever possible. All the trouble is over the inheritance—who's eligible—who's not.

"Once my Cub Scouts were so humiliated and hurt. I'd been promised my Cubs could serve the food, and then the privilege was grabbed away from them. I was furious—the boys lost honor points. It's always *THAT specific faction—lower-type-Makah*—that does nothing but cause trouble."

Minnie fumed in contempt. "You'd never believe the confusion—conflicts—rudeness—they created. It was deliberate interference—and ruined the whole affair for me and my Cubs." In scurrilous remark: "This type will get the inheritance—if anyone ever does!"

~

. . . and then, back to dinner with Ada. She gave the mystical blessing of food—a dinner prayer from the Shaker belief.

How I love to hear Makah! Harsh. Guttural. The power and expression of the ancient language is extolled in the songs of praise. A source of the spiritual, Ada contained within herself a mysterious wisdom—inner meanings to dawn-time prayers.

~

After Ada's outpourings—after subsequent eye-openers—I pulled down the shades and gave into reflections:

     . . . not aware of a rift in the Tribe
     . . . not aware of the vicious accusations—the feelings of hatred, jealousy, envy, bitterness
     . . . too busy to give credence to negatives, rumors, gossip
     . . . no time to bother about who was *higher-type*, who was *lower-type*—didn't know the difference—they were all my friends and I loved being with them

"Scoop!" shouted Jacqui—as she rushed into Journalism Class. "It's MY story. I've got all the five W's." Bright-blue eyes flashed behind thick lenses. Her long body folded into the nearest typing chair. She cracked her gum—clipped a pencil to the pocket of her blue plaid jacket—opened her notebook—whirled to the typewriter. Fingers clacked on keys. Through lips tight and smug, Jacqui tantalized: "WHO?—foreign students from the University of Washington. WHEN?—next week—Thursday—March 22—one o'clock. WHERE?—Neah Bay High School. WHY?—to tour our by-racial school and community."

"That's only four W's," smirked Lester. "You haven't answered WHAT?"

Jacqui's fingers arched above the keys. "Oh, yes. WHAT?" Puckering her lips, she grabbed her notebook, licked fingers, flipped pages. "Here it is: WHAT? What we're going to do." Sticking gum behind her ear, Jacqui announced, "At six-thirty, we all go to the Community Hall for a huge

Salmon feast, speeches, tribal songs and dances."

"How come you're so smart? How come you know so much? Where'd you get all this?" demanded Ernie.

Flinging her long blonde hair to one side, Jacqui turned to face him. "I stopped in the office. Mr. Perkins told me. He'd just heard about it. Here's my late slip."

"Good work, Jacqui," I praised. "You're a sharp reporter—on the spot at the right time to get the news first." I thrust the late slip on the spindle. "Your story's worth a by-line, Jacqui. Type it up as a feature article for Friday's *Chieftain*. Then do a follow-up for the next issue."

"Five of the athletic team won't be here," chirped Rose Mary. "The basketball coach is taking them to P.A. to an athletic banquet. I'm typing the article up now."

"We'll have more fun with the foreign students without them," said Annabelle.

A loud—scurrilous—"BOO! BOO! BOO!" from the Neah Bay Champions.

~

Excitement exploded down hallways—disrupted classes—burst out the double-entry doors into the village. A village perched on the tip of Cape Flattery—far, far from foreign shores—never invaded by Foreign Students.

"Shake, rattle, and roll," blurted Lester. "This place is falling apart. You'd think the Prince of Mars was coming to town. And the girls—the crazy girls!" Lester's lips twisted in disgust. "All they can think about is eloping to some island or sitting on top of the Sphinx or riding a camel across the Sahara. I'm glad I'll be in P.A."

"You said it!" snorted Stuart. "These dumb dames walk around with their noses stuck up in the air. They don't even see where they're going. I saw Cheree bump into Perkins and didn't even know it. What a silly dame."

"You're just jealous," Cheree snapped back. "I'm going to elope with an Arabian sheik and race a black stallion across hot burning sands."

Dreamy-eyed Mary Lynn tilted her head—musing—her thoughts drifted to a faraway place: "AFRICA!—deepest, darkest Africa! I want to paddle down the Zambezi at sunset. I want to watch snakes wiggle and twist down the river—and crocodiles with monstrous jaws snatch at us."

The bell shrilled. Mary Lynn called to Annabelle—turned to me: "Last year our history teacher showed pictures of Africa. He'd been there." She shivered deliciously.

~

"Have you heard?" Becky's black eyes glistened. "Natah's bringing out an ancient family mask—never seen in public before—one of those with strings and things and eyes that pop out!"

"I've seen masks like that. They're scary," chimed in Daphne. "My family has an old, old Thunderbird mask—with spooky eyes. The mask will be on display."

"My Aunty Helen is mending an old, old dance costume worn by her Nit-Nat cousin from Vancouver Island," volunteered Marie. "Our family will have some old whaling equipment out for the foreign students to see."

"Every night village dancers practice," joined in Elizabeth. "They wear costumes and masks hidden away for years."

Quiet, shy Sara spoke up, "The Makah Club is doing the dinner. The women are getting the sticks ready for the Salmon Bake. My dad goes out every day for fish. He's getting some for the dinner."

"Gotta have Indian bread," piped up Genevieve.

One thought dominated the scene: to honor students from alien lands with the most exotic, spectacular, extravagant, lavish festival since the old potlatch days.

~

Wednesday after school: SHE (Rega Buckthorn) butted in to order all teachers to bring a cake. FURIOUS! All of us! Especially me! Too excited and too busy to bother with a cake, I searched for a way out.

Thursday morning: Jane baked my cake and Deena frosted it.

"The Makah Club is in charge of the dinner," Deena, disgruntled, mumbled under her breath. "There's always someone who tries to take over. There's plenty of village women with nothing to do. They could have baked the cakes. But somehow Mrs. Buckthorn seems to be running it." Deena lifted her voice to remind me, "We'll pick you up at six. Don't forget."

I wouldn't forget. I remembered when nobody picked me up. I walked. "THAT WITCH . . . SHE'LL NEVER LAST UP HERE!"

~

While the girls romanticized and fantasized, the boys mimicked and ridiculed. But at last, their ecstasies and frenzies peaked. THE DAY found principal and teachers, boys and girls, in the Assembly Hall. Sheer effervescent energy bubbled to bursting. Only the calm presence of Mr. Perkins crushed the desire to jump up and down in joyous expectations. Controlled—the kids waited.

My role in this historical scenario demanded: FOOD! We, the Home Management class and I too waited. (A signal from the Principal would direct us.)

Minute by minute time ticked away. One o'clock. Two o'clock. No one in sight from strange, mysterious, distant lands.

School kids on edge, squirmed. Impatient, restless, wondering. WHERE WERE THE FOREIGN STUDENTS?

Cheree's tension erupted: "If they don't get here pretty soon, I'll never get to ride across the Sahara!"

Her erratic outburst released whooping, boisterous laughter. "You may never even see an Arab," Rose Mary squinted at the time. "Three o'clock! I don't believe it! Hey, someone's coming!"

One by one—in straggled the tour group—bedraggled and tired.

The signal: dismissed class—alerted me to coffee time. Genevieve and Lorna chose to stay and help. To my joy, Lissa, though graduated, returned to be part of the action.

"Oh, Lissa! I'm so glad you're here!" She turned the Home Ec kitchen into a theater of high activity. Quick and speedy, the girls raced to turn on ovens, slice frozen apple and cranberry tea breads, set out lemon-frosted cookies, heat water for coffee, assemble cups, spoons, napkins. "Don't forget sugar and cream," dictated bossy Genevieve. "Don't we got no Indian bread?"

Lissa probed in the freezer. "Here's some. Pop it in the oven, Gen."

Heated and buttered, the Indian bread and tea breads were lusciously arranged on serving trays. Plates of lemon-frosted cookies would tempt tour-weary guests.

Assembly-hall speeches yielded to the fragrances of coffee and hot breads. With the District Superintendent pouring strong hot coffee—with the girls serving delectable treats—the tempo lifted to festival time.

Lissa sparkled. Lorna beamed. Genevieve perked up. Grumble and complain they sometimes did, but in an emergency they never let me down.

"The foreign students liked our treats," Lissa smiled. "They kept thanking me over and over."

"Yah," grouched Genevieve, "one guy ate five pieces of cranberry bread. He'd never eaten it before," she grinned, setting the tray on a shelf. "Another guy asked if the Indian bread was a biscuit."

"A really cute guy from Turkey—his hair was so black and his teeth so white when he smiled," described Lorna. "I couldn't understand him very well. He said something about Turkish coffee was different—sweet and thick."

The ticking clock demanded respite—time for all to disband—to meet again for the Salmon feast—for the traditional Makah program of dances and songs.

Before Lissa left, she reminded me that her family would come for me at six o'clock.

Before I left, I found Ruth and Art and invited them to coffee. Grateful and pleased to be remembered—they relished the snacks.

～

A classy, bright, new Buick brought Deena and her family to my gate. For me, this moment was a sign—strong as steel—a sign that I had made it. I surmounted the prophetic "THAT WITCH . . . WHERE'D THEY GET HER? . . . SHE'LL NEVER LAST UP HERE!"

Members of a ruling Makah family had honored me with their gift of acceptance. Lifted into a realm of belonging, I happily joined the distinguished and talented family.

After greetings, Lissa took my cake. Then—click! "Oh, I forgot my dish and cup!" With her usual humor, Deena answered, "Never mind. I'll get them at the Hall."

Entering the Community Hall, I sensed the same vitality of spirit—the same energy peculiar to village gatherings. But tonight the intensity was heightened—charged by a distinctive vibration. In my mind, the air sizzled and crackled with unspoken words and emotions. I stood in the midst of a stirring awareness of nations—a mighty mingling of divergent races and cultures. Tonight—we were American Indian and white. Our guests were Chinese, Japanese, Iranian, German, Korean, Russian, Peruvian, and Syrian. Students from India and Saudi Arabia wore native dress.

Over the diversity of sounds—drum beats, squeals and squeaks from children, laughter and shouts, muffled conversations—a warm, friendly sensation hovered. The Great Spirit spoke to us all.

While Deena took the cake to the kitchen and picked up a dish and cup, Mrs. Norris (a village lady) whispered to me, "You are to come sit with the teachers." And like a child, I questioned, "Do I have to?"

Of course I had to! Just a formality? Just an obligation? PROTOCOL!

Forced to accept a hopeless decision, I faced Deena. "I'm so disappointed.

It wasn't my idea, believe me!" This left Deena alone. Luke, her husband, had been invited to sit at the head table. Deena playfully exclaimed, "I'm going to get mad and go home!"

"I'm mad too," I said. "I'll be with you for the dances." And so I joined Alta and her revolting perfume.

⁓

Lissa's Uncle Murakko stood as master-of-ceremonies. He carried the same Makah charm that marked all his family. With ease—with eloquence— he would narrate the evening's recital of events.

To quiet the whir of voices, Murakko raised his arms—a signal for Reverend Dale-Smith to offer the Christian dinner blessing.

Chanted in Makah, the ancient welcome song and feast prayer followed. Once again the mystical essence of the chant—in a harsh, guttural tongue—the drum beat background—enlivened my primitive instincts.

"WE ARE A PROUD PEOPLE . . ." In this way Murakko began his welcome to guests and foreign students. "The Makah custom to greet guests with song and feast food began hundreds of years ago—and is still the tradition of our Tribe. Our feast-food is Salmon (gift from the mythical Salmon People). The fish is tied on sticks stuck in the ground and baked around an outdoor fire, the old way."

Murakko lifted his arms in praise: "We give thanks to our Great Spirit for his abundant supply of Salmon. We hope you enjoy our food."

The ritual of food observed—my formalities resigned—my obligations satisfied—the way opened for ceremonial dances: Front row—ME!—an old, old Indian woman sat to my left—Deena joined me on my right. I was happy. Just where I wanted to be!

"Our ceremonial dances begin with the Thunderbird Dance." Murakko gave a brief interpretation—in story and symbolism—of each dance. What did this mean? Did this interest those with different ethnic backgrounds? Those with their own stories and dances?

The old, old Indian woman uttered comments now and then. Her uncertain English often puzzled me—but I did attempt to respond.

During the Paddle Dance, she murmured a soft melody. "Your song has a lovely tune," I complimented.

"Song—Paddle Dance—not belong to the Tribe . . . steal . . ."

Did she mean the song was stolen—copied—from another tribe or person?

"They're touchy about their songs," I had heard Deena remark. "Given by guardian spirit or in a dream, songs are sacred—belong only to person or tribe that received."

Champ danced the Medicine Man Dance with Levi Swan. The majestic rhythmic strength and energy of this dance expressed race vitality. Every stomp, lunge, thump, and lurch exerted spirit power.

A toying smile from Champ delighted me. Then, with a twist and a whirl, he was gone.

The thunder-beat of war drums rumbled an alarm. With high-stepping staccato leaps and screeching war cries, Cub Scouts lurched into an old Makah War Dance. Garbed in war gear—dabbed with black and red war paint—the young dancers created an illusion: ferocious little Indians on the war path.

Then, with a shriek and a lunge—with a twist and turn—the warrior Cubs whirled out of sight.

"Our program concludes by honoring each guest with a souvenir-gift. Beginning with the old potlatch days, this has been Makah custom," Murakko explained.

"Look! The Cubs are giving the gifts," Deena noticed. Each Foreign Student received a token of a cultural craft—olive shell necklaces and bracelets—small carving pieces—canoes, bowls, totem poles—tiny cedar baskets.

A change of focus began with the tour-conductor. He identified each student by name, country, university, and degree major.

"Among the group," he began, "are students willing to present songs and dances native to their lands. Umeko from Japan will sing. She accompanies her songs on the Samisen—a three-stringed banjo-like authentic Japanese musical instrument."

Exquisitely petite—her jet-black hair styled in Japanese coiffure—Umeko stepped out. With Oriental charm, she curtsied. Deena whispered, "Her blue dress looks like silk brocade." My attention glued to this elegant young lady, I barely breathed, "She's like porcelain—delicate—flower-like."

Through Umeko we touched Japan tonight—hidden messages in her songs carried us to the land of cherry blossoms.

Next, the trilling call of the high-pitched yodel—the answer from the trumpet-toned alpenhorn preceded Fraulein Wilhelmina—a music major from Switzerland.

In a clear, concise voice, she spoke: "Our yodel and long wooden alpenhorn are used as signals of communication—ways the Swiss mountaineers send messages of joy, sorrow, disaster, and calls for help and warnings. Tonight we are taking you from Neah Bay to Switzerland—to the grassy slopes and green valleys of the Alps—high snowy peaks rise to meet the dark-blue sky. We feel the bright sun and soft mountain wind. We gather in a meadow, fragrant with mountain flowers, sweet-smelling prunella, delicate red primroses, golden heads of cistus. There are blue bells and yellow buttercups. In this fantasy meadow, our group will join hands and skip into the rhythm of an Alpine folk dance."

Atop the blond heads of the boys perched sassy little green hats—a single feather marked the tradition. Snazzy black leather breeches—red plaid shirts—homespun leggings up to the knees—heavy hiking boots—made up the outfits of the young mountaineers.

Golden curls of the girls bounced to the rhythmic steps of the dance. Dirndl skirts swirled showing bare knees above white leggings. "I wonder if the dirndl skirts are hand-woven?" Deena questioned. ". . . and the bodices?"

"Look at the brilliant embroidery on the black velvet bodices!" I interrupted. "I love the bright stitchery on the sleeves of the white peasant blouses. I'd like one myself!"

Then with a rush—like an Alpine wind—we were back in Neah Bay—on scene with German students. In native dress—reflecting the Swiss style—the folk dancers of Teutonic origin delighted us with lively stirring steps and songs of their homeland. Joining arms in a round of whirls, they moved off scene singing *Auf Wiedersehen.*

In the dress of the ancient Incas, two Peruvian Indian students fascinated the guests with the unique hand and foot actions of the primitive dance. Then with a twist and a whirl, they were gone.

And—just like that—with a twist and a whirl—the evening was gone.

All at once it was time to leave—time to say good-bye—time to wish our foreign friends success, good fortune, and happy landing back in their homelands.

~

Then, an intermingling of races and cultures began. A high spiritual feeling of friendship—of understanding—of a mighty awakening. Above all—as from some great sign—we stood in a ceremonial gesture of good-bye. The Indians started a "hand sign." Their bodies swayed in rhythm to drum beats and chants. My obsession with this moment broke—when the old, old Indian woman whispered, "Come, come. You too." Always a beholder—a watcher—this unnerved me, surprised me. I felt awkward—self-conscious—but pleased to be included. So, I laughed and tried to follow her hand signs, her rhythmic sway, her chant.

Deep within us, an awareness of a great vibrant energy evolved. A great universal power was moving in waves through the atmosphere—melting negatives—prejudices—differences. I was swept up in this power movement with the Indians. I was responding to them—they were responding to me. As in the heart of Earth-Mother, I felt the powerful, vibrating waves like beams of light striking, penetrating, disintegrating the walls that encompassed my isolated self.

Bursting now into the marches of race and culture, I was one with the Earth—the Universe. I could feel all of life flowing through me—and yet I was part of that life: Yesterday. Today. Tomorrow. A part of all that ever was and is. "I" was the chant—the dance—the language—drum beat—laughter—living—dying. "I" was Makah—Chinese—Iranian—Israeli—Russian—German—grasping the oneness with life—meeting the call of the spirit in the cosmic vastness of their cultures. This was a moment of inspired, glorified KNOWING. I stood alone—feeling that nowhere in all the world was anything like this happening to anyone BUT ME!

Reality suddenly flashed around me. The flashes came from cameras. Students were taking pictures. Then pandemonium smote! The Neah Bay kids rushed into an excited phase of wildness—quite wonderful to experience! Hugs and shake of hands—smiles and praises.

All feeling: "We are one with you. We have touched your Land. We will never forget you."

When the doors closed behind the foreign students, our kids turned prankster—their bantering—their teasing—broke down more barriers:

"Where are YOU from?"

"Oh, Mars!"

"Where are YOU from?"

"Oh, from a mountain behind Saturn!"

"Where are YOU from?"

"Oh, from the outer rim of Olympus!"

"Who are YOU?"

"Oh, a Banshee from Vishnu!"

~

All night, I Indian danced. I could not sleep. All night long events of the evening charged through my mind—like starbursts—like sunbursts—like firebursts. I could not quench the flames of excitement—of wonder—of being a part of the whole. Over and over—repeating and repeating—I thought of me: just a spot down here on earth. At that precise moment in this mighty universe had we all sensed the depth of cosmic spirituality I had sensed that night? I will never forget the power—the uplifting of spirit.

Pieces of the significance came later—and later was Friday morning. My stopping for coffee in the school kitchen roused excited exclamations from Deena. "You're in now!" Several times she repeated, *"You're in! You're in!"*

In what? My mind quizzed. How could I know what she was talking about? I didn't, but I listened. Like standing in a vacuum, Deena's words bounced meaninglessly around me. Then the words began to signify a scenario involving me. Apparently my standing beside that old, old Indian woman won high favor.

"That old, old Indian woman is Mrs. Ember from La Push," Deena told me. "When she invited you to join in—and you followed her ceremonial hand signs and chant—that was IT! She accepted you—honored you."

Deena continued to explain: "For someone like you to take part in such an occasion, places you *on high* or *within* or is a matter of being *accepted* by the Makah Nation. *You're in!*" Deena repeated.

During the morning, I felt SOMETHING I could not define. Something different in the Indian kids—in our greetings and passing each other in the hallways.

Will I, someday, learn the real significance of all this?

 Lunch with Helen!
An enlightened happening!
A cultural phenomenon!

Helen's little house faced the water. Like entering a spirit power lodge, a cultural climate exuded from walls—from floors—from driftwood pieces—from artifacts—from Helen's very presence: her quiet charm, her grace, her touch of humor.

Lost in this picturesque atmosphere, Indian drums and chants pervaded my consciousness. Wondering, I turned to Helen. She spoke with gentle sadness: "I play this record when I'm lonesome for my Nit-Nat cousins. They live on Vancouver Island. I haven't seen them for a long time."

Nit-Nat power songs. An indelible impression to put in my Medicine Bag. To Helen: "I love the songs of your Nit-Nat cousins. Thank you for playing the record. The chants carry a mystical tone—like spirit songs."

The Nit-Nat drums and chants had drifted away. Helen relaxed on the couch—leaned against the cushions—closed her eyes. "One day—long ago—I walked in the woods alone. I heard a song—my song—my spirit song—my song to give me strength and protection."

An enlightened happening!

I revered this moment. It spoke good medicine: trust—confidence. Not often would I hear an Indian reveal guardian spirit power. My own spirit reached out—to hear more—to ask questions. But I did not. Questions can offend.

"Come to the kitchen while I make our lunch," Helen invited. "I'm so happy you could come." She spoke in a gentle dream-like voice. "I wanted to share my first smelt with you—like we used to do with the First Salmon. It was our custom. My brother-in-law brought the smelt to me. They're fresh—just out of the sea."

Helen deftly cleaned the very small silvery fish—peeled and sliced potatoes to fry. She moved about her modest kitchen—took plates from the cupboard—set out knives and forks. "Long ago," she began, "Indians believed Salmon were people—Salmon People—who lived with their families in villages—like we do—but in villages down under the sea." Helen tossed salad greens in a bowl—set it on the table beside a platter of fruit. Smelt sputtered in oil—potatoes fried to a golden brown. Scents of coffee—stimulated. Crusty baked Indian bread—tempted.

"According to my great-grandmother, the First Salmon Ceremony . . ." but Helen broke her story with, "Lunch is ready!"

Unforgettable: the savory delicate flavor of smelt. A real treat: crispy potatoes. Helen's Indian bread: sorta tough and chewy. "It's supposed to be that way," Cheree had told me. I admired the woven cedar placemats—the oblong cedar bread basket.

After lunch, I timidly referred to the First Salmon Ceremony. "Oh, yes, I must finish the story." With a low giggle—her typical humor—Helen continued: "The First Salmon Ceremony honored the first Salmon caught in the spring run. The tribes held the ceremony to thank and praise the Salmon People for sending the fish. An elder always sang the Salmon Spirit Song—a gift or tribute to the Salmon People.

"The whole village celebrated. The fish was cut lengthwise—in the old way—spread open—tied on sticks—stuck in the ground—cooked around a big fire—like we still do. After everybody ate, the Indians threw the bones back into the sea. The people believed the bones drifted back to the Salmon's own village—there the spirits made the bones into more Salmon."

A cultural phenomenon!

The First Salmon Ceremony! The romantic story of an ancient tradition.

The importance of the Salmon People—the Indians' dependence on the fish for survival was overwhelming. Not only was Salmon "food" but a mysterious invisible life force. The Salmon People, endowed with a conscious spirit, answered the Elder's song of thanksgiving . . . the Salmon Spirit accepted the honor and praise of the First Salmon Ceremony by giving themselves as a gift to the Indians' survival.

 Neah Bay Community Hall—Conference Day—awesome—inspiring—exciting panorama of spirit power.

I FELT more than I heard or saw.

Magnificent Indian tribes of Washington State—came over mountains—waded through Scotch Broom patches—crossed rivers—to meet as one mighty force—to gather in a power-swoop of native interests.

Drums pounded out a welcome—called the Tribes together—opened the doors of the Community Hall.

Courageous reminders of their ancient lineage, they stood to save their cultural institutions:

    . . . to revive language and traditions

    . . . to maintain arts and crafts

    . . . to protect tribal histories and spiritual concepts

Did Spirit Presence of the Old Ones dominate the Conference? Speak through strong leaders?

I could believe power vibrations emanated from vigorous minds—from deep emotions. Powerful messages of renewed dignity and recognition exalted my feelings of empathy and understanding.

As Tribal members, they bond to keep their individual definition—their own Tribal identify. Yet, to survive, they knew their future depended on expansion into the white man's world.

Troubled by existing conditions, Conference leaders explored many aspects: health-care programs—housing projects—job training courses . . .

An elder—an old Chieftain I wondered—rose to speak. A fringed deer or elk skin jacket—decorated with many bright beads—hung from his sagging shoulders. Elk-teeth necklaces—attached bear claws—appeared to be part of his style of dress. Leaning against a younger man, his voice quavered, "Many old ones sick—need nursing-home care. They not care for themselves—family gone."

Silence filled the Hall—alerting all Tribal members to the needs of their elders.

After the old one spoke, a leader volunteered to investigate nursing-home care. Another leader offered to inquire about employment markets and educational opportunities off the Reservation.

A prominent Makah called for attention. "We must begin to establish our own schools and colleges. There is much interest in this area. It may take time, but it will come. I have a brother who teaches in Oregon."

~

Conference doors closed. Tribal members, Chieftains, Medicine Men, Elders—on the long way back home—felt empowered by native instincts—revived honor, pride, dignity.

    . . . for all Tribes—the Conference inspired native interests and created power-visions of progress

. . . for the Makah—the Conference opened the Spirit Gate to their own
power-visions of progress

. . . for Me—the Conference left a powerful aura: awesome—inspiring—
exciting—my own power-visions of progress

~

Today is Palm Sunday. After last night's sensation of awe and excitement, I need to stay home and think:

. . . think about the Tribal meeting—its impact—its power

. . . think about the Makah dinner and entertainment

. . . think about the spirit quest—a gift granted to me by Perry, the old
harpooner

. . . think about Mrs. Ellis' coming to see me—beautiful, outstanding Indian woman—but not Makah

. . . think about her confiding in me—her anguish—her frustration because she feels an *outsider*— "unless you are Makah, you are not accepted as an Indian."

. . . think about Lucy coming right after Mrs. Ellis

. . . think about the might of information Lucy passes on to me

. . . think about her knowledge—her understanding—her seeking—her
power

. . . think about her Indian performance last night—sensational—glorious—the costumes of fringed deer skin, decorated with strings of
olive shells and bright colorful beads

HOW LONG THE TIME—OF WAITING?

How many twists of warp and filling threads
to weave a fabric strong enough
to give me the courage to ask:
"Did you go in search of Spirit Power?"

To question—to ask
. . . one dared not . . .

To reach out into the sacred realm
to glimpse into the innermost
depths of Indian spirituality
. . . one dared not . . .

Could he tell? Did he know?
    I was shaking and scared?

He looked aghast
    struck with amazement!

"How dare she!"
    but she dared!

And then he burst
    into his vigorous robust laughter
    ". . . AND I ALWAYS GOT MY WHALE!"

Others crowded around
    and this moment now
    belongs to another time.

I want to know more about
    this Makah harpooner
    this hunter of the Whale

It's been a time of waiting
    since fall, 1954
    I may never know any more

But I talked with the old Makah harpooner
    before it was too late.

 "Out there in the North Pacific right now, riding the waves of the great Kuroshio Current, are hundreds of thousands of desirable floats just waiting to be driven ashore somewhere along West Coast beaches." . . . *from* "BEACHCOMBING FOR JAPANESE GLASS FLOATS" *by Amos L. Wood*

"I found one! I found one!" Jule shouted, running toward me. "It's like a sign." Tears spilled over her weathered cheeks as she hugged her emerald jewel—a great glass ball from the Orient.

~

Never will I forget the day of Jule's trek to the Ocean beaches.

That morning, after months of bitter inner struggle, she declared, "I've finally decided not to teach here next year. I can't believe it though. It's been eight years." With shaky fingers, Jule lifted her glasses—rubbed her eyes—glanced toward Baha'dah Point.

Salty breezes whiffed in from the Ocean—ruffled loose hair across Jule's weary face. "I'm hiking out to the beaches." A sadness echoed her words.

I watched Jule tread through the school-yard gate. She would walk the beaches, I knew, to review in solitary amazement her decision. Leaving Neah Bay brought emotional shock that only the strong wild sea could soothe. Here, she could release her ravaged feelings to stretches of sea and sand.

Ocean—calm today. But yesterday—keening winds thrust white sea-towers fifteen feet high, purging the shore. I visualized in-rushing breakers that strewed hunks of lumber, broken orange crates, a bottle, a battered canoe, a cracked oar, and a mysterious glass ball.

Vibrant, glorious—this iridescent ball now glistened in Jule's arms.

In my own secret ecstasy, I fantasized a myth:

Who kissed the blue-green circle of glass to bring good luck to a fishing youth from Japan? A maiden—dainty—exquisite—flower-like—with almond eyes—and ivory cheeks? Did she whisper, "I will wait?" Did tears glint on black lashes?

After that kiss—after that tearful goodbye—the circle of glass traveled the seascape—ensnared in nets. But mystic fingers of sea spirits ripped the threads

to free the emerald ball. Spirit fingers pushed it into the warm, dark waters of Kuroshio—the Black Stream from Japan. Powerful currents and rogue waves charted the wander-ball easterly into the North Pacific Drift—to Makah shores— hurled it into tangled masses of storm wrack—bark and seaweed, broken branches, sea grasses. It waited—waited—for Jule—in its blue-green splendor.

I remember how she had longed to possess one of the great over-sized glass balls. Plentiful in Neah Bay, they hung in nets from ceilings, shone on window sills, clustered in garden patches, squatted on porch steps, and sparkled on gift-shop shelves.

But Jule must find her own. Over the years, she had scoured sand strips—dug into sea grasses beyond the drift—probed behind log banks. Searching. Waiting.

Now—at last—her gift.

A sign: PEACE FROM THE SEA.

Once again I sipped after-school coffee in Cerena's fourth-grade room. Windows warmed by April's sun were also streaked by April's rain.

I watched Cerena deftly set the coffee urn back on the hot plate—and thought: a woman in her forties with a rare fineness—a spiritual quality— an ethereal beauty—detaches her . . . then a bomb hit!

"Brad and I have decided to adopt a seven-year-old Makah boy."

My fingers tightened around the hand-painted, blue-violet cup. "You have!"

"Nathan Cederberry—a handsome, bright, little boy—charming and lovable," Cerena beamed.

Just then, her husband called from the hall, "Are you ready? Better make it home before it pours."

"Come in, Brad," Cerena invited. "I was telling Arlyn about Nathan."

A seriousness reflected in his face. Propping himself against a drawing table, Brad confirmed, "We're very happy to have Nathan. He's had it mighty rough—living with drunken parents. He's been mistreated and is undernourished." Brad pushed thin, graying hair off his forehead. "The social worker told us Nathan slept naked—crammed in one bed with several other children."

"We were shocked," admitted Cerena—shadows darkened her blue eyes. "The social worker reported the mattress and bedding were saturated with urine. The children were all bedwetters, and the bedding was hardly ever changed." Cerena shuddered and looked out the sun-warmed windows. "Reports stated his body reeked and his clothing was filthy. Ugly sores covered his body—his arms and legs were scratched raw from flea bites."

"With all legal matters finally settled, Nathan's coming home with us this weekend," Brad assured us.

. . . I returned to my room—my head reeled in wonder and astonishment.

Later, I pushed open the double-entry doors—walked into April sun and sprinkles. Over the Strait of Juan de Fuca a rainbow blazed—blazed over the life of Nathan Cederberry.

Nathan may never dip at daybreak in icy river waters to please the Nature Spirits. He may never quest his Guardian Spirit in mountains or seashore. But the great Guardian Spirit powers of his ancestors—Thunderbird, Whale, Bear, Wolf—reside within. Guiding. Protecting.

That year Cerena and Brad left Neah Bay. A new life opened for Nathan Cederberry in the white man's world. He will be given every opportunity—every privilege—every device—to find, to develop, his own Spirit Power.

~

Looking back, I remember another after-school coffee time with Cerena:

With precise movements, Cerena sorted Friday test papers. As I watched her, I recalled Jule's remark: "Cerena's so pampered and spoiled rotten by Brad."

Pampered and spoiled rotten she may be, but her distinctive, impeccable grooming set her apart. Her hair—styled in a flawless pageboy—snugged her neck. My hair—swished up in a ponytail—flapped when I walked.

Select eye makeup enhanced Cerena's deep blue eyes. I couldn't be bothered with eye makeup.

And her fingernails! Expertly manicured in shades of delicate pink or orange.

My nails? Nondescript. Filed short. No enamel.

Cerena's tailored wool jackets and skirts—not my style—but I admired her designer fashions and selections.

I WILL MISS HER NEXT YEAR.

"It's a package. It's for you. Open it!"

Back to Home Ec—after library period.

On the bright-green desk pad: a package. Puzzled, I picked it up—turned it over—wondering. By visual periphery, I glanced a figure in the doorway: Sidney! His grin teased. His black eyes snapped.

"It's a package. It's for you. Open it!" At his command, I opened it. Midst tangles of ribbon and wrapping, a ring emerged from under snowy-white cotton.

I could only whisper, "Oh, Sidney, thank you. It's lovely. It's so different. The variegated colors resemble . . ."

"It's abalone shell," Sidney interrupted. "I got it in Ocean City. I wanted to bring it to you. Gotta go. See ya." And out the door he went.

Turning the ring in my fingers, I admired details: a tiny engraved design attached the ring of sterling silver to each side of the oval-shaped setting. An edging of sterling encircled the abalone shell.

This ring—like the tiny gold cross—indelibly touched my heart—spirit gift for my Medicine Bag.

 Startled by a brisk knock-knock, I cautiously opened the door. "Marie!" I exclaimed. "Why are you and Dotti wandering around alone in the Neah Bay night?"

In Marie's hand, a little package: "For you," she beamed. "This will tell you 'why'."

Nestled in wrappings and cotton fluff lay the Makah Medicine Man doll—crafted by Helen. Yesterday at the Girl's Camp Fire Doll Show, I had gazed in wonder. A Medicine Man doll—powerful symbol of Makah culture.

I tingled. I couldn't believe my eyes. Helen knew I felt a strong attraction to this mystical totem of spirit power—of spirit healing. I never dreamed this sacred totem would ever be mine.

How dear of Helen. How touching. How thoughtful.

A spirit gift—the Makah way—to give a gift in friendship.

. . . the girls left—soon swallowed by fog and darkness.

. . . they left me to think—to value the true worth of my wonderful Makah friends.

May-basket night brought rain, a quick stout knock, scurrying feet, and giggles.

Left on the porch like drops of sunshine were three yellow May baskets. White lilacs spilled over crepe-paper edges. Chocolate kisses filled the bottoms.

Who had remembered me on May Day?

Picking up the baskets, I heard a motor race, saw a flash of pink—a Volkswagen—Lucy! I called, but she, Lylia, and Rita were gone.

Remembering Ada was coming for dinner, I gasped and rushed to the kitchen. I couldn't offer a Makah elder burnt Lobster a la Newburg.

Another knock.

Dripping wet, Ada stood in the doorway. Her gray hair hung in limp strands. Raindrops clung to her heavy cheeks. She clutched a flimsy shawl to her bulky body.

BASKET WEAVER

"Ada, you're drenched!" I cried. "Let me have your shawl. I'll hang it by the stove. Sit here." I pointed to the overstuffed chair with the white throw. "I'll get a towel to dry your hair."

While she ruffled the towel through her hair, I poured a cup of hot coffee. "This will warm you. What a night! I thought you might not come."

"I come," she chuckled. Groping in a brown paper sack, she pulled out a basket. "Here. For you. I make it for you."

"Ada! Oh, Ada . . ." I fumbled for words to thank her, but words were useless. The basket maker's jolly laughter told me she understood. "I bring May basket too. Makah May basket."

I held the basket in my hands. Suddenly I felt mists swirl around me, whirling me back to some primeval land. Transfixed, I stood facing a dawntime basket maker. I blinked my eyes. The mists scattered, and the ancient basket maker became Ada—respected, honored Makah elder.

To me this May Day gift was a sacred totem linked to the past. Ada had expertly woven the basket using the same skills as the ancient one. At this thought, tingles prickled through me. Was this feeling Indian Spirit Power?

"I tell about basket." Ada's voice pulled me back to the present. Pointing to inverted triangles on the lid, she explained, "This rainbow pattern. One time only black and white—now all color. Like here: red, black, green, yellow." Her finger jabbed at a design on the body of the basket. "Here whalers in canoe. Harpooner stand here. See. Harpoon lift to throw."

". . . Ada! This is Makah history—you've woven it on a basket. It's like a legend."

"Yes, yes. Story of old days before white man."

"What is the winged design?" I asked.

"That Thunderbird. Great Spirit helper."

Ada turned the basket upside-down. "All Makah basket have cedar-strip bottom in checker-work pattern. Side and top woven in bear grass."

She set the basket on the coffee table. "Woman name Queen Ann make first basket in Neah Bay. Twelve generations ago." Thoughtful for a moment—"Our girls this generation don't make basket."

"Not many are interested. One day in sewing class Grace remarked, 'My mother made me learn to make baskets when I was little. I won't do it anymore. Only old women make basket.' One day the old women basket makers will be gone."

"Everybody go to museum to see Makah basket," Ada laughed.

"Will May Day one day be gone too? I will always keep your beautiful basket. It will be in remembrance of the May Day you walked through the rain to bring it to me. Come, let's have dinner. I made Lobster a la Newburg as we planned. Lobster out of a can. I hope you will like it."

"I like it," Ada chuckled, clapping her hands.

We bowed our heads, folded our hands. Ada gave the dinner prayer from the Indian Shaker religion—a sing-song kind of tune. Then she gave the blessing of food in harsh guttural Makah. How I loved listening to this ancient tongue!

Sipping after-dinner coffee, Ada said, "Next week I go to University. Anthropologist take moving picture. I show old way make cattail mats— mats to sleep on. Last summer she take picture here. We tell story of cedar tree. How we strip bark—shred it for clothing. Cedar tree give us canoe and soft shred for baby diapers. Great cedar tree give us planks for longhouses and strips for twist into rope."

Ada jumped from one subject to another. She lifted her plump hands and plunked them on her lap. "Our family try to break up Takko and Irris.

They second cousins. We don't want them marry. Early tribes knew fresh blood must come in. Many intertribal marriages."

"More coffee, Ada? Have another ginger cooky," I offered.

"Yes, yes. So good. I get so big and fat I can't get out door." And her laughter rolled deep and friendly.

She paused—bit into the cooky. "In old days, chiefs or other tribal powers ask hand of daughters of other tribes. This way new blood come in."

I recalled one of the school girls had said, considering her own marriage prospects, ". . . there's already too much inter-marriage among the Makah."

Ada picked up another cooky—broke it in half. "After white man come, Indians use baking powder. They give us KC." Her broad face grimaced. She pushed back her glasses, and in contempt said, "Cheap stuff. Had alum in it. It ruined children's stomachs. My mother always use Royal or else we mix our own. After we got flour we mix it with water to make bread. That before baking powder. We knead dough on our laps for a long time."

Pushing her chair away from the table, Ada showed how the Indian women worked the dough. She used a kneading motion—pressing down hard on her broad thigh. "It first Indian bread. We bake it in hot sand. When bake in skillet, it Indian fry bread."

Ada talked and talked. I listened. Ada fascinated me. I sensed though that she was troubled.

Changing the subject to the minister of her church, Ada spoke in scorn, "That man. He not give my people what they need. He not touch their hearts. He not help them follow way of Christ's teachings.

"Minister told my son Bill, 'Stay away from your brothers who drink.'

"How *could* he tell Bill to stay away from his brothers who drink?" Shocked—angered—discouraged, Ada raised her hands helplessly. "He need tell Bill to love his brothers. Love them and love them. Try to comfort them and help them. That how Jesus taught."

I recognized strong spiritual maturity in Ada. Indian spirituality interwoven with Indian Shaker beliefs? Ada contends vigorous leaning to the early Indian Shaker revivalism. "I feel power in Shaker Church. I want old members to come together again—rebuild church." She sighed and closed her eyes—folded her arms across her breast. "I try," she murmured.

My thoughts drifted to a reading about the early Indian Shakers. It was believed to combine traditional Indian spirit-world beliefs with Bible teachings.

I poured more coffee—served cream from a can. Spooning sugar into her coffee, she chuckled, "Make me fat." Tasting it, she scowled, "More sugar." Another spoonful—it was just right!

"After a while, cows in Neah Bay. Milk for babies."

"Before cows, what did the Indians use?" I asked.

"If no one nurse baby, we squeeze halibut juice. We use catfish liver oil for babies too."

Shadows darkened her face. "I so sad. My family in troubles. Drunkenness, broken homes, illegitimate children. Not like old days."

Not one to dwell in shadows, her face soon brightened with smiles. I saw the same pretty dimples around her mouth inherited by granddaughter Cheree. "One son not drink. He teach in Oregon. Now work on master's degree. I so proud. Next summer I go see him."

Another knock.

"My daughter come. I go."

Into the starless night, through drenching rain, mother and daughter stepped softly over the ageless ground.

I closed the door. Ada's presence stood with me. I could still feel her wisdom, her wonder, her beauty, her magnificence. It all reached beyond the basket maker, the baking of bread in hot sand. A rock of power in her family—her tribe. She is history—legend—spirit—to all Pacific Northwest Indians.

So prim—so proper—so precise—so obedient to her Makah-Quillayute heritage. Daughter of an esteemed Indian family, Nadine Jorge inherited gifts of rare beauty—gifts that eclipsed her tribal mates: curved outlines of chin and brow marked refinement. Structured body outlines defined a slight delicate frame. Behind the outlines: a reserved charm—strength of her race. Spirit power of her own in-being emerged—undeciphered.

Not in my classes, Nadine enrolled to pick up Math and History credits required to graduate from a Washington State accredited high school—like Neah Bay.

Now married—mother of Jacob—cherished youngest member of the eminent Jorge family. Nadine's father—eldest member of the Jorge family—

distinctive tribal elder—held the traditional office of his family. Of arresting stature, his facial features seen stamped on daughter Nadine. His height—his silver-gray hair—gave credence to his nobility.

Alta claims Mr. Jorge is the most respected and wealthiest Makah on the Reservation. Jule declares he is from Ozette and does not live on the Reservation—but at La Push.

~

Ceremonial drums called guests into a hushed quietness—in subdued manner we entered the festive Hall—to the birthday party of Nadine's little boy.

A time to greet friends—mingle with school kids—praise the Red Devils for a basketball win.

Makah parties—always a high mood of festivity—contagious. Everybody entered into a state of hilarity. A time to feast. To celebrate. Quickened drum beats signaled all to the dinner tables.

"What beautiful flower centerpieces!" I exclaimed. ". . . and one for each table. A real touch of spring."

Seated for dinner, Jule whispered, "A card says Mr. Cartwright (he's owner of Jack's Place) sent the floral pieces. He's a close friend of the Jorge family—probably ordered from a florist in Port Angeles."

Alta spoke from across the table, "I heard they are a special gift to honor the Jorge family and the birthday of Nadine's little boy."

Before serving the birthday feast, Makah singers chanted low, soft, tribal songs to welcome guests—to give recognition to the famed family. Muffled throbs of primitive drums carried cryptic messages.

After the dinner blessing, plates of steaming hot food enraptured the starving feasters—BAKED SALMON: a sacred offering—a gift from the SALMON PEOPLE—feast food in deference to the Jorge family—by the Makah Tribe—by the guests—especially by me! Never again will Salmon be a cold-blooded sea entity with a skull and a backbone. But a fish—awesome—mysterious—a sacrifice—a spirit offering from the SALMON PEOPLE.

Traditional after-dinner activities began. Tables cleared—folded and stacked against the back wall—chairs moved to form an outer circle around the Hall—floor space ready for the procession.

Makah singers led—drums rolled in the background—chants invited guests to follow—to pay tribute—to present gifts honoring the birthday of Nadine Jorge's little boy.

Bound together by lineal ancestry and marriage bonds, this exalted and famous Indian family received in dignity the ceremonial gift-giving to the youngest member of the family.

An Indian birthday party! A festival! A potlatch! Just like the old days! Not in a cedar-plank longhouse—but everything else:

- cedar trees dripping rain
- fog drifts rolling in from the sea
- Tatoosh standing guard
- spirit dances
- chants
- drums calling for Spirit Power
- extravagant feasting
- elaborate costumes
- startling masks and headdresses
- lavish distribution of gifts
- not a canoe or a slave or an elk-skin robe, but gifts of today

Helpers, willy-nilly, passed a gift to each guest: a serving plate—a yellow or green salad bowl—Jule happily received a set of wooden spoons—just as happily Alta tucked two colorful kitchen towels into her purse—and I, happiest of all, treasured a cup and saucer set designed with purple violets.

Accelerated drum beats moved party guests to departure—but not without a heightened mood—a burst of hilarity!

Delayed at school. Home late. I mulled over the sixth period incident—wanting to crawl into hibernation. But a loud knock on the door demanded attention.

There—in the doorway—stood Ada. She barged her way in. Aggressive. Powerful. With hard, deep furrows, scowl-lines on her face spelled an immediate urgency.

Ada's words—blunt, abrupt. "There's a story going all over the village. Do you want to hear what I hear?"

I shook my head, "No. No."

We interrupted each other—talked at the same time. Ada was evasive—but I gleaned from bits of her rhetoric that someone had twisted the classroom incident into a vicious untruth involving Garth and me.

"I say to them—I go to her—she tell me."

. . . So, I tell: ". . . the last period of the day—Girls' Home Management class. A confused racket startled us. We turned toward the classroom door. Just then Garth crashed in. The last thing we needed was an extra-curricular activity in the body of Garth. But there he stood—in the doorway—clinging to Helmer who had come with him." Ada listened intently.

"His behavior was strange—awkward—yet it never occurred to me that he was drunk. And then, when he smashed his fist through the glass window in the door, I finally realized he was out of control and feared he had cut an ugly gash in his hand.

"We needed help! Warily, I slipped past the two figures staggering into the room. It was Medicine Man magic, Ada, for there at the foot of the stairway stood Mr. Perkins and Mr. Harris. Immediately they met the crisis.

"Oh, Ada, you'd never believe how Garth fought—riled into fierce revolt. He struck out with his fists—thrashed out with his legs—struggled and fought with the tenacity of an enraged grizzly. He crashed into desks—slammed against the wall—knocked over chairs.

"All the while, the girls and I watched: speechless, helpless, scared.

"Finally, by shoves—pushes—physical restraints—this Makah warrior was ousted through the doorway and into oblivion—thanks to Mr. Perkins and Mr. Harris.

"That's what really happened, Ada."

After she had heard my story, Ada stood—relieved by the truth which denied "the story going all over the village."

In contradiction, glad I could face Ada and declare, "No. Whatever you heard was not true."

"I go. I tell them." With that, Ada vanished into a mass of swirling mist back to the village.

∼

After Ada's departure into the mist, I recalled a little more about that afternoon:

Free from Garth's violent behavior, the girls breathed sighs of relief. Cheree jumped up and locked the door—a little too late—but no one laughed.

This was not an extra-curricular activity. This was different. Danger in the classroom—a former student—intoxicated—inebriated—just plain crazy drunk—Garth could be violent.

Garth had spilled his Makah blood on a chair—on my grade book—on a table—on everything he touched. Elizabeth—bless her dear heart—calmly washed the blood away—not about to leave her drunken tribesman's blood for me to wipe up. A cherished, thoughtful daughter of Makah.

This little Indian girl knows drunkenness and what whiskey has done to her people. She sees the tragedy and the heartbreak throughout the village every day of her life.

But what I'm wondering:

Why was I so determined not to listen to Ada's story? Knowing the stories of "goings on in the village," did Ada's distress suggest something else? What? Rape? Indecent behavior? Obscene language? Whatever—I didn't want to know.

Could some insidious gossip (SHE?) have intended to discredit or humiliate me? Could it have been a deliberate scheme to embarrass me? Force me to accuse an Indian youth? A crafty plot to arouse the Indians against me? Dare I burst someone's bubble?

Who started the story in the first place?

Never one word ever leaked back to me—not from any source—not even Lucy.

 "Have you heard the news?" exclaimed Lucy. "Three earthquake reports and a tidal wave alert. I'm so much excitement! Come, let's go to the Ocean!"
Darts flicked in Lucy's black eyes—dimples teased at the corners of her lips.

Oh, no, Lucy! I gasped in thought. NOT THE OCEAN. NOT TODAY!

But I couldn't squelch an Indian's instinctive pull toward Great Waters, could I? Not even if a tidal wave swallowed us—not even if the beach split open and we fell to never-never land—not even if a demon-pull of an undertow grabbed us.

I breathed in a long, deep breath—let it out slowly. "First we'll have coffee." Did my heart skip a beat? Earthquakes and tidal waves—not my excitement!

Lost in their own world of comics, Lylia and Rita (who had come with Lucy) giggled over the adventures of Bugs Bunny and Tar Baby.

Dumping sugar into her coffee, Lucy stared into the mixture. Scowl lines appeared. Engrossed in a stronger brew? I wondered. And then she began to talk:

"Lorna's dad, Jay, and Tony got into a terrible fight at the Pool Hall last night. Both were dead drunk. Tony's hurt real bad. Several ribs are broken. His face all bruised and bloodied."

I listened in despair. Whiskey will kill them all.

"Do you know what started the fight?"

"Tony's been dating Lorna," Lucy said. "I suppose he kept her out too late—something like that—and her dad got mad."

"Was Junior there?" I asked, picking up the coffee cups.

Sadness edged her answer: "Yes, my son was there." Clouds gathered in Lucy's eyes. "He was drinking too, but he got home all right. That's when he told me about the fight. It's all over the village by now."

Would Lucy rather face earthquakes and tidal waves than a whiskey bottle?

She shoved her bright-blue turban back from her forehead. Tightness across her brow relaxed. She reached for her car keys—a signal: time to leave the ugliness of the fight behind.

At the gate, I jiggled the lock. It held. No yard full of surprises—like horses—when I come back.

We all piled into Lucy's pink Volkswagen, bumped down the rutted sandy road, chattered all the way to Great Ocean.

We all piled out. Strong brisk winds smacked our faces. Fogs drifted close to shore.

Lucy scanned the stretch of sand—the immensity of sea. "March is Whale month, but I see no spout or spray."

Lylia and Rita skittered over damp sand in search of tidal wrack.

That day the might and energy of Great Ocean terrified me. Jittery—untrusting—I squinted at that water of history and legend—of sudden moods with fierce tempers. Far-reaching and turbulent, it rumbled and roared in gray danger and power. Its voice low—mysterious—growled a warning: "Don't come too close."

Defying fear, I rejoiced in sky and sea—high winds and wild waves. I'd forgotten Lucy's news of uncertain disasters.

Lylia's shout, "Look what we found!" jerked disaster-thoughts away.

On the sand she spilled limpet shells, a tiny bird feather, purple and bright-blue mussel shells, a sand dollar, curls of dried kelp.

Losing interest, Rita dared Lylia with, "Let's race to the rock." They shunted grumpy threats from Great Ocean.

Bouncing up and down before their mother, they begged, "Can we? Can we?"

"Not yet. Not yet. Stand still. Listen." Dutiful daughters, they stood, listened. "Sand and sea boundaries stretch unlimited. Yours do not. Wait for us at the rock. Don't touch anything metal," Lucy warned. "It might not be good."

~

What might not be good? I wondered. Ada's somber story of World War II struck my mind: "We believe Japan submarines in our waters. We fear Japan bomb us."

Reluctant to question Lucy, I invented my own answers: hand grenades? land mines? guns? a cache of explosives to be picked up later? Who knows the intentions of the war-minded?

~

"Now race off," Lucy urged her bright-eyed daughters. We watched the carefree girls race down the beach. Like frisky spring colts, they kicked up their heels—sand clots flying behind them.

Again, Lucy stared into the surging sea—then turned toward me. "We must have walking sticks."

While Lucy rummaged in driftwood heaps, I rummaged in spirit with the sand and the sea. A sunstreak pierced the misty, dampish fog. Like sprays of spindrift, the fog spun around me. Again I was aware of that mystical, indefinable SOMETHING. Like a mist-haunted, spirit-haunted entity of wildness that rolled away into the unknown. Unreachable. Intangible. Like wind-voice echoes.

Not wind-voice echoes I heard, but Lucy's "Here's your cedar walking stick. There's a knot on the end, and it's crooked and covered with barnacles. But it's strong and sturdy."

Before giving me the walking stick, she paused. "We believe when an Indian gives a gift he has touched or worn that he gives a part of himself."

Her words pulsed Spirit Power. I gazed at the cedar walking stick: gnarled, knotted, barnacled, a power image, a bond between Lucy and me.

I stood silent midst the force of high winds and sea voices—but it was Lucy's voice that called me to her yesterdays. "I always say I came along just in time to see the last of the old ways and the first of the new ways. I was only a child but I remember living in my grandfather's longhouse at Coupeville on Whidbey Island. Indians split cedar planks to build longhouses. Some were one-hundred feet long and twenty feet or more wide. They were our permanent homes—and always faced the water."

Lucy stared down the beach toward the rock. Her daughters, like tiny dots, bobbed up and down. Devoted mother—she watched their every move. "We always had several relatives living with us in our longhouse. Our beds—like bunks—were built around the walls. I still remember the sweet smell of grass mats and cattail blankets."

I soon recognized Lucy's longing—her remembrance of the old way.

"We dug shallow pits in the earth floor for fires. They ran down the middle of the longhouse. Each family kept its own fire and living space. Smoke curled up and out through a hole in the cedar-planked roof." Lucy shifted her basket—lifted her arms to show how planks were shoved aside to make an opening.

"Mom! Mom! We're starving!" shouted Lylia and Rita, skipping toward us.

From her basket, Lucy spread lunch snacks on the huge, flat-topped rock. Cheese and crackers washed down with orange pop quickly vanished. Squawking seagulls—mouths open—wings spread—attacked each other for pieces of cracker and bits of apple.

"Look at that big bully!" shouted Lylia. "He's grabbing food from that little bird." She rushed to frighten them—waving her arms and whooping, "Go away!" The birds scattered—circling into the storm sky.

Forgetting the quarrelsome seagulls, the girls pocketed apples and Hershey bars and hippity-hopped down the beach.

Salty, snappy wind whipped around us. Black clouds rolled—hiding the sun. But for one moment a tiny shining arrow of light stabbed the blackness. Rumbles in the Olympics alerted Lucy. "We need start back soon."

Never changing our pace, we walked in silence—as far as the river—the Sooez—that twists into the rough and stormy Pacific.

With the incoming tide, the wind turned—temperish and cold. An uneasy growl from Great Ocean triggered an eerie alarm. "We turn back now." A smile twisped Lucy's lips. "I fear no earthquake or tidal wave. The morning news report—false alarm—but storm coming in."

On our trek back, Lucy stopped. Across the angry water, she stared into some distant place. When she spoke, she flashed into the past again:

"I remember winter storms when sitting around pit-fires in Grandfather's longhouse. Winds howled through the cracks of the split-cedar planks. Rains hammered on the roof. Cold crept in. But—wrapped in blankets—we children huddled together and kept warm.

"With my older sister—and our many cousins, uncles, aunts—I listened to the old stories." Lucy looked beyond the wet sand at our feet—looked beyond the menacing gray swells of the Ocean. Her voice softened, "I still see the loved faces of the Old Ones. I still see how they looked as they sat around the fire telling their stories. I remember how shadows from the firelight crossed their wrinkled faces. Long into the night, the Old Ones sat. Finally, the stories stopped and everyone slept."

"Who will tell the stories when the Old Ones are gone?" I asked. "The young don't seem to care."

Lucy leaned on her cedar walking stick—poked her toe at a half-buried shell—"As long as Grandmothers sing to the new-born and Old Ones tell how Thunderbird fought Whale and how Raven stole the Sun—as long as Grandmothers teach that every seed, bird song, cedar tree, Salmon from the sea has a spirit with mysterious powers—legends will live on."

A shattering clap across the sky sent us all scurrying to the car. Our day now surrendered to Storm Spirits. We bumpety-bumped back to the village.

At the gate, Lucy braked. NO HORSES. I clutched my walking stick, grabbed my tote bag—jumped out—rushed for shelter.

"Look!" Lucy pointed. "Hail stones coming! I'm so much excitement! Hurry," she urged. "Get inside!"

Aware that hailstones bounced off my head, I hurried inside—leaned against the door—sighed in joyous relief. To be knocked out by over-sized hailstones—to be scared to death by rumbles from Thunderbird—NOT MY EXCITEMENT!

On another day, in the still, deep forest—away from Juan de Fuca's shore—Lucy walked softly beside me. Above the evergreens, sun flamed with warmth of beginning summer. Forest sounds hushed. Songs of sea winds quieted.

Again I entered Lucy's Indian past—listened to the old lodge-fire tales that often began: "I was only a child . . ."

Abruptly, Lucy stopped.

On the floor of this forest trail, trampled in sandy soil among dried twigs, weeds, and tiny pebbles lay an old piece of wood with strings. Unnoticed—at my feet—stepped on by me—nothing could have appeared more worthless.

Lucy stooped—as if touching a spirit totem. She gently lifted the rough wood. "This is a piece of red cedar bark." She turned the wood in her hands. "This is the hard outer bark that protects the smooth inner bark. These strings are shredded strands."

Revering the tree that towered above us, Lucy said, "The red cedar tree was our way of life. It gave us our whaling canoes, our longhouses, our clothing."

Walking back to the beach, Lucy recalled her past: "The Old Ones believed a Guardian Spirit lived in the red cedar tree. When the tree was cut down and carved into a whaling canoe or war canoe or traveling canoe, the Spirit lived in the prow."

Now, back on the beach, we walked toward the uprooted tree sprawled on the shore. Lucy pointed to the old log with roots uplifted. "Let's sit here awhile." Relaxed against a pronged root, she held the strands I had stepped on. "For hundreds of years, women and girls wore fringed skirts woven from cedar-bark strands—like these. The skirts hung below the knees." Gently, Lucy fingered the strands.

"We wove blankets and mats from shredded cedar bark. From twined cedar, we wove capes. From narrow cedar strips we wove pointed hats that shed the rain. From the softest cedar bark fibers we lined a baby's cradle."

RED CEDAR BARK FIBERS! What a gift to my textile class from their own heritage! Why not include wood fibers with the natural aristocrats: silk, wool, linen, cotton? Red cedar bark fibers extend an indigenous quality to the textile field—to the textile industry.

I saved the red cedar bark with shredded strands. Placed in my Medicine Bag with spirit rocks, sand dollars, barnacle-covered driftwood—I treasured them. They belonged to my life in Neah Bay.

Again, sea breezes sent Cerena's message: ". . . there is SOMETHING here for you, and you want to find it . . ."

Find it—as I live the old lodge-tales with a direct descendent of the powerful Indian Chieftain, Seattle?

. . . six-forty-five in the morning!

. . . and there I sat in the Seattle Bus Terminal waiting for a ride back to Neah Bay—my only chance to squeeze in time to write the Camp Fire Picture Story—promised Lucy—using the Indian symbols she had given me.

How to begin—where to begin—I didn't know—but begin I did. I created my own interpretation of the symbols—juggled words—jiggled phrases—until a story unfolded with some semblance of meaning. I meant to rewrite it.

The picture-symbol-story NEVER had a chance for a rewrite—NO TIME!

Later—after school—all bright and bubbly—Lucy rushed me to Camp Fire meeting—first stopped at my apartment to pick up her Camp Fire Manual.

On our way to the meeting, I told Lucy I had written the symbol story. Pleasure and admiration beamed in her soft, dark-brown eyes. So glad I had managed to write it. Anything I can do for her little group is so greatly appreciated.

. . . no time for a rewrite—no chance to hide it—even think about it or remember what I had written. I read the story. The little girls laughed and clapped their hands. Lucy was delighted. So was Mrs. Johns—a visiting mother—a spy for SHE?

I am now the AWARDS COMMITTEE!

~

CAMP FIRE PICTURE STORY

Within my Camp Fire *hogan*,
I hold the *seed-pod* of life.
Night and day I behold the
rainbow of my hopes.
Down the Camp Fire trail I see
the *Morning Star* bright
with my desires.
If *lightning* and *rain clouds* appear
to dull life's rainbow hues,
the power of the great *Thunderbird*

shall bring forth again
the *sun's* pure rays.
And once more, the *crossed arrows*
along the Camp Fire way
shall direct my spirits to the path
of the *Shooting Star.*
Thus through Camp Fire building,
the seed-pod of my life
will be fulfilled.

Apologizing for her cluttered house, Lucy scowled, "All this for-eign living has been hard enough . . ."
. . . cultural overtones that meant: "I don't keep the floors waxed—the rugs swept—the windows shining . . ."

Cluttered or not, I loved Lucy's little cottage. Hidden in the woods—among salal bushes, rhododendrons, madronas—it gripped the edge of Juan de Fuca's narrow sea.

A path led from the back door to the beach. How I loved being out here on this historical strait! Many times I walked with Lucy on the pebbly beach. Here we poked our walking sticks into eel-grass, seaweed, kelp—in search of tidal-drift curios. Here stories of her childhood spun out for my very eager ears.

Did sharp zesty sea air open her memory cells? Did choppy sea winds blow in images of the old days? Did Lucy's mind vanish to a longhouse—to Coupeville—to Whidbey Island—to the old ways?

Frisky winds snatched at her words. "I remember how I used to sit be-fore Grandmother. She was my teacher. I was five years old. I sat very still. I had to pay attention. I listened. I watched. I did as I was shown. I dared not ask questions.

"In the same way, I learned family dances—tribal dances—and our songs and chants." Again that look into the past shadowed her eyes.

"This was our education." Lucy looked away—as if remembering . . . "Little girls learned early woman's work in the tribe—how to weave cedar baskets—cattail mats—how to do beadwork. We learned the ritual way to clean and cut Salmon. To please the Salmon People, everything must be just right—the old way."

For a while, again we walked in silence. A seagull's screech broke the stillness—brought Lucy's thoughts back from the past. "From the old days I still remember how our Indian families moved about from place to place in our dug-out canoes. We valued our big dug-outs. They were our only way of travel. At night the men pulled the canoes up on the beach in front of our longhouses. In those days my father used to say: 'Always be ready in case of an attack.' Nowadays we have different kinds of attacks to worry about."

Before she spoke again, Lucy noted the clotted cloud formations. Rain threatened. "Every day liquor attacks—kills—our people—like the smallpox it runs uncontrolled." Sadness darkened Lucy's facial lines. Her next words sounded deep concern: ". . . we must learn to survive in the new way."

The NEW WAY brought whiskey—survival threatened by every drop.

"I pray for strength to meet these changes. Makahs—a whaling nation—hunt no more."

With a distressed sigh, Lucy lifted her eyes in supplication.

"We needed and asked for so little. Life was so easy and free."

. . . often I'd heard that the Indian offered his pipe as a token of friendship. The white man reciprocated with liquor. Hunting had ceased—leaving the Makahs destitute. Liquor promised a way of release.

 Bright! Sunny! Glorious! Memorial Day with Lucy. Her demure little cottage—snug in the woods—off the Reservation: a spirit-place for happenings.

Enticed by the brilliance of sky and water, we followed the path to Juan de Fuca's shore—a strand to probe for agates and things. After last night's high and mighty bout with Storm Spirits, the smash and crash of tides swept in MORE THAN AGATES AND THINGS.

On this great expanse of pebbles and water, Lucy and I—like a couple of excited kids—picked the beach. Lucy—for driftwood and shells for her crafts. I—for tokens to stash in my Medicine Bag. Distorted curlicues of seaweed—black and stiff from sun and wind. Barnacle encrusted wood and rocks.

. . . and there again stood the huge silvered structure of driftwood—violently and recklessly thrown on Juan de Fuca's shore—ages ago.

Before we left the beach, we faced the Strait. What mysterious elements compound its icy-blue depths? Under its spell, I fantasized . . . If I sailed to the right, I'd follow the sea, plunging through white caps to Puget

Sound—to a great mountain—THE MOUNTAIN THAT WAS GOD, TAHOMA—named by Indians a long time ago. And then if I sailed to the left, my sea craft would pass Fuca's Pillar into the North Pacific—an Ocean with its own mysterious elements . . .

Back at the cottage, the girls had dinner ready—beef stew and a special treat, Indian fry bread.

Once we ate squirrel—once a piece of bear meat—once venison steak. No time for a squeamish stomach. No time to shun delicacies from the forested wilderness.

On Juan de Fuca's shore, again I walked with Lucy. Turning toward the old cedar tree, Lucy breathed easier. "The wind slows," she noted. By the faraway look in her eyes, I knew she was thinking of the old days.

"Even as a child—living on Whidbey Island—I'm always so much excitement to go on family berry-picking trips. We had plenty of food—but not all in one place.

"I remember how our Indian families started out every summer. In our big dug-out canoes, we piled blankets, fishing gear, baskets of dried fish and roots. We children—happy and laughing—scrambled in last. Our paddlers took our canoes into coves, up creeks, and into small inlets.

"The woods were full of all kinds of berries: blueberries, salmon berries, huckleberries, blackberries. We dried berries in the sun and stored them in baskets. Dried foods helped us survive the winter months."

"Berries and bears go together. I'd have been scared of bears in those woods," I interrupted. "Did you ever see any bears poking their noses into berry patches—prowling and sniffing for the fattest, ripest berries to feast on?"

"Bears stayed in the backwoods," Lucy replied. "They were no trouble—but feast we did! These summer outings were a part of our way of life." Lucy's round face brightened with her native impish grin. "These were happy days—summer Pow Wow days!"

Lucy probed her walking stick into the sand. "We built huge driftwood fires. We baked Salmon tied on sticks stuck in the sand. We baked bread and potatoes in the ashes. We ate berries. Sometimes we dug wild carrots and onions. That's how we lived.

"At feast times, we chanted Suquamish songs of praise and thanksgiving.

To drum beats we stomped our native tribal dances. Our shouts and laughter rang across the Sound. Days like those are no more."

 Lucy comes again: "I'm so much excitement!" Smiles of joy—of happiness—wreathed Lucy's face. "We've been asked to do another program in Seattle. They want us to do Suquamish tribal dances and songs. We'll wear our Suquamish costumes and olive-shell necklaces."

Drinking sugared coffee at the kitchen table, Lucy's excitement persisted: "June is set up to sing Indian songs at a radio station in Port Angeles. The program is dedicated to the signing of a one-hundred-year-old treaty. WE'RE ALL SO MUCH EXCITEMENT!"

. . . and I'm so much excitement just knowing these talented descendants of Chief Seattle!

Not forsaking the ancient tribal identity of the Suquamish, did this Suquamish-Makah mother turn each child's first words into a song of praise? Turn each child's first steps into a dance of the Great Spirit?

. . . one brother—three sisters—spark attention in any gathering

. . . their inherent dignity—their poise—their obedience—their closeness to their mother— reveals their training

ROYALTY!

. . . when I'm with them, the past flares all around me

. . . I hear chants—follow dance steps—hear thunder-roll of drums pound out messages of PAST—PRESENT—FUTURE

. . . and I'm living it with my Suquamish-Makah friends.

SUQUAMISH INDIAN DANCES—BY JUNE

All our Indian dances are an achievement of a craft or a diploma of our Indian schooling.

As we children reached the age of five or seven, we began our early teaching to understand nature and acquire a totem.

Only children of the royal family or middle-class family were taught. The third and lower classes were not eligible for any teachings.

Youngsters, boys, were taught in secret. The granddad or uncle would awaken the boy at three o'clock in the morning, give him a stick—called the home stick—tell him to take this to a certain place, say three miles away, the first day. The number of miles would be increased as the lad grew older.

He would be gone for five or fifteen days sometimes, over rivers and across mountains. When the lad returned, two slaves were sent out to return the stick.

All the time the lad was out he would be fasting and swimming—as the first rule to acquire a totem was cleanness of body, as well as mind, honesty, humbleness—were those that acquired the prize totem as Chieftain.

Totems were crafts of Chieftains, Medicine Men, gamblers, songs, hunters and food callers. Those who could sing a song during famine and call Salmon or fish, to load the canoes enough to feed the whole village.

And then the Shaman Spirit Songs for entertainment called the Healing Song, where the singer would take a knife and cut through his middle, and dance when he was through. He was to stay in public for twenty-four hours to prove he didn't use anything but his song to heal himself.

He would earn his song and get his powers from the animals. Only when he had learned to understand nature, would he be given power.

Chief Seattle's song of thunder came from the powers of thunder and belonged to the great Chief Seattle.

 Wonderful and exciting happenings every day! This time a CAMP FIRE POW WOW in Port Angeles—impressive and stirring panorama of artistic and impressive Indian songs and dances. Lucy's children—June, Ernie (Junior), Lylia, Rita—all danced. Lucy in costume enlivened her role as she beat the drum.

The four children danced in spirit—in essence with their heritage. In action, they appear withdrawn—unaware—only listening to the Indian call within—answering the drum beats. Junior is a compliment to his sisters. A strong dancer, he too answers the call within.

~

Driving back to Neah Bay after the Camp Fire Girls' Pow Wow: Midnight. Dark. Moonless. Spooky. Black trees stood ghost-like—watching.

But protective fog spirits watched too.

Along the Strait of Juan de Fuca, Lucy steered her pink Volkswagen. To keep us awake, Lucy chanted strong, spirit-powered war songs.

In the back seat, Lylia and Rita and Junior strengthened the war chants—while June pounded war drums in rhythmic beats.

I listened—a phantom shadow harbored by sounds and shades from another time.

~

. . . abruptly, the sounds in the car changed all around me—being pushed back—back to the days before white man: war drums, war dances, war parties, raiding bands.

. . . only an illusion—only fantasy—to be drawn into the mysteries of a culture far different from my own

. . . to be with my Indian friends—I never forgot who they are—who I was—never forgetting the Indian within me

. . . wildly excited by the spirit-stemmed happenings—ecstatic because I knew WHO THEY WERE

. . . the chants—the drum beats—opened the spirit-gate for me to FEEL their past with them—to be part of their today-lives

 Against the side of Lucy's cottage—the side that praises the rising sun—huddled amazing fragments of driftwood: native artistry in bizarre shapes and sizes.

In this rustic background of sky and sea, Junior worked on a strange, mystical shape. *My inmost thoughts unveiled a derelict ship stranded on some coral reef.*

"Where can you find such unusual shapes?" I quizzed Junior.

"I found this piece on our beach after a big storm. We find lots of good driftwood after storms."

"The children work with me on the driftwood. We rub and polish each piece until it's smooth," Lucy said.

Varnish had lightly brushed the surface of several fragments. The glossiness brightened the dull gray wood. But the ones untouched by varnish—the ones carried in from the beach—captured my feel for the natural—the belongings left by ocean currents.

In Lucy's craft room are found a loom and spinning wheel—from a long time ago. She cards and combs virgin wool—spins it into yarn—knits

sweaters, scarves, caps, bags. Native designs—Thunderbird, Duck, Whale—
are knitted or woven into Lucy's craft pieces.

I see a sweater in black and white wool—the great Thunderbird designed across the back. I WANT IT!

A specialty shop in Seattle buys most of Lucy's handwork.

". . . other pieces and knitted things will go to the Craft Shop here,"
she said.

And so, in this way, Lucy's craft skills help her to survive in the white
man's world.

Yesterday: a gladdening day in winter solstice. A glorious day on
the Strait of Juan de Fuca.

Above the horizon line, silver slices of sky wedged between charcoal shadows. A strange mystic moment prevailed . . . a spirit . . . blending
of two cultures . . . that I may never know or feel again.

Winds brisk and frisky pushed Lucy and me to the uprooted tree.

"We'll sit here awhile," she decided. In a pensive mood, I surrendered
my thoughts to this ancient image of a culture past. Its mysterious energy
enfolded me—once a seedling . . .

Then soon I relinquished my thoughts of the tree to Lucy's voice:
"This little bead is called WAMPUM. She touched a tiny cylindrical object
fastened in an arrangement of colored beads.

"Wampum beads are made from shells. Indian tribes on the Atlantic
Coast used them for money. They carried much power. You may have
this."

Overwhelmed! Stunned again. I wondered how she could part with
such a sacred piece? Did I understand the essence of this gift—understand
it as an invincible trust in me?

I felt its power—its force of communication—its language.

How could I thank her—reveal my true wonder—my true admiration of
her—my true bonding with her.

Did she understand what I was feeling? Did she understand how overcome I was?

I finally spoke: ". . . such a rare and special gift . . . how can I ever tell
you how much this means to me . . . I'll put it in my Medicine Bag with all
my spirit gifts."

Happy with my reply, Lucy smiled, "In the old days, one small white wampum bead would buy a canoe, a slave, a woman . . ."

. . . one small white bead: primordial system of power—of wealth—of prestige.

This morning I revel in the remembrance of yesterday with Lucy—on the Strait of Juan de Fuca. I revel too in remembrance of her gift of wampum beads.

And now, today, I think of the crusty old mariner, Juan de Fuca, and the inland sea that carries his name.

On this scene of myth and history—where I live and teach—my thoughts wing back to the Great Spirit and his creation: the Strait of Juan de Fuca—one of the most ravishing, bright, and shining water strips in the Pacific Northwest.

Seen yesterday as a glittering streak of water, it may gleam and glisten in sublime innocence one minute—then turn stormy black, and dangerous, the next. Mocking storm spirits hover over its rocky shores—its treacherous sandspits. Boulders and reefs are hidden under its wicked tides. High winds, driving rains, deceitful fogs paralyze water crafts in any age of sea travel.

With Lucy on this ancient waterway, I cringed from a bit of history: within her knowing, some of the bloodiest intertribal battles in Indian history were fought here.

"Armed with bows and arrows—stone-headed clubs and knives," Lucy recalled, "great numbers of fierce northern warriors from Vancouver Island arrived in huge war canoes and savagely attacked the tribes living near the Strait."

So serene and peaceful my day with Lucy, the shock of terrorizing attacks of blood-thirsty warriors didn't fit in with the picturesque, romantic Strait.

Never-to-be-forgotten: Ada's spirit-stirring comment: "I glad when white man come—we not have to worry anymore about other tribes making war on us."

Everyone detests hall duty—trying to subdue screaming, yelling kids. How can they play outside under a waterfall in the mud? They don't! They race pell-mell through the halls until caught.

"I'd rather be in hell!" a teacher twists the words from the corners of his mouth. Who wouldn't! To save us from insanity—the bell clatters and everyone beats it to class.

. . . and working in the background—beyond hall duty—on a wetter-than-average day—are sincerely dedicated teachers—devoted to their jobs—seeking to help—to inspire—to improve.

Another youth group—formed in one of the churches—promises to enlighten young lives—and reduce drinking.

 Gazing into the distance—over the seascape—Lucy braced against her walking stick. "Winds yank words right out of my mouth," she laughed into the blustery gusts.
"Let's sit a while on this driftwood log."

I sat in quiet submission—felt the mists off Mount Olympus—watched sea-spirits dance on the white caps.

Something drew me to the silvery sheen of the log. In random touch, my fingers traced the grain lines.

I mind-traveled again:

. . . transported by an invisible vitality, I saw the old uprooted tree that once grew in a forest of red cedars. Vibrant. Living. Majestic. A Guardian Spirit tree.

Once rooted in Earth-Mother—drenched by rains and misty fogs—I could believe primeval ferns and berry bushes flanked its trunk. Strings of lichen—filaments of moss—hung from its branches. Soft gentle breezes of summer sang to nesting birds sheltered on sturdy boughs—deep gouges dug by cougar claws scarred its tough bark.

Who knows what Storm Spirits ripped the mighty tree out of the forest?

What gigantic force hurled it to rest on Juan de Fuca's shore?

What shattering catastrophe ages and ages ago? A mighty earthquake? A sweeping cataclysm? A tsunami?

Lucy reached for her walking stick. A sign to move on. A sign for us to forsake my mind-travels with the uprooted tree.

∼

Lucy and Rita dropped by to chat—to coffee—to plan a Camp Fire program. Later, when they stepped into the winter dusk, I closed the door to wonder: Will June dance her Suquamish dances—sing her Indian spirit songs?

   . . . to watch June dance is to watch a sacred Indian prayer in motion
   . . . she moves in spirit with the mystique of her race
   . . . she moves with native dignity and grace—with poise and beauty
   . . . her footsteps change in rhythm to the beat of tribal drums
   . . . her arms uplift as to a legend's song
   . . . her eyes close as to the mystical whisper of a wind's song
   . . . what radiant light shimmers within?
   . . . what spirit voice guides her?
   . . . does she hear the power-chants from dawntime?
   . . . does she answer to a secret vow pledged long ago?
   . . . June—in dance—moves to the call of her Indian heritage

1957-1958

Today I helped Helen in her Craft Shop.

Forlorn—despondent—the look on her face was soon resolved: "I can't believe the number of school girls who are pregnant. In the old days, teenage pregnancies didn't happen very often."

Troubled by girls dropping out of school, Helen reflected: "If this had happened to us when we were girls, we would have been so ashamed. We were closely guarded and watched until ready for marriage."

Helen arranged cedar baskets on shelves—hung olive-shell necklaces on jewelry racks—then slowly added, "It happened more often in slave families."

Helen spoke for the OLD CULTURE. Who speaks for the NEW CULTURE?

In this wilderness Land of rocky shores—black-green forests—guardian spirits—I love being free: uninhibited by marked demands—psychological as well as emotional and physical.

"A self-sufficient unit of purpose!" a friend once said.

How right! And I am living it!

Where did it come from? An appreciation for the people—the race—the culture—a wanting to understand—to belong. Is there an awareness of SOMETHING?—something here for me and I want to find it—as Cerena said.

A visiting friend deplored, "How can you stand to live up here with these Indians? Indians are filthy dirty and stink. That Indian baby made me sick to look at it. It was so ugly. How can you stand it?"

One Saturday a guest-teacher from Port Angeles fussed about the isolation—the loneliness. "How do you stand it up here? I couldn't. You must have *something* within you that I don't have."

They reject and think I am mad. But I shall never cease to learn up here:

> Beyond the schoolyard:
> horizons stretch into vastness
> distant—far from reach
> untouchable—inaccessible.
> Always seeking a goal:
> hoping for a promise
> reaching for a rainbow.

"If the weather holds, I'm driving to Tacoma right after school Friday," said fifth-grade teacher Miss Pugh. "If you don't mind my cat and dog, you may ride along."

For a weekend away from classes and kids, I could tolerate a couple of animals, I thought. But did I really want to miss the Makah party? The drums? The ceremonial dances and songs. The Salmon feast?

Friday morning I met Miss Pugh in the hall. "I'll pick you up at 3:30," she announced, plucking at pins in her mop of stringy gray hair. "Be ready. I want to be out of here before dark."

When I climbed in her car, my toe hit a box. "Oh!" I exclaimed.

"Never mind that. It's just Mouse's potty box. Can't trust a cat. I always travel with it. A bit smelly." She twitched her nose, "But you'll get used to it. Haven't had time to change it."

We were out before dark. In the front seat, between their tall, angular mistress and me, rode the pets: the cat Mouse, the dog Yakki. Each was fitted with a harness. Fastened to each harness were long leather straps wrapped between Miss Pugh's strong slender fingers.

Mouse hissed at me between lips that snarled a tiger smile. Her long straggly tail switched in jerks. Yakki's snippy yips and flat-back ears sentenced me "unwanted." The pets wiggled and twisted and strained on their straps.

"Your animals seem to be very unhappy with me. Why don't I sit in the back seat?" Dared I hope!

"Indeed not! Stay right where you are," she commanded. "I have absolute control over my pets. They'll settle down." To Mouse and Yakki, "Stop it! I've had enough of this nonsense." And yanked the straps in discipline.

All this while driving! I couldn't believe it. But when I looked at her profile accented by gold-rimmed glasses, the embossed hump of her nose, the straight cut of her thin lips, the stern jaw edge, I believed it.

Yakki. Mouse. I love animals. I do! But these: so nondescript, so common and unpretty. Panting in my face, through ugly yellow teeth, Yakki's tainted breath repulsed me. Small scrubby and short haired, this dingy, white mongrel dog had no pizzazz. Looking through weak watery blue eyes, he saw only Miss Pugh, straps, and Mouse.

Poor Mouse. Her long fur in blotchy patches of black and white emerged mangy and bedraggled. Out of faded gray eyes, she squinted at me. Twitching black whiskers were her only personality charms.

Tangled in straps, squeezed in between Miss Pugh and me, the animals dozed. Mesmerized by the glaring sweep from headlights, I wanted to doze too. But Yakki's soft snores jumped into hard snorts. "Oh never mind him"—followed by: "Yakki's just dreaming. When he snorts like that his feet and tail twitch. Thinks he's chasing a cougar, I guess," said his mistress.

Mouse, curled in a semi-circle, stretched, digging her claws into my cashmere coat. Instead of contented purrs, I heard a low-throat growl. Who was *she* chasing, I wondered. Me?

After a while, my mind drifted. Mists danced on the Strait of Juan de Fuca above purple-rose cloud patterns. Thinking of the party I was missing at Neah Bay, I wished—by this time—that I could turn around and go back.

Then, unexpectedly, from somewhere, erupted a strong revolting smell. What *was* it? Where did it come from? Then I remembered. Mouse's sand-box reeked at my feet! Clamping my lips tight, I muttered not a sound. I had accepted a ride. But qualms and near-gagging gripped me. Nauseous odors seeped into my nostrils, skin, hair. They penetrated the fabric of my clothes. Did they reach into the marrow of my bones too?

Contaminated, I thought. Will I ever feel clean again?

I squirmed.

"You're too warm," assumed Miss Pugh, and snapped off the heat. "I'll open the wing-window to let some air blow through." A jungle of cat and dog hairs had clumped on the dashboard. The sudden gust sent them into brisk activity. Like tumbleweeds, they rolled across my nose and mouth. I'll suffocate, I thought. "Whew!" I gasped, catching my breath.

Over and over the wheels turned—mile after mile vanished into the darkness.

I released a stress-filled sigh. The Narrows Bridge that connected my Neah Bay world with Tacoma spanned ahead.

Miss Pugh scolded her uneasy pets and slapped them with the straps. "I've never seen Mouse and Yakki so restless," she said, puzzled. "It's not just because of you. Must be a storm coming in."

"Oh, no!" I wailed. "I can't think of anything worse than driving back to Neah Bay in a storm." Through cables and girders of the Narrows Bridge, I watched cloud-clots scud—threatening.

In silence we followed the black pavement. Suddenly, Miss Pugh braked to a stop. I leaped out, dragged my suitcase behind me. At last, my mother's apartment. I crawled under an electric blanket—forgot storm threats.

During the night, the weather switched. A fair November, from the Cascades to the Olympics, was snatched into blitzing winter. Chill wind-blasts dropped snow and hung icicles.

"I can't believe this weather. How will we ever make it back to Neah Bay?" I moaned over morning coffee.

"You never can tell. Trust a chinook to blow in and melt the snow by Sunday," my mother consoled.

Sunday morning the phone rang with an extra shrill. I knew who it was. "I'll pick you up at one o'clock. Be out on the sidewalk so we won't lose any time," Miss Pugh demanded—her voice tense but determined.

Waiting on the sidewalk, I felt the pinch of cruel winds. Snowflakes fluttered. My thoughts fluttered, too. Back to Neah Bay. Back to classes and kids.

"The weather sure tricked me," Miss Pugh ventured, as I slid into the front seat. "All roads are open though, according to weather reports." Through clenched teeth, Miss Pugh warned her pets, "No foolishness out of you two." Her grip on the straps was taut. Mouse and Yakki huddled together, cowering.

"Well, are you settled?" she asked, slipping the car into gear. "We've a long way to go."

"Yes. Yes, I'm settled." Settled, I thought—but barely breathing—stinky kitty box still at my feet.

A look out the window and I too cowered. Snow had sprayed the evergreens. Snow had ridged at road sides. Inwardly, I was tight and cramped with anxiety. Danger menaced every turn of the wheels. A freakish skid on a patch of snow-covered ice *could* hurl us down a vast ravine. A sudden lunge of the dog, a startled jump of the cat, *could* send the car whirling into a guard rail. But when I looked at Miss Pugh, my fears disappeared. I knew by the iron-set of her jaw, her bulldog stare, her cold silence, that we *would* make it back to Neah Bay.

Long ago, without a word, she had switched off the heat. I was numb.

Relief: Like an aurora borealis, city lights lit the sky above Port Angeles. In the icy-darks of a short November day, this was a port, indeed!

After miles of silent tension, Miss Pugh relaxed her hold on Mouse and Yakki. "We'd better stop in P.A. for dinner and a chance to get warm." She shivered. "I turned the heat off. Didn't dare get drowsy."

Better freeze than slip off a curve, I thought.

Dinner? Eat dinner? My stomach churned—verging nausea. To disguise fears, I faked joy! "Dinner sounds wonderful! I'm starved!"

From the confines of Mouse—Yakki—and pollution—I stepped into AIR! Magiked air! Fresh and salty from the sea, it filled me with life, vitality, spirit!

With Mouse and Yakki stoutly strapped in the car, we dined at Aggie's famed restaurant.

Back to the car, I braced for the odors of the kitty box. Grappling with a network of straps and animals—twined and intertwined—Miss Pugh discovered Mouse had wet on the seat. And wouldn't you know . . . my seat! Why not Miss Pugh's? I wanted to scream, pull my hair out, and hitchhike the rest of the way to Neah Bay. Instead, I groaned and wondered how she would fix this.

"Oh, I am so sorry," apologized Miss Pugh. "It's all in a day's work. Must have tied Mouse's strap too short," she mumbled. "But I'm always prepared for an emergency." She grabbed an old dirty rag from under the seat and smeared the puddle back and forth, back and forth. "This will have to do." In curt decision, "We must be on our way."

I had accepted the ride, so I had to sit where the puddle smeared. What did imperturbable Miss Pugh care if my coat smelled like a cat? What did she care if the cleaners failed to get the smell out and my coat was ruined?

On this last perilous stretch, the car powered along the Strait of Juan de Fuca. In the cold cutting night, this narrow sea was unseen. I sought oblivion from the sounds and wiggles of Mouse and Yakki, the smell of the litter box. My mind reached out to the huge rocks halted at the edge of the shore. Jagged, they sliced sharp against the circle of Luna, rising. Harsh, brazen in their nakedness, the rocks resist the clash of seas, the winds of cruelty, the darks of life.

Will I ever be strong, unflinching as the rocks? As Miss Pugh? A snort from Yakki returned me to my real world.

The car swung around a curve. Lights blinked: Neah Bay!

I shuddered. I dreaded entering my apartment—chilled like an ice house. But to my amazement I walked into tropical warmth—oil heater and gas range burned full force. Glorious relief! How come?

Slipping out of my coat, I rushed to Alta's for briefs.

"Oh my! I'm glad you're back. Come in," she urged. "The radio announced all roads were open—but we all wondered if you'd make it."

". . . a scary ride over patches of ice and snow and slippery turns. Thanks to Miss Pugh's expert driving, we're back."

Staff members had worked all day in teachers' units to thaw frozen water pipes. Workers had turned on stoves for heat.

Winter Storm Spirits: cold, callous, unfeeling, had ripped through Neah Bay.

~

Monday morning:

Stinging ice-splinters pierced my cheeks on the way to school. To beat the sharp cold, I scurried into the building. Crews had worked all night to thaw frozen pipes. But a puddle here—a puddle there—kept us gingerly stepping over water pools. Burst pipes had flooded floors: part of the storm's rage. But it didn't stop the roaring furnaces spewing hot heat into classrooms.

With my Prop Pals—Deena and Marta—in the cozy warmth of the school kitchen—I could forget yesterday's plight.

But winter—cruel and severe—didn't stop in the friendly kitchen. Record-breaking grips with November storms continued.

For days, Storm Spirits blasted in from the Ocean. With savage, relentless attacks, they besieged the village. They raked ice-tipped claws, scarring Neah Bay homes. They blew gusts of ruthless, bitter winds between window cracks and down chimney stacks.

Cold paralyzed—increased hardships—suffering—sickness. Stories eked from village families:

". . . only a heap of rugs on the floor for a bed . . ."

". . . only a covering of newspapers for warmth . . ."

". . . food? Money gone for whiskey . . ."

". . . then the story of drunken parents who neglect their unhappy children: the innocent ones.

". . . last night twelve-year-old Dane walked his little sisters to an elder's home—the girls could not sleep—they were hungry . . ."

". . . and the boy—he boldly claimed that he was tough—'a guy like me can sleep even if he is hungry'—emptiness gnawed at his stomach—same as his little sisters . . ."

Cold that snapped and chilled, urged all school-age children to classes—seeking shelter and hot food. Today's tally was the highest lunch count of the year.

The frigid weather continued. Bitter Arctic winds persisted.

A gas burner in Home Ec kitchen emitted alien odors—an oven was labeled "out of order"—unworkable parts removed for repair at a later date. Petty inconveniences overshadowed by the power-path of Storm Spirits. Will their fierce grip never break?

It did. Followed immediately by torrential rains—then to return to freezing temperatures—icy roads—and again pouring rain.

When will normal weather patterns of drizzle—rain—fog—return?

Perhaps for Makah Day next August?

 . . . no sleep last night—just a wink—now and then
. . . too excited thinking of today's adventure
. . . out of bed—in early dawn—village enfolded in a sheath of fog—I love mornings like this: quiet, serene, sunstreaks burst through the mists—breaking up the heavy dew

~

At the Ocean, I watched Zettah dig two big holes in the sand—watched her lay pieces of driftwood—dried grasses and weeds—in each one. From home she brought paper and matches—not like the old days!

"I have to tend the fire for two hours. The sand has to boil before it's ready to bake the dough. You can look for glass balls down the beach, if you like."

Out in this majestic setting of ancient forests, sand and sea, I felt again the primitive rise around me—wanting to escape down the beach into the mystery of the past. But the chill March wind told me to stay near the fires. And Zettah's voice put me in tune with the present:

. . . a birthday party, a baby shower, an Indian wedding, teenage drinking and what to do about it. She poked the fire—added more driftwood and grasses—then we talked about the basketball schedules.

. . . the one coming up with Port Alberni—the game Friday—players stay overnight. Saturday morning I serve breakfast in the Home Ec kitchen. Zettah offered to help. Grateful, I thanked her.

In rhythmic sequence, minutes ticked away. Soon two hours had passed.

With sticks, Zettah scooped ashes from one hole—placed the floured dough onto the hot bubbly sand—covered it with ashes from the second hole— "just the right temperature to keep the sand from sticking to the dough," she said. An amazing and thrilling creation of an old way. The bread was delicious and wonderful.

. . . and here I sit on the beach where sand and sea meet

. . . a lone Indian woman shares her bread with me—bread baked in hot sand—and all because an explorer's ship crashed on the rocks giving up sacks of flour

. . . out here in the great spaces of sand and sea, I face primitive encounters: Legends, Guardian Spirits, Thunderbird and Whale—rock towers—cedar forests—seasons passed over them in periodic movements of time

. . . the sound of a motorboat intrudes on the primitive—a Makah elder, Jerry McCarty, shoves the prow of his boat to a stop—gouging a cleft into the soft sand. He sits with us around the dying embers—shares bread with us: "When I was a boy, this was the only bread we had."

. . . wispy strands of ghost mist floated by.

Deep in the green-green wonder world of the Olympic forest, Zettah listened with me to songs of the wilderness. Willowing through evergreen boughs, birds trilled in happy freedom. Soon the tranquillity of song was shattered: "My father is dead—he died in a family tragedy—we lived . . ." Zettah broke into sobs. After a while, she began again: "We lived up near Everett. One summer night our families all gathered in a party . . .

"One of my uncles started an argument . . ." Sorrow crossed Zettah's face—her eyes filled with tears. "I wasn't there but I heard later they were all drinking too much—soon others joined in the argument—then they began fighting—then suddenly gun shots were fired. Nobody knows what really happened—but when the shooting stopped, five of our family lay dead. My father was one of them.

"I was eleven years old. I loved my father more than anybody in the world." Zettah held back her sobs. "My father wasn't involved in the fight and shooting. Later my aunt told me stray bullet hit him in the chest. He lay all night in the backyard dying—terribly wounded. No one knew he was there until I found him in the morning."

In anguish, she covered her face with her hands. "I'll never forget the look of agony and pain on his face. He died in my arms. My father's death will never leave me. It is part of my life every day."

I listened. Memory opened a cruel assault on a long-forgotten story—a story that blared in the headlines: INDIAN FAMILY MASSACRE . . . FIVE LEFT DEAD

In shock and horror, my family in Tacoma talked about it. Everybody talked about it. Crazy, drunken Indians—killing each other.

My young impressionable mind never forgot. I remembered my reaction—the sadness I felt—like a pall—the killings hung over me for days . . . and now I connected the tragedy to Zettah's story. In my wildest moments, I never dreamed I'd relive the massacre of blood and death with a family member.

. . . they weren't just a bunch of crazy, drunken Indians shooting each other to death

. . . they were strong, close, loved uncles and aunts and cousins crazed by white man's whiskey

. . . an Indian father lay dead—his little girl left to grieve the rest of her life

 This week I talked with Lucy for a long time. Moments like these I do truly cherish. I enjoy her so much and feel the depth of her sufferings: personal afflictions—family disruptions—dissension. Lucy is not well. Her energy is low and family disturbances devastate her mind and body.

Ernie, her husband—white—World War II veteran—shell-shocked—suffers periods of anger that develop into violent rages—ones that are frightening to the children.

Last weekend Junior ran away from home.

"I was so upset and frantic with worry." Hands trembling, Lucy described the search: "June and I looked and looked for him. We went to friends' houses. I feared he'd gone off drinking. We went to the Pool Hall—to restaurants—even looked on the beach and in the woods. We looked everywhere. No one had seen him."

Lucy crossed her arms—pressed them against her breast. "My heart beat so fast I could hardly breathe. Finally we found him at Kelly's." Lucy sighed heavily—tears of relief flooded her eyes:

. . . Tears of relief—only brief respite—mental anguish and distress continue . . .

~

. . . an indomitable force of invisible energy—Lucy carries strength—
spirit power

. . . an indomitable sense of humor—not always angry and violent—
characterizes Ernie, Sr.

. . . after an evening with the family, they all drove me home, left me
at the gate

. . . to my horror, I discovered the yard full of huge horses

. . . running back to the car—waving my hands in wild, frenzied signs,
I shouted, "Horses! Horses!"

. . . roaring with laughter, Ernie jumped from the car—chased the
horses away

. . . thus liberating me—Ernie also endeared himself to me

. . . Ernie may still be laughing—but I could still be sitting on the gate post

Saturday afternoon, and in walked Lucy.
"Guess what? I have news!"
A self-sufficient-unit-of-purpose look smirked across her face.
. . . cups on the table—filled with coffee: WHY THAT LOOK? I wondered.

"You are now SPONSOR to my Camp Fire group. You've replaced
Mrs. Carr," Lucy smugly declared.

I froze—but uttered not a word. Mrs. Carr was an ally of SHE. Wow!
Strong medicine.

With purpose, Lucy stirred more sugar into her coffee. "At a meeting
of Camp Fire Girls' leaders in Port Angeles, Mrs. Carr claimed to represent
Neah Bay. I'm the leader of the Neah Bay group. Mrs. Carr ignored me as
though I wasn't even there."

Stung. Snubbed and offended, Lucy dismissed Mrs. Carr as Sponsor,
choosing me instead.

. . . so merrily I go on my way in spite of conflict—of prejudice—of what
SHE and other white women plot and plan behind village coffee klatches.

Once Jule remarked: "THEY say Lucy uses you."

SO WHAT? I love it.

Jule had already warned me: "You have an enemy in Rega Buckthorn
just by being here."

Intrigue thickened. Another warning. This time from Lucy. Before she
left for home, I learned she believes one of Junior's friends stole money

from her purse—hidden under the mattress. "He's in and out of the house all the time. He's part of the family. He knew where I kept my purse."

Upsetting—unbelievable—involving difficulties.

"To accuse him openly would split the Reservation." Lucy bowed her head in resignation. "I've decided to remain silent and offer prayer."

I listened—shocked and startled. I knew the boy—the suspect.

Later in the week—after class—the accused student complained: "I haven't been able to sleep."

"Why?" I asked.

"I don't know."

Guilt?

Cast aside in a corner of Lucy's craft room lay an old scrubby blackened basket.

Forgotten? Neglected? Perhaps. But when Lucy held the basket in her hands, the woven cedar fibers sparked life. For me, they sparked romance, history, imagination.

A slight tremor quivered across Lucy's lips. "My mother gave this basket to me—Chief Seattle's daughter, Princess Angeline, wove it."

In wistful reflection, Lucy spoke slowly: "This basket was used for stone-boiling—a soup kettle."

STONE BOILING? SOUP KETTLE?

In answer to the question mark that blazed across my face, Lucy explained: "The Old Ones tell about the stone-boilers—the way ancient peoples discovered how to boil water."

To boil water had to be discovered? What an amazing revelation! What steps did the primitives take to learn how to boil water?

To boil water today is so uneventful. Who could believe the dynamic energy needed to bring water to the boiling point?

Lucy continued: "I was only a child at Coupeville on Whidbey Island—among the Suquamish—my mother's tribe. I listened to the old storytellers pass on the story of the stone-boilers.

"In those days iron stoves and cooking kettles were unheard of. I remember hearing about the first stone-boilers—how they learned to heat stones in the campfire until they were red-hot."

Lucy picked up the old burned basket woven by her ancestress. "Tightly woven baskets like this one were filled with cold water. Then, with wooden tongs made with two sticks tied together, the hot stones were dropped into baskets." Lucy paused—thoughtfully traced the discolored designs on Princess Angeline's basket. "When the stones cooled, they were brought back to the fire to be heated again. To keep the water heating, other hot stones were added to the basket. In this way, the women changed stones many times until the water boiled."

Turning toward me, the look in Lucy's eyes told me her thoughts drifted to another place—another time.

Like being drawn into a vision, I was there with Lucy—in a mystic place—a trysting place—a place of sea and wispy fogs—a place of glaciered peaks. A trail led us into a mysterious silence—a primeval silence—to a place where stones heated in the campfire.

. . . in the silence, I wondered: Where is she? Where am I?

. . . soon we left the mystic place, where stones heated in the campfire, to follow a voice—soft, gentle, memory-like, that called us away from the silence:

"No one knows when stone boiling began with our tribes—but like legends, the story of the stone-boilers lives on."

Lucy placed the basket near a pile of raw wool. "Old pieces like this basket are part of our family heritage—our history—our customs. They hold families together—tying past to present—not that I would want to go back to stone boiling."

Not back to stone boiling—but Lucy is still part of that past.

"While living at Coupeville—I've told this story many, many times—mostly to visiting anthropologists—it goes to follow that after the early peoples discovered how to boil water, they learned to add wild meat, Salmon, or clams. They added vegetables or plants and herbs. This gave the people SOUP—never dreamed of before."

What mighty sweeping discoveries: How to boil water! How to make soup!

What a mighty upheaval in the eating habits of primitive man: hot food—cooked food—SOUP: easier for children to eat—for Old Ones to chew—for sick ones to digest.

What an unprecedented red-hot discovery! A revolutionary change in food preparation—techniques of skills and talents that spread far and wide over primitive lands.

And now I held Princess Angeline's basket in my hands. Just to touch a piece of Indian history shot shivers through me—to learn the dramatic progress of the stone-boilers.

What an exciting—picturesque—romantic—historical narrative—and all because I saw an old, blackened, discolored basket tossed aside in Lucy's craft room.

What a dynamic period. What an amazing story to carry into my nutrition class!

On this sunny, spring afternoon, Helen and Natah had walked from the village to chat a while over coffee. In pristine comfort, these two Makah storytellers now sat before me. Like arrows in a quiver, their stories held intrinsic powers. Secretly infatuated with Indian legends, I gloated over this cultural treat. For this first-time narrative, I waited in a rapturous mood.

"Long long ago—when world very young," Natah began, "Destruction and Tatoosh live together in Pacific Ocean—down from Cape Flattery—near mouth of Hoh River. Little rocks and big rocks—on shore—their children—many children.

"Oh how Island parents quarrel and quarrel. Destruction stamp foot—Tatoosh stamp foot—they shout—they shake fists." Natah doubled up her fists—shook them to show how. "Destruction and Tatoosh always mad at each other. Fights went on for thousands and thousands of years. One day after very bad quarrel, Tatoosh—very mad—left husband, Destruction."

Natah relaxed—glanced at Helen—who nodded in approval. In delirious suspense I waited. What next? I didn't want to interrupt.

"Tatoosh grab all her children—pile them in dug-out canoe—paddle up coast." Natah leaned forward—moved her arms in paddle action. "Tatoosh very mad at Destruction—faster and faster she paddle—passed mouth of Quillayute River—passed rocks and inlets and coves. Finally she come to place call Point of the Arches. Still mad at Destruction—she stares at children—shout 'You'll all grow up to be just like your father' . . . and dump them all overboard into water."

With an impetuous, imaginary tossing action of her hands—Natah mimicked Tatoosh throwing children into icy-blue sea.

So moved by the vivid story, I gasped at the heartlessness of Tatoosh . . . and waited for the storyteller to continue . . . *to a happier ending . . but that was the ending!*

"Over her mad spell—Tatoosh paddle on alone—to her place in the Pacific at the tip of Cape Flattery—Guardian at entrance to Strait of Juan de Fuca."

Bizarre and spectacular, the rugged arches rise up as Guardian to the children. Flung into the sea—alone and deserted—they stand between their Island parents.

 "You come to the meeting too," Lucy invited. "Two woman from Port Angeles and one from Bainbridge Island are coming. They want our craft shops to organize into one group. They want to stimulate interest in a craft shop that sells to tourist trade."

The meeting was fun and interesting . . . something was accomplished . . . committees suggested . . . election of president proposed.

At a later meeting, Lucy was elected president. Committees formed. Charter discussed.

"Already some are fighting her—but Lucy's the only one capable enough to run it," said Zettah. "Villagers are jealous of Lucy because of her background, her education, her abilities and skills—superior to many."

The Makah Arts and Craft Club has decided on the Thunderbird and Whale for their symbol, and Helen asked me to write about it.

At another meeting, later in April, Helen presented "my" Thunderbird and Whale story. Now it's causing controversy: "Not authentic," Lucy said. She didn't know I wrote it. DOG HOUSE FOR ME! . . . just condensed from James Gilcrist Swan's historical-mythological creation. Where else could I find a Thunderbird and Whale story? Helen offended by Lucy's reluctance to accept it unconditionally as a story for Craft Club's symbol. Should be passed by Tribal Council, Lucy decided, and based on authenticity. I thought James Swan was authentic.

Lucy dropped into Home Ec. . . . Marrs Henry referred to some as "crooks like those people." Heavens! All resulting from difficulties over Arts and Crafts Club.

Moves are being made to put a ban on white people learning the Indian arts. Weaving is being taught. Believes their arts are sacred. Should not be given away. Art skills part of their cultural heritage and should remain confined to the Indian peoples.

~

White people stealing the arts away from the Indians, but Indians may let the skills die, some fear.

One utterly, ghastly day in April—cold, rain, wind—worse than winter—Lucy stopped by before Tribal Council meeting. Important. Wanted me to go, but I could not bear the thoughts of sitting through four hours of wrangling. Genealogy ratings coming up—Co-op deal—whites stealing crafts involves Tribe's decision.

Once before, I'd heard: "They took the best of the Reservation—kept pushing us back to this rock. They still have the best: businesses, stores, restaurants, motels. Now they are still trying to get our best: the Art."

Again—worst wind, rain, cold storm all year—just terrific! Settled for peace and quiet. Then Lucy came to take me to Arts and Crafts rummage sale. We sorted items for sale. My job to sell coffee and donuts, pineapple-cranberry pies and pumpkin. Made $20—pretty good!

What confusion! Lucy's ready to give up as president, but Marrs Henry and Reverend Dale-Smith tell her to hang on. Other group trying to cut in. When I left with Helen, Lucy called, "Remember you're a Crafts member now!"

～

Later, in April, Elizabeth thrilled me in an interpretive reading at the Band-Chorus Concert. Elizabeth has come so, so far.

Recalling Champ's basso: "I'm just a tumbling-tumble weed . . ." Is that what I am—just a tumbling tumble weed?

Lucy, still as Arts and Crafts president, may dissolve Minnie Atwater and her gang who seem to be taking over. That's her reputation. What a mess—just petty rivalry all through the village.

In May, Lucy has big plans for Arts and Crafts Opening Day. A dinner—corned beef stew—wedding soup, so it was once called Helen said and someone said to tell me it was a Makah dish—Indian bread—delicious cherry pies. After dinner, Lucy opened the meeting. Then for two hours I took minutes. Wow! Plans are developing . . .

～

A Grand Opening of the Arts and Crafts Club. We all wore Thunderbird and Whale tags. Lucy came for me. Wonderful old photos on display. Old Indian faces preserved—beautiful—priceless—many valuable relics on display.

Later, when we went to the Community Hall, Ada and Natah barbecued Salmon in the pouring rain. "Here comes the Salmon!" Joan and I cashiered. It was all great fun.

Tourists galore. Supper—more Salmon. Wonderful to watch. I loved it!

Lucy's family danced. Others participated. Gave gifts to the Apple-Doll Lady. Bone games in session. A real thrill—the drums—the chants—the louder the better. I loved it too!

～

Once we spent a day at the Arts and Crafts for the Camp Fire Salmon Bake. As always I had a wonderful time. The Salmon was more elegant than ever—just super delicious. It poured down rain, but who cares. Lucy drove us out to the Ocean—in the fury of rain and waves—wild and spectacular!

How can I ever leave this Indian village and its people when I love it all so much. And yet I am pulled this way and that way. Some day I'll just splatter.

I love the Ocean in its moods of stormy madness trying to upheaval the beaches—tear the rocks in halted splendor from their moorings.

Breaking away—mesmerized—but resisting the pull to stay and become part of the great surging movement of the sea—we had to leave—had to get back—had to count the money we made at the Salmon Bake. I now have to keep it—a keeper of the Camp Fire treasury.

~

Lucy came and went. We talk and talk. So much drinking and wrong doing on the Reservation. It hurts her so to be aware of all the troubles the kids are headed for. ". . . just little babies," Lucy says.

Always planning for Camp Fire. Always baking pies for Arts and Crafts—apples from Lucy—beautiful, delicious pies—but all the juice ran into the broiler rack.

~

Arts and Crafts Dance—lots of drinking and noise—rowdiest crowd ever, said Lucy—so many Air Force drunks. Dance success financially though. Helen and Zettah helped. Kids danced into a frenzy—crazy and wild. No wonder Gloria rejects dancing—says all evil stems from their dancing.

~

Out of my Medicine Bag:

. . . adviser: the Annual, *The Chieftain*, Girl's Club, Junior Class

. . . classes to teach: Junior Homemaking, Seventh Grade Language, Home Ec I and II, Study Hall, Typing, Home Management, Journalism

. . . Neah Bay social activity started with a fantastic party at Community Hall for Perry's daughter—baked Salmon so terrific—left early with Lucy, T-Birds for ice cream

. . . gorgeous weather—golden—sunny

. . . first full day of school—in a whirl though—so many books and classes

. . . typing Intertribal Conference minutes for the Henrys

. . . Gloria here for dinner—so was Bob

. . . Zettah and Dorris came—Lucy came—began to work on the minutes—not to bed till midnight

1958-1959

Many times my thoughts have linked to Lucy's remark: ". . . all this foreign living has been hard enough . . ."

White man's way uprooted native traditions of longhouse families at Coupeville on Whidbey Island—gouged a trailway through the evergreen wilderness—cut a passage over waters of the Sound—forced its way between the cracks of the cedar-plank longhouses—and took over.

Many times I recall Lucy's saying, "I came along just in time to see the last of the old ways and the beginning of the new ways . . ." A tone of sadness reigned in her gentle voice.

Once again we walked on Juan de Fuca's shore—leaned against the silvered log—the uprooted tree.

Once again my mind-travels unmasked this mark of devastation—unveiling its native dignity in the forest stand.

Rent from Earth-Mother—stripped of bark and branches—the great red cedar surrendered on Juan de Fuca's pebbled beach. In stark silhouette, withered roots reach skyward: in request? in promise?

In Lucy's stories, I find a culture uprooted—just like the uprooted tree—deprived of native dignity—force ripped from Earth-Mother—stripped of traditions, language, spirit power. Lucy's people struggle—bereft—arms uplifted, they reach to the Great Spirit: also in request? also in promise?

 Steadfast, dignified, proud—Lucy, Camp Fire Leader—taught her little maidens (Indian and white) native Indian songs and dances. Her voice carried the melody in deep pure tones to the soft velvety beat of the drum.

The warrior woman enriched my life—the essence of her nativity—the harmony I feel when I am with her.

I love being a part of an *indistinguishable something* not understood by me.

Yesterday—discussing a program—Lucy's comment: "IF IT IS TO BE—THERE WILL BE A WAY."

⌒

A request from some Indian Agent resulted in: "Do you know how he talked to me? He treated me like I was a dumb old Indian."

What would he have thought had he known who she was? Or was he too dumb to care?

⌒

. . . her heart beat as one with the heart of her people

. . . she knew their concerns—their fears—their nostalgia

. . . she feels their loss of power—their loss of language—their loss of traditions and legends

. . . but through her songs and dances the legends live on

. . . how vast her knowledge—her understanding—her seeking

. . . she lives to help her people

A WARRIOR WOMAN: LUCY MILLHOLLAND! GREAT-GREAT-GRANDNIECE OF CHIEF SEATTLE!

⌒

And there was the wounded heart from the Camp Fire Girls' breakdown. . . .

SHE—Rega Buckthorn—responsible? SHE knew I worked with Lucy—knew we were friends. Someone deprived Lucy of leadership—forced her to resign.

Shouts of: "The Northern Lights! The Northern Lights!" brought us all rushing out into the night to see a spectacular phenomenon of color!

Expecting to see the sky aflame with brilliant splendor—radiant and vibrant with reds, purples, oranges, greens, all colors of the rainbow in shimmering, glorious display—but on the far distant sky there appeared only a pale light above the horizon.

What a let down! My expectations of what the aurora borealis should look like were greatly exaggerated:

> No "merry dancers" in dazzling colors—
> No titillation of imagination—
> Just a non-descript light—
> not even blinking—
> Just a non-descript light—
> far far away!

~

Once—after Ernie graduated—joined the Marines—home on leave—he and Dane stopped by.

A cultural factor brought forth a comment from me: "Never let your language die."

Dane pointed his finger right at me.

"Who took it away from us in the first place? YOU!"

 Ada recounted that the Indians at Neah Bay believe the black rock came from a meteor. Some Indians say they saw it fall— blazing red—then became the black rock. A symbol of strength— power—purity. Smoothness of the surface symbolizes no evil will cling to it. "Be like the Black Rock," they said.

~

In 1855 Lucy's ancestor was the second Chief to sign the treaty of Neah Bay.

~

Went to evening church—coffee for the graduating seniors. One of the village men came just reeking with liquor—and tobacco. Could smell him all over the place. I poured him some coffee. Clouds of sadness wave over me at times like this.

~

Bender said, "You can't leave now. You like it here."

"How can you tell?"

"I can tell by the way you look. You like us dumb Indians."

Oh, Bender!

~

Ronnie says, "Gee, you're spoiled."

Yes—Simon, Helmer, Bill, Bender, and Larry do a <u>lot</u> to spoil me!

~

Margo and Jean made a cake to celebrate Dotti and Genevieve's birthdays. We served it sixth period . . . and Larry did get Gen's piece!

~

Me: "Who are the Puget Sounders?"

Lucy: Oh, those silly people who want to modernize the Pacific Northwest. They want to put a Statue of Liberty down on Peter's Rock and build a bridge—soon!"

~

The Major (a teacher) left his combat knife in the drawer. I sent it back via Larry. Have enough to worry about. Would have stabbed myself next period trying to teach punctuation and letter styles!

~

Yesterday Bender and Simon engaged in unpremeditated fight. Knocked over table, chairs. I could have killed them, and they should have been expelled on the spot. Rolled over and over on the floor. Simon cut his finger—hurt his shoulder. Bender hurt his leg. "Just love them and take it in your stride." Reported them. Bender said, "We didn't think you'd tell." I suppose not!

~

T'hlu-kluts—Thunderbird
Chet-up-uk—Whale
Ha-hek-to-ak—Lightning

~

Lucy came and coffeed after school. I said something about leaving. And she said, "No, you couldn't do that." If I leave it will be hard for them to understand. As though I betrayed my Indian race.

~

I told Bill Mahone that Lucy said some people are made so ill from eating seafood, and I said, "I'm just a tough old Indian." Bill said, "You are just a tough *little* Indian." For Bill to accept me as an Indian was the highest compliment. He's too proud to accept just *anyone* as an Indian.

~

Lucy said there was much resentment rising. "Indians had discipline. Whites took it away to civilize them and now what have they done."

~

Simon, Bender, and Larry all went Caruso in Journalism. Simon scooting around in that wheel chair. (I'm going to have it taken out. Nothing but a problem and something for the kids to play with.) The rest yodeling at the top of their voices. Bender is impossible. In no place but Neah Bay could such things happen. No dull moments though.

~

 "T-clop—t-clop—t-clop—t-clop!"
I jumped up. Stared into faces: Horses faces! Horses again! Horses on Ocean Prairies! Horses on Front Street! Now horses at my very door!

To watch Makah kids gallop wild horses across Ocean Prairies is picturesque but hair-raising to meet horses and riders face-to-face on the very steps to the very door of my apartment.

Threatening snorts. Warning stomps. Switching tails.

These huge beasts still terrify me. One look from a skittish eye and I cower. Besides, in my busy day, there's no time for a class in equestrianism—horseplay, no less. Enough of that goes on all the time—without horses.

Before ungentle hoofs kicked down the door or crashed out a window, I called through the screen door: "Sorry! I am not serving tea and crumpets today!"

With a howling war whoop, they whirled—riders charged their mighty steeds down the school-yard turf. Hoofs flipped up rocks and chunks of dried grasses. Off they galloped back to Ocean Prairies—I hoped.

 MAKAH AIR FORCE STATION: *The new name sent out a triumphant message: Believed to be the only Air Force Base named after an American Indian tribe, the 25th Air Force Division evolved into a universal structure of spirit power . . . but I remember what my students thought of the Air Force.*

". . . have you noticed how the Indian boys bitterly resent the Air Force fellas?"

". . . Sue's been dating a guy from the Base—Chuck got mad and beat him up."

". . . the village blamed the Air Force for the bloody fight at the Pool Hall Saturday night."

". . . officers from the Base are taking it up with the Tribal Council."

". . . who stole Chet's car?"

". . . I heard a guy from the Air Force 'borrowed' it—he wanted to get to P.A."

". . . the Base Commander canceled all leaves."

Stuck out in this wilderness fortress—bored, homesick—maybe too much whiskey—these recruits were first to be suspected.

Whatever the reason, all I ever heard was in reverse to regimental codes.

~

MARCH 12, 1958! AN UNFORGETTABLE DAY IN MAKAH HISTORY!

Military letters and figures that once identified this isolated outpost turned into vivid prominent letters that spelled: MAKAH AIR FORCE STATION.

The new name sent out a triumphant message: Believed to be the only Air Force Base named after an American Indian tribe, the 25th Air Force Division evolved into a universal structure of spirit power.

That day I remember climbing into the back of a truck with Zettah. Leaving late, we were lucky to find a ride to the Base. Merrymakers greeted us. Arrows of excitement—like firecrackers—shot through the air. But I remember what my students thought of the Air Force.

Over heads—over giggling girls—over serious-faced Makahs—I listened to Zettah brief the morning's schedule: Marrs, as Tribal Council Chairman, stood for the Makah Nation. Helen's sister introduced the Makah dancers and singers—who gave their traditional song of thanks. At lunch, Perry Ides gave the blessing for food.

Abruptly, Zettah curbed her briefing. From somewhere in the ether a bugle sounded. Alerted by military drums, attention riveted on military uniformed airmen and flag carriers who marched toward the Base entrance.

Then a triumphant roar! Five airplanes split the air lanes—they dipped—they dived—they circled low overhead in a mighty tribute—a spectacular splash to honor the new name.

Exciting to hear! Thrilling to watch! Sensational to experience!

In a twinkling, this isolated wilderness Air Force Base had been transformed. Now: Prestigious. Dignified. Distinctive.

Swooped up in this moment of power, I watched more marching—more ceremony—more songs and dances from the Makahs—even an ancient song of appreciation. Then more merits, more badges, more more more. After a while, Marrs Henry honored the Base Commander with the name Chief Too-Too-Che (Thunderbird).

Zettah whispered, "To give the Commander a former Chief's name makes him an honorary member of the Makah Nation."

That evening—in fantasy—I followed—again—the pathway of ghosts and shadows—the trail of Ishkoodah the Comet—this time into the Community Hall. The gathering created a Pow Wow-like theme that wavered throughout—connecting two worlds and a United States military unit.

. . . after the Welcome Song

. . . after the dinner prayer

. . . after a superb feast of Salmon and Indian bread, I watched Marrs Henry. Proud, dignified, a skilled speaker. Tonight, as Master of Ceremonies, he assigned added honors and awards. Then as compliment to the Base Commander and his wife, Marrs called for the GIFT DANCE.

THE RITUAL OF GIFT GIVING! . . . an amazing achievement of dances, chants, drums, and Makahs' giving of gifts.

A potlatch! Not the old way, but a potlatch 1958!

"Oh, my! This is awe-inspiring!" whispered Alta, who sat beside me.

I didn't answer . . . but thought: a powerful evolvement of living on Cape Flattery.

Again, exciting to hear! Thrilling to watch! Sensational to experience!

After the Hoo-Hoo-Su (the fun dance)—after the Paddle Dance—Marrs gave the Commander a hand-carved, hand-painted canoe paddle—a most significant gift.

This day I had lived a real-life story with the Makah—an unforgettable triumph in their history.

Sunshine brightened the sky over Neah Bay. Out from winter hibernation, the ground hog crawled from his den in the ground—looked around—saw his shadow—became frightened—crawled back into his den. Legend dictates to sleep and wait out six more weeks of cold, rain, wind.

All quiet until afternoon. Then Helen walked from the village to chat a while. Refreshed. Relaxed. Helen leaned against the back of the sofa-chair—

closed her eyes. I watched the placid calm on her face turn to shadows. They wedged their way into lines of her forehead—into creases under her eyes—into tiny wrinkles in her cheeks.

Silent for a long time. When she spoke again, her voice carried a tone of despair: ". . . for years I've worried about our Makah history—it should be written by a Makah. No white man can understand our ways—our thoughts—our feelings. Only a Makah can really understand our culture."

Helen was right, of course.

If I were to write Makah history—WHERE WOULD I BEGIN?

. . . with Great Red Cedar—tree of power—of dignity—of stateliness that shaped Makah culture?

. . . with Great Whale Spirit—that gave secret messages to the harpooner?

. . . with Words from Helen: "My father was a whaling chief!" . . . The bravest—most powerful men led the hunt . . . the Whaling Chiefs . . . their Chieftainship had been established by ancestral inheritance of power creating Makah society.

Helen was royalty—a princess.

WHERE WOULD I BEGIN?

I might begin with a legend.

Ada wove Makah history on a cedar basket.

In the meantime, I'll think about it . . .

Before she left, Helen invited me to a seafood dinner—Tuesday at the Community Hall.

Intriguing menu: China Slippers, devil fish, mussels, barnacles. Do they really EAT all that stuff? Yuk! The Makah Club will serve boiled rice with raisins, also buckskin bread.

Later—I wondered—was this a test—revealing the unpalatable food?

Would I really come?

Helen stood on the threshold—"You don't need to come if you don't want to."

I wouldn't miss it—not a real, old, Indian party.

WHAT'S A CHINA SLIPPER?

On Tuesday, I stared at the strange shell fish—shaped in a bony curve—sharp shells formed across the back. They looked exciting? fearsome? hard to deal with? FORMIDABLE?

Placing several of these weird aliens before me, Helen said: "In the old days, we had slaves do this for us. Today you are my slave."

Did I gasp? Then she vanished . . .

I stared again: CHINA SLIPPERS!

HELP! HELP! What to do? Where to begin?

Frightened—helpless—like trying to climb Fuca's Pillar . . .

Then Zettah rescued me from my despair. "It's fingers all the way!" And down to the very bone, I thought.

. . . and here I sat—where lots and lots of Indians also sat. But where was Perry? Where was Ada? Where was Lucy?

A strange feeling of belonging—of not belonging—overcame me. Aware of an unknown—a mysterious culture—far different from my own.

. . . nerves frazzled—squeegeed—all eyes on me—all these Indians watched.

. . . now I struggled furiously with these weird fish—scared to death I'd make a horrifying mistake—I did! Zettah discovered I'd pulled the bones out upside down. How could that be? No wonder the task was so treacherous—no wonder slaves did the work.

Expecting the roof to collapse on me, I lowered my head over the desecrated bones. Helen smiled—forgave my clumsy effort. With her native, casual grace, Helen moved to sit beside me. "You are my slave," she remarked again. I laughed—not knowing what else to do. "I'm honored to be your slave."

Then a switch in status: "Now I will be YOUR slave." As my slave, Helen brought food: mussels, barnacles. I never thought I'd live to see the day I'd eat a barnacle—just sharp-crested shells stuck on rocks—to cut up my legs—swimming at Vashon during summer vacation.

Then, some way—some how—the barnacles slid down. I didn't dare gag or choke. What a relief. Then boiled rice with raisins! Buckskin bread came next—tough and chewy.

. . . in dread, I waited for devil fish—an octopus—with long scary, creepy, crawly tentacles. Scared—tense—I couldn't wait any longer. In a quivering voice: "Where's the devil fish?" I asked Helen. She answered: "No one could find any." With a huge sigh of relief, I wondered how I would have managed THAT!

At the end of the sigh, the president began his after-dinner speech: "Today we celebrate the birthday of the Makah Club." Again, I thought: Here I sit in this culture so different from my own. I swirled in a tidal current of judgmental faces—as at the first Mother's Tea. But tonight I sensed a strangeness—an unrealness—a tenseness—not present at ceremonial feasts and parties.

I felt SOMETHING WAS ABOUT TO HAPPEN. I heard the Makah Club president announce: "As of tonight, everybody here becomes a member of the Makah Club."

I laughed and clapped like everybody else. "Me too?" I asked Zettah. "You too!" I thought she was only teasing.

Later, the president spoke again—TO ME: "Let's hear how the Home Ec teacher likes our cooking." WOW! THIS WAS REAL. But I stood—gave a speech—survived.

We rose to leave. The Marrs Henry family had brought me. Now they were taking me home. I was one of them.

Moving into the night, I was filled with the warm glow of belonging. Somehow I had won their trust—their confidence.

How wonderful to have their approval—their acceptance. I REALLY WAS A MEMBER OF THE MAKAH CLUB!

Then I heard Marrs Henry say—sincerely—emphatically: "WE used to never accept white people—but now, once you are accepted by the Makah, and become a member—these Indians will be your devoted and loyal friends for the rest of your life."

 When Helen came she brought the Black Prayer Rock. Another gift of her acceptance of me. I feel such awe and reverence for these special gifts.

. . . the Black Prayer Rock—symbol of strength. "Hold it in your hands when you pray—it will make you strong . . .

"In olden times, prayers were held in secret. To confront an elder or anyone in prayer was very serious—you'd just better look out. That's one thing you people gave us—to make prayer open—and not keep it secret."

～

When Helen and Natah walked from the village last Friday, Natah cried: "My heart is broken—my heart is broken. I shall die of a broken heart—a broken hearted old lady."

More of Natah's land has been taken by the government for timber. I wondered. And Natah will die of a broken heart. And there is nothing I can say to comfort her.

~

Helen made a Makah Medicine Man doll for me—from cedar bark shreds. She wove two cedar mats. Exciting events continue to happen. I was the only white person present at a baby shower the other night. This thrilled me. One old woman spoke Makah. Helen won a dear pair of earrings. She brought them to me, smiled, "I won these for you because I made them!"

 I've decided not to come back next year . . .
The same invisible, mystical SOMETHING that pulled me to this Makah Land is now pulling me away.

But Helen reminded me: "You can't leave now—you're one of us—you're a full-fledged Makah—we won't let you go. If you do, we'll come up in a canoe and bring you back."

Her words held powerful medicine—powerful spirit power—and tugged at my heart.

Thinking back over the years, I remember Cerena's saying, "There's not so much rowdiness in the halls since you came. It's all because of you and your influence. I give you all the credit. The girls are better groomed. It's SOMETHING intangible—something you don't do by force—but by day-to-day contact."

I recalled how enlightened I felt—at that first Mother's Tea—by words from one of the guest-mothers, "This is the nicest and loveliest Mother's Tea Neah Bay has ever had."

. . . and from Mrs. Walter, "I've never seen a more beautiful tea table—and the girls were so lovely and lady-like." She had seen all the Tea's.

Jule's comments left me tongue-tied, "You made the loveliest impression at the Tea. Both Indian and white mothers expressed to me how fortunate the girls were to have the guidance and instruction of one with such dignity and humility."

Once when Lucy asked me to help her with Camp Fire, she smiled, "I'll teach the little girls beadwork—you can teach them charm."

And when Perry said, "I guess we'll have to adopt you. What would you think of that?" So wonder struck—I said nothing—so flabbergasted!

Again I recalled words of advice from Cerena, "You've brought an indistinguishable SOMETHING here. Give to this culture the traditions and talents that formed you. You came up here looking for something. You will find it."

Did I find it? Did I succeed? Did I complete what I unknowingly came to do?

I surmounted the prophetic: "THAT WITCH . . . WHERE'D THEY GET HER? . . . SHE'LL NEVER LAST UP HERE."

. . . but Alta's words still ring in my ears: "You have the greatest following of any teacher we've ever had up here . . ."

Epilogue

The same invisible, mystical SOMETHING that pulled me to this Land now pulls me away.

" . . . we used to never accept white people, but now once you are accepted by the Makah and become a member, these Indians will be your devoted and loyal friends for the rest of your life."

Al Zantua's cover design has been approved by the Makah Tribal Council. Bender is Tribal Council Chairman, and Champ is also on the Tribal Council.

Over the years, whenever I returned, I felt as though I had never been away. Devoted and loyal friends they were. And also, over the years, my friendships with older Makahs and my school kids continued. They came to see me. They called.

One winter, snow drifts—icicles—blizzard winds—controlled our area. A phone call from Elizabeth: "Thought I'd better check on what's going on down there in Tacoma. The wind nearly blew Ruth's little red house into the bay."

Once, during a New Year's Eve party: "Just wanted to wish you a Happy New Year!"

And once, a call from Simon's fishing boat off Cape Flattery: I exclaimed, "How come?" His response: "Modern tech! We're having a party! Wish you were here! Come up for Makah Day!"

Their acceptance—their trust—their loyalty—give spirit power to my life. They will always be a part of my heart!

And now, more than forty years later, Elizabeth asked me to return for a class reunion and for a book-signing party on Makah Day.

ORDER FORM

RED APPLE PUBLISHING
Peggy Meyer, publisher
P. O. Box 568
Vaughn, WA 98394
253-884-1450, fax 253-884-1451
1-800-245-6595, e-mail: redaple@aol.com

Date _____

NAME _____
STREET _____
CITY, STATE, ZIP _____
PHONE _____

DESCRIPTION   *"NEVER TRUST A WHITE MAN"*
                      Arlyn Conly (Cover art and sketches by Al Zantua)

QUANTITY _____

LIST PRICE $16.95

SUBTOTAL _____

SALES TAX _____
(8%, WA residents only)

S & H _____
(1-2 books $3.00, 3-5 $3.50, 6-7 $4.00, 8-10 $6.00)

TOTAL _____

Thank You For Your Order!